LARRY SILVERBERG'S

MEISNER I TRAINING PROGRAM

"A most inspired teacher of acting"
Academy Award® and Pulitzer Prize
winning author Horton Foote

CALL : 212.462.3005

Teresa Spoon

ACTORSCRAFT.COM PRESENTS

Act New York 2005

The Actor's Pocket Guide to New York City

Includes our special book within a book:
The Actor's Guide to Qualified Acting Coaches

"This is a marvelous and invaluable book for all actors. It should surely be one of the staples in every actor's arsenal. I recommend it highly!"

Robert Kim, Robert Kim Photography, NYC

"*Act New York 2004* is the best resource I have seen. Books like this inspire actors — regardless of their ultimate goal — to take control of their careers."

Betsy Capes of Capes Company, Private Coaching for Actors, NYC

Published by
Smith and Kraus, Inc.
177 Lyme Road, Hanover, NH 03755
www.smithkraus.com

First edition: September 2004
9 8 7 6 5 4 3 2 1

ISBN 1-57525-392-5

Cover and text design by Freedom Hill Design, Reading, Vermont
Illustrated by Lisa Goldfinger

DEDICATION

True actors understand the word *hunger*. We are hungry to create, we find it essential to express our most intimate voice, and we ache to make a difference in the lives of those who come to witness us work. Along the way, we need to be reminded that what we do actually does make a difference. We need to be inspired by masters of the craft whose courage, simplicity, and spirit make it possible for us to go on.

This last year, the staff of actorscraft received this kind of life-affirming inspiration when we attended a workshop led by Alan Arkin and experienced one of the most profoundly moving weekends of our lives. And so, this year, *Act New York 2005* is dedicated to:

ALAN ARKIN

Thank you Alan for sharing yourself so completely, with such love and openness. Thank you for opening our hearts and, in this very difficult time, thank you for reminding us that we are human beings and that we need each other.

Contents

ONE. GETTING COACHED

TWO. GETTING SCHOOLED

THREE. GETTING THE JOB

FOUR. GETTING THE LOOK

FIVE. GETTING SOME SPACE

SIX. GETTING IT TOGETHER

SEVEN. GETTING THE FACTS

EIGHT. GETTING INSPIRED

NINE. GETTING HEALTHY

TEN. GETTING AROUND AND STAYING THERE

ELEVEN. GETTING IT ON

Welcome Back

WE'RE A HIT!

Last year, when we released our first edition of *Act New York*, we believed we had created a book that would make a significant difference in the lives of our fellow actors here in New York and all the actors coming here. Well, we had no idea how big a difference we were about to make!

Act New York 2004 quickly became the number-one selling actor's resource book in the country. At New York City's Drama Book Shop, the book was literally flying off the shelves. Knowing that the comprehensive information we had compiled was being put to use by thousands of actors from coast to coast gave all of us a deep sense of satisfaction.

PRESENTING 2005!

Act New York 2005 builds on the 2004 edition with tons of new feature articles, interviews, reviews, and listings. So, take your time and enjoy the great people, places, services, and events featured inside.

2005 also brings some staff changes here at actorscraft.com. Key to this year's book has been Senior Editor Liz Berntson. Liz has worked as a writer, reporter, and teacher for the past four years in North Carolina and Florida. Her contributions to this book are just a few of the ways she continues to explore film and theater careers in and around Manhattan. She lives in Brooklyn with her husband, Ken ReCorr. Liz has given *Act New York 2005* a tasty, fresh flavor. Thank you Liz!

Of course, we have to thank Josh Young, our passionate executive director here at actorscraft, who, due to the sale of his screenplay and his first feature film directing job, is busy on location out in Alaska. Josh will, of course, be leading and inspiring us from the set. We also send big hugs of thanks to Kimshelley Garner, Stephie, Doobie, Lionel, Martha, Kirk, Sarah, Aaron, Curly, Buttons, and Ethel.

We invite you now to enter the book and enjoy! As you travel your own path as an actor in New York City, if you discover information you think would be useful for other New York actors to know about, please tell us so that we can consider including it in the 2006 edition of *Act New York*. You may do so by contacting Mrs. Anne Jillian, assistant to the executive director, at: www.actorscraft.com.

Good luck to you and be well!

All the Staff at,
actorscraft.com

ONE

Getting Coached

1. THE ACTOR'S GUIDE TO QUALIFIED ACTING COACHES 2005

SECTION A: *ACT NEW YORK'S* MASTER TEACHERS

We are proud to present four teachers who have devoted their lives to the art and craft of great acting. Their classes, year after year, are filled to the rafters, and they have students who come to study with them from all around the world. The comments we received from their students were profoundly moving. Also, these teachers have done highly praised work themselves as both actors and as directors, which gives them a broader perspective on the demands of the craft.

As for the interviews you are about to read, rather than list all of our questions, we simply deleted the questions and what remains is a very candid and personal look at the hearts and minds of these extraordinary acting coaches. We know you will enjoy meeting them as much as we did.

Master Teacher 1: Larry Silverberg

Editor's Introduction: Our first master teacher, Larry Silverberg, is known as one of the world's leading proponents of the Sanford Meisner approach to acting. In fact, the Academy Award–winning playwright and screenwriter Horton Foote wrote in his preface to one of Silverberg's books that "Larry is a gifted actor and director and a most inspired teacher of acting!"

Silverberg has also become the world's most widely published actor/ director, with an impressive list of books that have become the standard acting texts in the drama departments of universities, colleges, high schools, and private acting studios around the globe.

Most well known of Silverberg's books are his hugely successful four-volume series, *The Sanford Meisner Approach: An Actors Workbook,* as well as his revolutionary book *Loving to Audition.* Silverberg is also featured in the video production, *The Actors Journey: Larry Silverberg Teaches the Meisner Approach,* which we learned is now the number-one selling instructional video at the Drama Book Shop in New York.

Besides working as an actor and director all around the United States and in Canada, Silverberg founded an award-winning theater in Seattle, Washington—The Belltown Theatre Center— for which he served as artistic director for ten years. A couple of years ago, while in Seattle, he won the Seattle Critic's Association's "Stellar Acting Award" for his perform-

ance as Teach in the David Mamet play *American Buffalo* (directed by the gifted director, April Shawhan). Silverberg, living back on the East Coast again, now runs his rigorous, professional acting class —The Meisner Intensive Training Program — right here in New York, and he leads visitng master classes at acting schools around the world.

Here now is Larry Silverberg

I have been very lucky. I have worked with the best acting teachers of our time. I had the enormous privilege of being trained by Sanford Meisner at the Neighborhood Playhouse. After graduating from the playhouse, I did more advanced training in the professional class with the gifted actor/director/teacher, Suzanne Shepherd. Suzanne introduced me to another wonderful actor/ director/teacher, April Shawhan, who later directed me in a production of David Mamet's *American Buffalo.*

I was also very fortunate in that I had an extraordinary college acting teacher who trained us in a physical, improvisational process, which was all about unleashing our impulses, getting out of our heads, and taking big risks. When I began my classes with Sandy Meisner, I had already acquired one very useful thing: I was able to leap into the work without wasting a lot of time questioning it or trying to figure out where it was going. I saw many of my classmates spending more of their energy fighting the process than doing the work, and when I was invited back to attend the second year of the program, I noticed that the students who argued more than they worked weren't with us. Also, for whatever reason, I wanted very badly the things Sandy wanted to teach us.

My classes with Sandy were not only thrilling and incredibly demanding; they were profoundly eye-opening. My senses came to life for the first time, and I saw the world around me and myself in that world in completely new ways. Class after class, I felt as if I was shedding every possible layer of who I thought I was as I opened to the vibrantly alive present moment and to the discovery of who I truly was. Over time, I began to work from a deep well of personal meaning, and I experienced a power of expressing myself that I had no idea I was capable of. Also, for the first time in my life, I learned how to be truly available to another human being. I can honestly say that my classes with Sandy not only strengthened me as an actor, they saved my life.

Of course, it is my very biased opinion that the most healthy and organic of all the acting techniques is the Meisner Approach. Nothing else gets close. It is the most meticulous, step-by-step, and specific process. And what I know, after fifteen years of teaching the approach to students all around the world, is that if a student actually does the work with a ruthless consistency, he or she is going to grow as an artist in the most beautiful ways. At the same time, I must tell you, the work is clearly not for everyone. Students discover that the work is more demanding than anything they have encountered and in ways they never

could have imagined. There is a cost to this pursuit; the cost is personal and the price is high. You see, not everyone is willing to pay that price — but for those who are, the rewards are great.

If I boiled the whole thing down, I would say that one of the most important and elusive places an actor must arrive at in his or her work is "embracing everything, denying nothing." In other words, you must always say "yes!" Now, for this to occur, certain things have to be operating.

First, the actor must have his attention completely off himself. As opposed to life, where we are often completely self-absorbed (as are most actors in their work because their biggest concern is "looking good"), the true actor must become deeply available to life all around him, which, of course, includes his partners on stage. I call this kind of availability "listening with the ear of one's heart." This suggests that the actor's mind and heart must be wide open to his partners; wide open to what is actually happening in each moment. In this way, he embraces what his partners are giving him rather than rejecting it because it may not be what he would like or what he has previously planned.

The flip side of this is the ability to respond spontaneously, authentically, and fully to what the actor gets from her partners. This means that she must allow her natural, organic impulses to lead her, in other words, her humanity. You know, the head's function is survival and it is the great control mechanism. And because most actors want to be comfortable and "right," they never rise from the level of imitating what has already been done, what they already know. But what does this have to do with the creative process? Nothing! The only place we can really create from is the surprising place we suddenly discover when we enter the unknown. In this way, we embrace all that we are and everything we are experiencing moment by moment by moment.

As a concept, embracing everything sounds easy, but to get it into your body, into your heart, guts, and soul in a way that becomes as effortless as breathing takes rigorous work and tremendous desire. Desire!

The other major part of the work at this point has to do with learning how to really do something. Sandy taught us that acting is doing and that the basis of all acting is the "reality of doing." This alone is so exquisite it takes my breath away. The problem with most actors is that they are not "really doing" anything. They are merely speaking empty, hollow, and meaningless words, which they have no need to speak. But as the actor learns how to "really do what he is doing," a whole new world of living truthfully on stage or in front of the camera opens up that is not only enlivening for the actor, it gives the audience the experience that they are spying through a peephole and looking in on something absolutely and intimately true. This is when the audience member has the very rare experience of sitting on the edge of his or her seat not breathing, totally captivated by the life being lived out in front of them.

The other huge gift of this part of the process is that the "reality of doing" gives the actor the most simple and human answer to all the questions related to "emotion." I'll tell you, there is no bigger trap for actors than the realm of the emotions! Many approaches push, shove, and manipulate actors into the most unhealthy and inhuman ways of working with their emotional instrument. So most actors end up continually watching themselves and judging their own performance by how emotional they are in any particular moment. Emotional masturbation! Disaster!

The simple human truth is that in life our emotions happen naturally and freely when we are involved in doing things that have meaning to us. Imagine you were saving your mother from a burning car. Where would your attention be? It would be on your attempt to get your mother out of the car. Would you stop in the middle of this activity and think, "I should really break down and cry right now so all the people passing by will believe that I am an emotional person." Of course not, only bad actors do that! No, you would put every ounce of your being onto getting your mother out of the car, and as you really did that, you would have all kinds of emotional responses. Your emotions would come to life on their own without any extra effort on your part. Doesn't that make simple, human sense?

Anyway, all these things are the first things we work on in class. Then, once these skills have been made habitual, we can really get into working on text because now we have a passionately alive, available human being ready to lift those words off the page and fill them with life! So this is when we get to all the advanced elements of script analysis, interpretation, and character work.

Every person who wants to act has a choice. He can choose to be the "me, myself, and I" kind of actor and work at getting as slick as he can in hopes that the audience will buy all his mugging and faking. And there are plenty of very slick actors around. But you have to ask yourself, "Is that enough?" David Mamet once said the difference between a real actor and the slick actor is like the difference between a wood fire and a fluorescent light.

What does it mean to be an acting teacher? A few years back in one of my books, I wrote a paragraph listing the values I have experienced in my great teachers and the values I strive for in my own classes. Here's what I wrote:

The acting teacher must hold sacred the trust the students offer. The teacher must hold to the highest integrity, always championing for the highest good of the students. The teacher must be like an arrow, always aimed at the goal of teaching the skills that will lead each student towards discovering and improving their own, individual craft of acting. The acting teacher must not turn the learning space into a therapy session or an emotional war zone. The acting teacher must not break the student or abuse the student in any manner. The acting teacher must guide the students in such a way that the students become not more like the teacher, but more the expression of who they themselves truly are. The teacher must be a great listener. The teacher must be fully available in each moment so as to learn from each student what that student most needs. Finally, the teacher of acting must model simplicity, generosity, and humanity in the classroom; for these are the deeper components of the art of a true theater.

I love being in class. I just love it. I am continually inspired by the courage of my students, and I love working with them, facing the rigors of this grueling, exciting, and joyous process together. To me, it's the greatest, most thrilling place in the world.

Here are some comments from students of Larry Silverberg

"Larry is the best acting teacher I have known so far in my career. He has a ceaseless passion for the craft and demands that his students approach the work with the same awe and reverence as he does. He has been a taskmaster, and I learned quickly in this class that to do less than your most is to undermine not only the work, but also your own sense of well-being. I admire Larry so much for his discipline and his compassion. What I leave class with is the understanding that all the imagination, creativity, truth, and life I will ever need to be an actor is already inside me. Larry has opened me up to the world of myself and for that I shall be forever grateful."

D'Vorah Bailey

"Larry fearlessly challenged us to be present, to strengthen our points of view as human beings, as actors, and as artists. We all felt treated with integrity and respect at all times in our work with him. Larry's combination of good humor, warmth, and sharing of himself, while encouraging a dedication to hard work, made us all trust ourselves to go further than we'd ever been.

"As an actor, I continue to look for greater depth, a fuller revelation of my truth, a strengthening and opening of my imagination, and I believe my work is becoming richer as a result of the work we did together; my own faith has been strengthened and my passion has been nourished. It has been a pleasure and a privilege to work with Larry. Lucky are they who become his colleagues and students."

Garry Davey, Director
William Davis Centre
Vancouver, Canada

"I am so grateful to have had Larry come and work with me and our resident acting company. We were all impressed with his generosity of spirit and his desire to help us find our most artistic and dynamic selves. Larry challenged all of us to be more specific; to toss away all that was unnecessary and work from our most truthful and creative selves. Over the course of the workshop, our work became more exciting and meaningful. Larry enriched us and reset our compass, and we will continue to nourish the seed he has planted here."

Dave Demke, Artistic Director
Stark Raving Theatre
Portland, Oregon

"After having taken eighteen months of classes from another teacher, I felt that my acting was only truthful about 30 percent of my time and that I was spending far too much time thinking and not time enough being. My teacher had often sung the praises of Sanford Meisner, so I jumped at the opportunity to take Larry Silverberg's class, even though it meant driving for twelve hours a week from my home to the class.

"Larry opened my eyes and my soul to what acting is about. Starting with simple exercises, he took the whole class to a place of complete truth, a place where we followed our instincts safely, and where we were completely emotionally involved in the lives of the characters. Larry's classes have allowed me to live permanently in a world on stage of which I had only had brief glimpses before."

Robert French

To study with Larry Silverberg, call (212) 462-3005.
Web site: www.actorscraft.com

Master Teacher 2: Suzanne Shepherd

Editor's Introduction: Suzanne Shepherd is renowned as one of the finest acting teachers of our time. A very busy actress and director, Suzanne is currently playing Carmel's mother on the hit series, *The Sopranos.* You can also see Suzanne in her many movie appearances, which include, *Mystic Pizza, Working Girl, Second Sight, Uncle Buck, Goodfellas,*

Palookaville, Trees Lounge, Lolita, Lay of the Land, Never Again, On the Run, and *Jacob's Ladder*. On television, Suzanne has appeared on *Law and Order, Third Watch, One Life to Live,* and *As the World Turns.*

As a director, Suzanne has had a very special relationship with the plays of South African playwright Athol Fugard and has directed his plays *The Blood Knot, A Lesson From Aloes, Master Harold and the Boys,* and *Boesman and Lena,* and she has worked with some great actors, including Danny Glover, Joan Allen, Olympia Dukakis, and James Earl Jones.

Suzanne offers her professional ongoing scene study class at her own studio in New York City, which she has had in operation for over thirty years. Some of the staff here at actorscraft have studied with Suzanne, and the word is, if you are fortunate enough to get into her class, you've struck gold, my friend!

Here now is Suzanne Shepherd
The first indelible influence on me as a person in the theater, was Larry Arrick, a teacher at Bennington College. He introduced me to the active pursuit of an objective and the naming and playing of actions to achieve that objective. He challenged me and the class to use the most passionate means to that end. I was intoxicated by it — the total sense it made. The second major influence on me was Kenneth Burke, a literary critic with whom I was fortunate to work for two years. He taught me how to look at a piece of writing like an x-ray and to see its underlying meaning based on its specific use of language. The next major influence on me was and is Sandy Meisner. His approach and the vital exercises he developed focused me to work emotionally, spontaneously, and, finally, unintellectually. These three people are the cornerstones of my training, and in combination, they created a dialectic on which my work is based.

The essential thing in training is to ground the actor in specific and truthful behavior. The poet Marianne Moore said: "A poem is an imaginary garden with real toads in it." She hit the nail right on the head! That's what a play is too — an imaginary garden in which the real toads are the actors. That sounds high-falutin', but it really isn't. As Sandy Meisner says: "Acting is living truthfully under imaginary circumstances." Many actors don't know what that means. They do those monologues and talk to an empty chair. You can't look at that chair and tell me your brother's sitting in it — because he's not. Sandy said "imaginary circumstances," — not imaginary people. That's a lie; it's making believe. Acting is not making believe — acting is believing. I tell my students and the people I direct that an actor shouldn't do anything that people do not do. Good lord, the possibilities and the repertoire of what human beings do is infinite. Infinite and always, always grounded in the truth of their circumstances.

I read in the *New York Times* a few years ago about an earthquake in Russia: A mother, trapped in rubble, bit her own arm until she drew blood and made her child drink that blood. That was not a theatrical gesture. She was not a cannibal. That woman was doing what she had to do to keep her child alive. That is very extreme behavior, but it is utterly truthful under those circumstances. To be an actor is to inhabit another human being and to do, with all the courage and the passion, what that human being might do under specific circumstances.

An actor came to me the other day and did something from *Richard II*. Her husband was killed three months ago, and now her father-in-law has been killed and she's alone at his coffin. When she had finished, I asked, "What are you doing?" She said, "I'm working on the physical behavior of a queen." I said, "You're telling me your husband died. Did you like him?" She said, "Oh, I loved him." And I said, "Your father-in-law is the last connection that you have with your husband. So take it that it's your husband in that coffin. You might as well, right? And then, how do you feel about saying goodbye to him? Are you grief stricken? Is this a time to worry about if you're a queen, or if you look like one? Shakespeare wasn't writing queens. He was writing human beings responding articulately and emotionally to the specific events in their lives moment to moment. Have you ever seen a queen mourning? You're trying to show some theatrical ideas, not anything that is human and real."

A boy in another class did something from *Julius Caesar*. When I asked what he was doing, he said, "I'm venting my feelings." I said,

"No, the words do that. What are *you* doing?" He answered, "I'm expressing my anger." I said, "You're describing what you're doing. You can't act from a description. You can only act from a key. A key starts an engine; a description of a key does not."

I want to teach actors to be independent and to know how to x-ray a scene and see what's underneath it so that they're not acting the words, but living what it is that's going on in the circumstances and what their point of view is about it. "What do I want?" "What am I doing here?" I want an actor to be able to ask those questions and come up with some answers so that when he goes into a rehearsal room, he's not a helpless puppet. I'm dedicated to teaching actors to look at a text and to make choices that are doable and that excite the actor into emotionally vital and believable action.

The next thing I am interested in is character. Certainly, character has to do with many things, but one of the predominant things is point of view. A character has a specific point of view about everything. Characters like Stanley Kowalski or Blanche Dubois are distinctive, unique human beings. What makes them that way? Well, many things, but I'm not interested in going into what their mommy and daddy were like, what the tree was like in their backyard. That's not going to help you get out of the dressing room. A character has a globalized point of view — he sees everything the same way. Stanley Kowalski's got to be the king of the hill whether he's at work, at home — wherever he is. He's going to respond to everything and everybody from that point of view. Character comes from within you — how you see the world around you and how you relate to it and respond to it every moment.

I don't make a mystery of anything about acting. The only mystery is talent. No one knows where it comes from. It's a wonder and a holy thing. In training actors, I dedicate myself to respecting their talent by helping them make the best use of that talent.

All actors are insecure to some measure — I'm very careful about looking after that to the best of my ability. You see, I left acting for many years because I had no confidence and didn't feel I had the right to walk on stage. I'm mindful not to allow that to happen to people with talent. I try to help my students get rid of anything that stands in the way of their doing the work and enjoying it.

When interviewing students, I'm looking for a couple of things. I'm interested in working with serious people. I'm looking for how hungry they are to be an actor. God knows it's a crazy thing to want to be, but if you're going to be one, nothing will stop you. Also, I have them do some work, and I look to see how they respond to what I say — whether they light up with excitement, or whether it intimidates them. If it intimidates them, they may be wonderful, but I don't want to work with them. I don't want to work with somebody if I intimidate them. This forty-five minute encounter is the beginning of our rela-

tionship: how we are with each other, how we work together, how I feel being with them, and how they feel being with me. I am also interested in their intelligence. You can't be an actor and not be intelligent. They have to have a sense of humor. They have to be serious and alive. Ultimately, I have to have a good feeling about being with them or else I can't teach them. And they have to feel good about being with me or they shouldn't study with me.

I have been so lucky for the twenty-one years I have been teaching. I don't know how it happens or why, but the actors in my classes are genuinely supportive of each other's work. I have such beautiful people come to me. I have been blessed, and I'm deeply grateful for it. I'm not being sentimental, but there is an enormous amount of respect, an enormous amount of love and very serious attention to the work — theirs and their fellow actors'.

Value and respect your own experience. You can't act without a complete acknowledgment of your own experience. If somebody makes you feel lousy and weak, get away from that person. There's a sign in a Las Vegas casino that says "You must be present to win." Work with people who encourage your ability to be here now, claim every moment and enjoy your experience living in the imaginary gardens.

Here are some comments from students of Suzanne Shepherd

"After meeting with seven different acting coaches, I audited one of Suzanne's classes and knew immediately that I wanted to work with her. I have learned from Suzanne to trust my body, to stay in the moment, to relax, to prepare better, and to take risks. She also taught me how to have fun and enjoy myself in my work. Just listening to Suzanne respond to a scene in class, whether I was in it or not, was always exciting. "Not only is Suzanne completely available in class, she gets everyone involved and supportive of the other class members; the energy in class is fantastic. Suzanne once said something that I will always remember: 'Everything is grist for the mill — including the mill.' That's Suzanne!"

Gregory Hines

"Suzanne's approach in dealing with the actor is a kind of *via negativa*— the belief that if you get the block out of the way, what remains will be perfect. She frees actors to be in their own experience. I have learned so many important things from Suzanne. Some are: people don't try to feel — only actors do; What time is it? if you are an actor, the answer is always now; your body never lies; if you really do A — it will take you to B; when you read a script, listen to it very quietly and it will speak to you; dedicate yourself to what you want to be and do and the rest will take care of itself. Most of all, I have learned about truth. Studying with Suzanne you develop an allergy to bullshit, to things false, theatrical, sentimental, and romantic.

"Suzanne helps you create good habits so that when you've flown the coop and are doing your thing in the world, you'll know what to do. Re-

ally, the most supportive thing a teacher can tell you is the truth. Suzanne does that."

Irene Glezos

"By the second week of working with Suzanne, I knew I had never seen a teacher in any field work so passionate and with such precise intelligence at the same time. Also, there is nothing frivolous or jaded in Suzanne. She is serious without the pretentiousness of "Art with a capital A," and she is spontaneously and endlessly funny. In Suzanne's presence, it is impossible to think that the large enterprise of acting, directing, playwriting, and filmmaking — the whole set of dramatic arts — is anything except directly expressive of the most important things in life and deeply necessary to living.

"On any day of class, it's a good bet that you will see something more alive than anything you could buy a ticket for in New York. Again and again, the natural power and beauty of a particular student is suddenly unleashed, and you see that student do more than you had thought possible. I attribute this to Suzanne's genuine interest and great patience."

Leo Rubinfien

"In my work with Suzanne, there are constantly moments of self-revelation so intense that it is as if she has magical abilities to read right to the core of my being. She knows how to plumb the proper depths, touch the right nerve, and guide the intellect with a simple phrase. Through her passion, Suzanne infuses the art of acting with joy and shows you how to take the ride with abandon.

"Suzanne provides a place where experimentation is welcome; there is permission to make mistakes and trust is given. Outside class, I feel comfortable reaching out to Suzanne as a touchstone to get through the minefields of professional life."

Leigh Silber

To study with Suzanne Shepherd, call (212) 873-5324.

Master Teacher 3: April Shawhan

Editor's Introduction: We are very proud to bring you our third featured acting coach, renowned actress, director, choreographer, and teacher, April Shawhan. Although April currently offers her private classes and coaching sessions out on the West Coast, as well as teaching at UCLA, she comes to New York from time to time, and if you can get into a class when she is here, don't miss the opportunity to study with her. If you are heading out to Los Angeles, be sure to call April for classes and private coaching.

April has worked in film and has had recurring roles on television, but it is her extensive experience acting on Broadway and Off Broadway and in national tours and the country's finest regional theaters where we really see the depth of her impressive and award-winning career. On Broadway, April appeared in *A Streetcar Named Desire, Rex, Over Here, A History of American Film,* *Much Ado About Nothing, Dinner at Eight, Three Bags Full,* and *A Race of Hairy Men.* She has worked with director greats, including Larry Arrick, Nikos Psacharopoulos, Hal Prince, Tyrone Guthrie, and Gower Champion.

In regional theaters, she has appeared in *Betrayal, Who's Afraid of Virginia Woolf,* and *A Lesson from Aloes* (wonderfully directed by Suzanne Shepherd). April's credits here are way too long to list, but her beautifully crafted performances have been enjoyed in the great regional theaters, including Yale Rep, Pittsburgh Public Theatre, Trinity Square Rep, Williamstown, and the Asolo.

Here now is April Shawhan

From a very young age, I wanted to be and was a dancer. Oh, the freedom and power to be able to leap and spin and to be accompanied by great classical music! In high school, I had a teacher named Leah Funk. She taught English and drama. She introduced me to literature and plays. I entered Forensic League contests. The best part of my week was Saturday. I worked privately with Ms. Funk, and she gave me a passion for reading. We worked on scenes from *The Heiress, The Glass Menagerie,* and *The Diary of Anne Frank.* It was then that I realized I must be an actor.

Although I've had superb acting teachers, my biggest influence as a teacher has been my professional acting career and my continuing work as an actor, director, and teacher. When my husband, Larry Arrick, asked me to conduct an acting class at the Trinity Rep Conservatory, which he was heading at the time, I replied that I didn't know the first thing about teaching acting — and that was the beginning of my teaching career.

I had been a professional actress for many years on Broadway, Off Broadway, television, and in regional theaters. I worked with such directors as Tyrone Guthrie, Joseph Papp, Gower Champion, Nikos Psachorapolis, Hal Prince, and Larry Arrick. Now my job was to organize and articulate what I had learned from these experiences so that others could learn from them. Nothing I had done before prepared me for trying to explain how I'd done it. Even more daunting was to translate what I worked at every day into a language and procedure that could result in a viable and teachable acting technique.

An actor needs tools, and it is our job as teachers to furnish these tools. I have drawn from many techniques, including the so-called Method and also from Meisner techniques — but mostly from what I have discovered and developed over the years as a practicing professional actress. Perhaps it was my very early training as a dancer and singer that convinced me of the importance of warm-up exercises to bring the creative instrument to its maximum efficiency.

It is also important for an actor to have experience with exercises for relaxation, concentration, imagination, and improvisation. I often use games children play to help actors understand strong actions, specific objectives, and varieties of adjustments. Sometimes I ask the student to observe a fellow student in the class and try to inhabit his or her behavior or mannerisms. This is not for the purpose of imitation — but for the actor to search for the essence of another human being. In other words, the beginning of work on "creating a character." This exercise can be expanded to include work on animals (actual, imaginary, literary), people observed on the street, family members, and so on.

Storytelling is an important part of the actor's skill. Exercises to help the actor recall and reexperience memories from her past can work as an introduction to "substitution" and "emotional preparation" work. The deeper the actor's personal emotional connection to her character's situation, the more profound her work can be. I particularly like exercises involving singing because I believe music is the easiest, best connection to our emotions.

Virginia Woolf said, "Writing a novel is like walking through a dark room with a lantern which illuminates the things that were always there." I think exercises are our lantern. In an exercise, you *do,* you don't perform. This can and must be transferred into our working on the text.

As a teacher, I have utmost respect for the text. Once we illuminate what is there within us, we need to bring that light to illuminate the worlds we are trying to inhabit. I encourage my students to ask questions about the circumstances of the text, the relationships of the characters, and the back story of the characters. I do this by giving them a list of questions and by asking the questions myself until they learn to question, question, and then question some more. Then I encourage them to make choices that are informed by their understanding of the text and their imagination. Making a commitment to your choices will result in your being "in the moment."

Besides the exercises and techniques that are necessary for all students to master, it is necessary for a teacher or a coach to know what each individual actor needs at a particular moment of development. Just as an actor must be in the moment, so must the teacher. I believe that it's not only what you teach but how you teach that is important.

As a young actress I was cast to play Ophelia opposite Martin Sheen in a production of *Hamlet* directed by Joseph Papp. Every rehearsal was exciting, daring, playful, and revealing because Joe brought so much passion, and his passion infected the whole cast. Anytime I walk into a classroom or a private coaching or a rehearsal hall, I am reminded of how infectious appetite and passion can be. I took forward to my students or fellow actors surprising themselves and me and to us making discoveries that are dangerous and unpredictable. But for there to be danger and passion, there must be an environment of trust and freedom. Nothing grows unless it is nurtured.

To quote one of my students, "When I first came to class, I thought acting was all about me. But now I realize I am a small part of a much larger thing." I quoted to her from the artist Anselm Kiefer, "I want to communicate through my work. All I want is something that goes through me and results in something." That's what makes me act and direct and teach because it becomes more than itself.

Here are some comments from students of April Shawhan

"April is both precise and gentle, and she is able to create an atmosphere of safety and compassion in her classroom. I quickly grew to love April for her patience and her uncanny way of nudging me to greater places with my work. I refer her far and wide as the best acting teacher I have ever had. I call her my 'secret weapon.' Her extensive study and decades of experience allow her to always approach a student on his or her level. She was able to build on the craft that I already had and push me to take new risks with my work.

"April also directed me in a play three years ago. Her direction was much like her teaching style: direct, sure-handed, respectful of the actor, and always gentle. She chooses to make a play a collaborative process in which the actor's character choices and visions contribute to the final direction of the work. Her lack of ego and obvious love for the work itself are always at the heart of her directing.

"I consider April to have had the greatest influence of any teacher on my growth as an artist. If I were cast in a major role today, she is the first person I would call for coaching because I have total faith that she brings out the best in me as an actor."

Sarah Liwnicz

"I did individual coaching with April over a period of five years. We met weekly and worked primarily on monologues. April is a truly outstanding teacher. She brings tremendous focus and energy to every session, communicates clearly, directly, and with lots of humor, and creates a safe and supportive environment in which one can take risks and experiment.

"April opened my eyes to a whole new array of tools I could use to develop a character. She was always ready with an exercise or an improvisation about a character's circumstances that would help me deepen my connection to the material. She encouraged me to explore text with movement and sound. I learned that 'homework' on a character can be experienced on your feet and not just imagined. Then I saw how this eclectic approach informed my performance of a piece. It was an exhilarating, successful, and joyous process!

"April was also able to convince me that no acting problem is unsolvable; there is always at least a way to work on any obstacle. She taught me that with hard work and imagination, one will move forward. To me, this is a sign of a truly inspirational coach."

Anne Stockton

"April has given me what I like to call a tool belt of skills. And each tool on my belt has prepared me for the different directors and actors I've come up against in the professional world. For a few hours a week, in April's class, I had a safe environment to take risks and be guided by a nonjudgmental, sensitive, artistic soul. On numerous sets, auditions, and rehearsal rooms in my career, I have been so thankful to have the resources given to me by April."

Michael Fitzgerald

To study with April Shawhan, call (310) 441-9578.

Master Teacher 4: Carol Fox Prescott

Editor's Introduction: We are thrilled to bring you our newest master acting teacher, Carol Fox Prescott. Carol has worked in the professional theater as actress, director, and teacher for close to forty years, playing featured and leading roles in New York, national touring companies, and regional theaters throughout the country. Her roles include such varied characters as Tzeitle in *Fiddler on the Roof* with Zero Mostel and again with Luther Adler; Agnes Nolan in *George M!* with Mickey Rooney; Catherine in *Pippin*, directed by Bob Fosse; and Guitele in *The Rothschilds* opposite Hal Linden. She appeared as Kate in Shakespeare's *The Taming of the Shrew* and Celia in *As You Like It*, as well as the title role in Ibsen's *Hedda Gabbler*. Most recently, she was a standby for Ellen Burstyn on Broadway in *Sacrilege*.

Carol's teaching career began with a nine-year tenure at The American Academy of Dramatic Arts and Five years at the T. Schreiber Studio in New York City, after which she created her own studio where she teaches classes in her unique approach to acting, based on breathing, awareness, and joy. Carol also coteaches special workshops in musical theater with Broadway musical director Edward Strauss, "Acting with the Camera" workshops with award-winning filmmaker Geoffrey Sharp, and "Off Balance & On Target" weekend intensives with master improvisation teacher Gary Austin.

Here now is Carol Fox Prescott
I didn't have what I would call a mentor, but I certainly had influences. Why I say I didn't have a mentor is that where I had professional relationships, they never passed beyond the classroom. It may simply have been because I was very shy when I was young, and I got what I could and snuck away with it.

Peter Brook had a tremendous impact on me. From his work, from his productions, from his books, and from hearing him talk. Morris Carnovsky was an enormous influence on me. I spent a summer when I was in college at the American Shakespeare Festival and was with him and watched him work. He made me realize clearly, in no uncertain terms, when I was twenty years old, that he never became the character. I sat there in his living room and watched him literally transform himself in just talking about different characters, and when

I commented on that, he got very upset and said, "I'm not a different person. It's just what I do that looks different." So, I count that as my first real acting lesson, because I really got it.

When I got out of school, I worked with two people who were my primary acting teachers. One was a guy named Joshua Shelly, who was a group theater person and then was blacklisted in the early fifties, so he never had the kind of career that the other people had. He was a wonderful teacher. And I worked with Charles Nelson Reilly at the HB Studio because I was a singer. And so I have this kind of traditional method training on one side with Josh, and I had this buoyant, exuberant, thrilling, based on nothing but, "Are you enjoying yourself?" training with Charlie. I worked with Bobby Lewis for a while, and that was very wonderful, too. And then the other big influence was Michael Moriart, who was the first person that I heard say, "It's all in the breath."

By that time, I had been teaching a few years already. I was acting and teaching, and I was basically teaching everything that I had been taught, and sometimes it worked and sometimes it didn't. I don't have a good memory — I don't remember my childhood very well, and so you know, in emotional memory exercises, I was lost. It never meant anything.

Then, I did a scene and just worked on noticing where the tension was coming from and relaxing it. And that was my total point of focus. And you know, that was the best work I did up until that point.

Carol *Fox* Prescott:

Acting Classes

A Physical Approach to Acting

Based on Breathing, Awareness and Joy

Acting Technique and Scene Study

Musical Theatre Scene Study and Audition Skills

Off Balance/On Target Weekend Improv/Text Intensives

The Basement Space
102 West 75th Street
New York, NY 10023
(212) 501-7776

www.CarolFoxPrescott.com

And I never understood what that was. Interestingly, as a singer, I had much more access to my emotional instrument, and in a very easy way, than I did in my early acting training. And I couldn't understand it, and nobody could explain it to me. It was such a bleak discomfort for me. And I realized many years later that it was because I was breathing kind of funny. It was that simple. But we didn't know. Nobody knew.

So there's something about my experience back then that I have come to find out kinesthetically. I don't necessarily experience visually. I don't necessarily experience literally. So I had to go about finding a way of working that fit the way I learn. And now in my teaching, I'm very mindful of how people learn, so that I can adjust what I'm doing. The easiest people to teach, of course, are the people who receive things the way I do. The challenge is, when somebody is very literal or visual, to find ways of translating what I do so that they get it.

I teach a method of acting based on breathing, awareness and joy. If you're having a good time, it's very likely that everybody else is too. And that's all there is to it. I teach mixed level classes, so that in any given class, I'll have people who are beginning actors, people who are more experienced actors but who are beginning with me, people who have been with me for a long time, as well as people who are working and then come back to class when they're in town.

My classes are four hours long. The first hour or so is a warm-up exercise. It's a physical vocal/breathing warm-up, and within it, it contains the seeds of all the concepts that I work with. Then I'll do an exercise that gives people the experience of working with the breath without the pressure of text. It's all group work; everybody's doing it. And it's very simple work. The problem with learning it is that it's so simple that people want to complicate it. The only thing that is difficult about it is that the breath is a very direct route into very deep emotional responses. I think of it like learning how to ride a bucking bronco: For some people, when the feelings come up really intensely, they're home free. But for other people, they need to learn how to move with that energy rather than sitting on it and going up into their heads and trying to make it right.

As a teacher, I think my strongest suit is how much I love to teach, and it's always a surprise to me. I can walk into class feeling like the whole world is falling in on me and find myself — in a moment — blissful. So I don't know where that comes from, but I'm very grateful for it. I think I have the ability to listen so that I can address each person very specifically. I love acting, and I think that's the reason I focused on teaching, because it's the ideal world of acting that really turns me on.

I try to create a learning environment that is as safe as possible. I can be tough. I can be very demanding, but I make sure that before I do that, there's a safe, loving environment from which to learn. My first choice is always to be as gentle as possible, to get people laughing a lot. I've had experience with put-down teachers and dangerous teachers, and I work very hard to create a healthy environment. When I give the students feedback, I make it's positive and that I am teaching what works, because people know what doesn't work. People know when they don't feel right. So I find that the safer I can create the environment, the harder that I can be, and people seem to appreciate that.

This is not one of the traditional techniques. It is simply a useable, tangible, delicious acting technique that works. I had a conversation with a woman recently who's a student at the Strasberg Institute, and she asked all these questions about my work, and I was talking and talking, and she was really probing, and then she finally said to me, "So, what technique do you use?" So I said, "What are you, the method police?" So I think there's a part of me that keeps expecting the method police to come and close me down. But I love this work, and it works, and it's very exciting when it works. So I guess if anything, it's not just who I am and how I do it, but that this is a very reliable, tangible, body-based technique that I can take with me anywhere.

I like to work with passionate students, people who have to act. I don't care about the rest. I don't care how old they are or how experienced or inexperienced they are or anything. People who really want to do it are the people that I want to work with. If the passion is there, the instrument is there. I really believe that.

Here are some comments from students of Carol Fox Prescott

"Carol tries to instill in her students that each one of us is 'enough' and that we have everything we need; that through inspiration (literally, through the breath) and with the playwright's words, the universe will give me a full and satisfying experience. In the three years I have been with Carol, I have learned to act fully; to trust myself and my fellow actors; to live in my body while honoring my intellect; and to carry around inside myself the safe place that Carol provides in her classroom."

Cathleen Charleson

"In the eight months I have been with Carol, I have learned to take risks in my work. Before I started working with Carol, I was very rigid and unable to bring a physical life to my work. I am now able to have fun and enjoy the work. I am able to let go and follow my instincts, which is very exciting and wonderful. Recently, I brought in a song that required a great deal of movement and after working with Carol, I got the job.

"Carol's warmth, support, her joy of teaching, and her availability have had tremendous impact on me. I now am able to work with love and without worrying about being judged. Need I say more? She's the best."

Jessica Frankel

"Carol has drilled into me that I am responsible for my own creative process and that if I am really working, the role will always be new for me. She emphasizes how important it is to really listen and to never rest on past accomplishment. That no matter how badly a role is written or how long we have been performing it, we must always approach it with an open heart and be willing to experience it anew each night.

"One of the most meaningful moments in class was watching a man who couldn't sing a single note on key, sing a Sondheim song straight from his heart. And class is exciting weekly because Carol never lets us just 'get through' a piece of work. Carol is always a phone call away and never minds taking the time to help me with acting problems. Many of her previous students return to class to work on new roles or to continue developing as actors. The other people in class and myself are growing and struggling to become artists. Carol has created the environment for this."

Carol Grose

To study with Carol Fox Prescott, call (212) 501-7776.
Web site: www.carolfoxprescott. com

SECTION B: QUALIFIED COACHES

Josh's Spotlight On: Rebecca VerNooy

Rebecca specializes in a technique called "Authentic Movement." Here's what she had to say.

Authentic Movement offers one a profound experience and understanding of what it means to be unedited, nonjudgmental, and in one's body (and so recognize your harsh, inner critic because that is the voice that will put a stop to any creative impulse).

What inspires me to teach is that I get to see the potential for growth and change every day. The inspiration to teach is also really selfish: I learn so much from my students — about truth, fear, desire, and our capacity for compassion. I also get to give people permission to play, and I get to be a part of that. By the way, it is also important to live well and have fun! Because if it's not fun, why bother? Allowing oneself to play is a big piece of the puzzle.

Students should know that I value hard work and honesty, and that, to me, acting is the exploration of human behavior and motivation as dictated by the text and informed by life experience, being in the moment, and working from impulse. So I always look for students who have a real curiosity about life and who are willing to take risks. I also want to know that the student and I understand each other on some fundamental level.

Rebecca VerNooy
Rebecca VerNooy: (212) 765-7021
E-mail: vernooyr@aol.com
Private Coaching: Yes, $60–$80 per hour
Admission Policy: By interview.

Classes
Authentic Movement and Creative Process
Fee: $120 per month
Schedule: Sat., 1–3:30 PM

Beginning Professional Acting

Fee: $210 per month
Schedule: Tues. and Thurs., 6:30–
9:30 PM (twice a week)

Movement for Actors

Fee: $120 per month

Joanna Beckson

My Own Training

BS, education and social studies, Temple University, Philadelphia; Neighborhood Playhouse School of Theatre New York City (two-year graduate program). Member of Circle Repertory Company-LAB for five years (New York City).

My Performance Background

Off-Off Broadway, Off Broadway, and regional theater/summer stock. Also numerous commercials, *Law and Order* episodes, and independent feature films.

My Teaching Philosophy

1. To trust one's instincts, because they're perfect.
2. To support and nurture the most human qualities in the artist.
3. To create a safe environment to explore the above.

What Inspires Me to Teach

Being present and witnessing the fulfillment of self-discovery and self-expression, through the craft and artistry of another human being.

Other Important Things for Prospective Students to Know

Adjunct professor, New York University, SCPS (Department of Film and Video); director of Off Broadway and Off-Off Broadway plays; consultant for Disney and Paramount studios.

How I Would Describe the Art of Acting

The ability to be in the moment, truthfully and without self-consciousness, so that the actor can express fully his or her responses and to take the facility to play seriously.

What I Look for When I Interview a Prospective Student

1. Willingness to discuss oneself through the practice of the craft.
2. Commitment to taking risks, to grow, to change, to feel the work.

The Kind of Student Who Gets the Most Working with Me

Someone who learns to trust their instincts, who isn't afraid to fail and begin again, and who has a passion for the art of acting.

The Facts

Years Teaching: 21
Address: 325 W. 38th Street,
Suite 204
New York, NY 10018
Studios: J. Beckson Studio and New York University, S.C.P.S, Department of Film and Television/Video
Phone: home (212) 620-0098; work (917) 749-6922
E-mail: jtbeck417@aol.com
Private Coaching: Yes, $85 per hour
Admission Policy: Business and personal recommendation along with personal interview.

Classes

Meisner Foundations
Fee: $285
Schedule: Mon. and Wed.,
5:30–8:30 PM (9-month commitment;
Tues. and Thurs., 7–10 PM (9-month
commitment)

Professional Workout Workshop
Fee: $200
Schedule: Mon., 8:30–11:30 PM
(monthly commitment)

Intermediate/Advanced Class
Fee: $200
Schedule: Wed., 8:30–11:30 PM
(8-month commitment)

Sitcom Workshop
Fee: $395
Schedule: Intensive, one-month
audition class

Tanya Berezin

My Own Training
Boston University School of Theatre;
James Tuttle (Meisner Technique);
Chuck Jones (voice); Clive Vinson
(Shakespeare); Patsy Rodenberg
(voice).

My Performance Background
Circle Repertory Company (cofounder and member of acting company); Lanford Wilson's *The Mound
Builders* (Obie Award); film and
television.

My Teaching Philosophy
As a teacher, I concentrate on developing the actor's instrument through
helping the artist meet specific challenges until he or she is confident in
risk taking. As a coach, I want to get
the richest life of that instrument to
performance.

What Inspires Me to Teach
I'm inspired by the limitless possibilities in the study of this craft —
by my students, their myriad imaginations, and the joy of discovery.

Other Important Things for Prospective Students to Know
For five years, while I was working
with my private clients, I was serving as resident acting coach on a
number of daytime TV shows. The
large amount of material to be accomplished demanded that I find
ways to help the actor grow while I
focused on bringing the fullest work
to the set each day.

How I Would Describe the Art of Acting
The study of acting is the study of
humanity. It begins with the artist's
own humanity and goes on to be inspired by what we see in others, in
the world, and, finally, in the vision
of a writer. We go from knowing
ourselves and being free with who
we are and progress, through the
imagination, to infinite possibilities.

What I Look for When I Interview a Prospective Student
I want to see true curiosity, the
courage to say, "I don't know," a
commitment to explore.

The Kind of Student Who Gets the Most Working with Me
The students in their early careers get
a sense of the possibilities they can
bring to their work as artists. With
the more accomplished artist, I work
to open doors, remove roadblocks.
It's important that a student see this
work as a process.

The Facts

Years Teaching: 10
Address: 171 W. 79th Street
New York, NY 10054
Phone: (212) 874-1945
(646) 322-5452 (West Coast)
Fax: (212) 874-3862
E-mail: Tberezin@bellatlantic.net
Private Coaching: Yes, $110 per hour
Admission Policy: Interview.

Classes

Acting technique
Fee: $650 for 10 weeks
Scene study
Fee: $650 for 10 weeks

Kathryn Bild

My Own Training

Frank London, California; Lorrie Hull, Ed DeLeo, and Stella Adler.

My Performance Background

Palace of Fine Arts, San Francisco. Television commercials, produced television commercials and videos.

My Teaching Philosophy

I look at acting, as I try to do with everything in life, from a spiritual perspective, because I think that is the truest one. My sense of it is that each man and woman is an individual expression of all that is magnificent in life and that our privilege is to continue to grow into that understanding.

What Inspires Me to Teach

I love to teach. It's one of the most effective ways to learn.

Other Important Things for Prospective Students to Know

I help students to determine, for themselves, their own current most probable "castability," the types of roles they think they are best suited to play. I am the author of the books, *Acting From a Spiritual Perspective* and *The Actor's Quotation Book* (both published by Smith and Kraus).

How I Would Describe the Art of Acting

As does all art, acting elucidates truth for an audience.

What I Look for When I Interview a Prospective Student

I trust that when a student comes to me, it's because he or she has been led to me, that the universe matches us up. And I let the student decide whether or not he or she wants to hire me as his or her next teacher; I take the role of employee.

The Kind of Student Who Gets the Most Working with Me

I do best with the student who is enthusiastic and has an innate sense that something bigger than ourselves is running the show and is prompting him or her to step up onto stage and be part of it.

The Facts

Years Teaching: 13
Address: 1341 Second Avenue, #5N
New York, NY 10021
Studios: Private and the
New York Film Academy
Phone: (212) 517-3265
Fax: (212) 517-5713
E-mail: kmbild@aol.com

Web Site: www.kathrynmariebild.com
Private Coaching: Yes, $80 per
90 minutes
Admission Policy: All are welcome for
private coaching. Must audition for .
workshop.

Classes
**8-week Advanced Student
Scene Study Workshop**
Fee: $400

Robert Dagny

My Own Training
An acting career starting in my teens,
two years training personally with
Stella Adler, and on the job as a professional actor.

My Performance Background
Off Broadway, regional theater, film,
television, commercials. I am a member of AEA, SAG, AFTRA, SSOC,
and the Dramatists Guild.

My Teaching Philosophy
Actors should control their auditions. Creator of "The Performers
Audition Package," I find material
suitable for each actor and use exercises for control and confidence at
auditions to show their talent and
choices — not their insecurity.

What Inspires Me to Teach
My inspiration is watching raw talent blossom into confident actors
able to impress agents and casting directors enough to get them work.

Other Important Things for
Prospective Students to Know
Show me your passion and commit-

ment for acting and you will find an
acting coach willing to assist you in
your goals.

How I Would Describe the
Art of Acting
It is an equation: talent, imagination,
passion, commitment, and total discipline added to physical and mental stamina required for the realities
of the business.

What I Look for When I
Interview a Prospective Student
Assuming real talent is evident, the
necessary requirements are intelligence, presence, and a willingness to
be fearlessly creative.

The Kind of Student Who
Gets the Most Working with Me
Students who believe that acting is
serious business, do their homework,
show up on time, and move beyond
technique and process to become
artists.

The Facts
Years Teaching: 26
Address: P.O. Box 852, FDR Station
New York, NY 10150-0852
Phone: (212) 371-8258
E-mail: Robert@actorsauditioncoaching.
com
Private Coaching: Yes, $60 per hour
Admission Policy: Interview/audition is
obligatory.

Colette Duvall

My Own Training
I started training at the Alley Theatre
in Houston, Texas. Graduated from
the American Academy of Dramat-

ic Arts, three years with Daryl Hickman, and one summer at BADA.

My Performance Background

I'm still acting and now directing theater and film. Twelve years of appearing in commercials, sitcoms, soap opera, and film in Los Angeles and ten years in New York film and theater.

My Teaching Philosophy

I'm not a critic or director in the classroom. If it's not working we fix it, explore it, and make it happen now.

What Inspires Me to Teach

Every week my students open up and share their humanity and dare to live their dream. So beautiful!

Other Important Things for Prospective Students to Know

My training and technique is Stanislavski based, but with more specificity to attain performance level on your own without a director.

How I Would Describe the Art of Acting

Emotional creativity. Making the subconscious, conscious. Moment to moment, through a choice, honoring the script.

What I Look for When I Interview a Prospective Student

The courage to claim and explore your emotional life and work through socialized blocks.

The Kind of Student Who Gets the Most Working with Me

Artists. Acting is artistry and craftsmanship: "The more you know, the higher you climb, the higher you climb, the less you know."

The Facts

Years Teaching: 11
Address: The Creative Acting Company
122 W. 26th Street, 11th Floor
New York, NY 10001
Phone: (212) 352-2103
(917) 304-8870
E-mail: c.duvall2@verizon.net
Web Site: www.allinoneacting.com
Private Coaching: Yes, $60 per hour
Admission Policy: Weekend Film Intensive prerequisite for all on-camera classes. Advanced Technique requires an audit.

Classes

Weekend Film/TV intensive
Fee: $325
Schedule: Every 3 weeks throughout the year
Audition for Film/Sit-com
Fee: $325
Schedule: 6 weeks alternating film and sit-com on Wed. eve.
Advanced Technique
Fee:$195
Schedule: Ongoing monthly on Thurs. eve.
Film/Sit-Com Workshops
Fee: $325
Schedule: 6-week specials during the year

Catherine Gaffigan

My Own Training

MA in speech and drama, Catholic University of America, Washington, DC; two-year program at James Tuttle Studio, New York.

My Performance Background
Broadway, Off Broadway, summer and winter stock, National Tour, Shakespeare, musical comedy, film, daytime, commercials, industrials, television broadcasting.

My Teaching Philosophy
Aspiring artists bloom at different tempos; therefore patience and persistence are necessary from both teacher and the student. Talent, even in undeveloped state, always reveals itself.

What Inspires Me to Teach
Love of the work.

Other Important Things for Prospective Students to Know
My goal is to see my students acting on stage and on screen.

How I Would Describe the Art of Acting
Truthful human behavior in fictional circumstances.

What I Look for When I Interview a Prospective Student
Passion!

The Kind of Student Who Gets the Most Working with Me
Disciplined, intelligent, intuitive, emotionally available.

The Facts
Years Teaching: 30
Studio: My own studio in the theater district.
Phone: (212) 586-6300
Web Site: group:yahoo.com/group/catherinegaffigan
Private Coaching: Yes, $100 per half hour.

Admission Policy: Personal private interview with prospective student.

Classes
Sat. 11 AM–3 PM
Fee: $205 per month (16 hours)
Thurs 6–10 PM
Fee: $205 per month (16 hours)

Bill Galarno

My Own Training
BA degree in theater, Michigan State University, with additional work at Ohio University and the Royal National Theatre Studio in London.

My Performance Background
For over thirty years I have supported myself as an actor, theater director, playwright, and coach. My performing has included Broadway, Off Broadway, and TV and film, ranging from comedy and musical theater to the classics with emphasis on Shakespeare verse speaking.

My Teaching Philosophy
Having been blessed with a wealth of fine training, I aim to share it with today's performers, who will (I hope) digest it, make it their own, and pass it on to future generations.

What Inspires Me to Teach
As director, actor, and coach, I am intimately aware of the sacrifices talented individuals make in pursuing the theatrical life. We are never finished learning our craft and must continually maintain and upgrade our skills, vocal technique, physical preparedness, and emotional responsiveness.

Other Important Things for Prospective Students to Know

My focus as a coach is primarily on the text, be it contemporary comedy, Shakespearean tragedy, a piece of commercial copy or a song. I am extraordinarily patient with my students, yet do see acting as work, not play, and therefore expect them to work diligently.

How I Would Describe the Art of Acting

I think of acting as a craft in which the actor conveys the author's (and, yes, the director's) intentions. Acting, then, is the task of clearly telling the play's story, using voice, body, and emotion to propel the forward action of the play.

What I Look for When I Interview a Prospective Student

A sense of purpose, an open mind, plus an awareness of what the student feels he or she is lacking (and hoping to remedy). Also, a willingness to practice at home and bring improvement back into the studio.

The Kind of Student Who Gets the Most Working with Me

Both advanced professionals and motivated beginners who wish to move forward in their craft and who respect that balance of work and study that constitutes the working actor's life.

The Facts

Years Teaching: 19
Address: 461 W. 44th Street, #1-E
New York, NY 10036
Phone: (212) 765-9002
Private Coaching: Yes, $40 per hour

Gillien Goll

My Own Training

MA in directing, Hunter College; BA, Barnard College; study with Harold Clurman, Lloyd Richards, Darryl Hickman, Rae Allen.

My Performance Background

Circle Rep, MTC, Lincoln Center, SNL, Conan, 100 Center Street; *ER*, *Sex and the City* scenes with Robin Williams, Mary McDnell, Elliott Gould, Kristin Davis.

My Teaching Philosophy

Create a safe, supportive environment where the actors can learn to trust their instincts and not feel the need to predetermine their feelings.

What Inspires Me to Teach

To constantly learn and grow, to see my students blossom into actors who have a confident, healthy technique that works.

Other Important Things for Prospective Students to Know

I offer on-camera coaching. I believe in working though our imaginations and in understanding the character the author wrote, rather than reliving our own life traumas.

How I Would Describe the Art of Acting

Being real in any imaginary circumstance, being in the moment and communicating with one's acting partners, being true to the script.

What I Look for When I Interview a Prospective Student

A responsible, professional approach and openness to exploration of an acting process. My student are often refugees from destructive teaching methods.

The Kind of Student Who Gets the Most Working with Me
Any actor willing to do the work!

The Facts
Years Teaching: 16
Address: P.O. Box 250795
New York, NY 10025
Studio: American Musical and Dramatic Academy (AMDA)
Phone: (212) 501-6196
Fax: (212) 280-6758
E-mail: gollmark@aol.com
Web Site: www.gilliengoll.com
Private Coaching: Yes, $60 per hour
Admission Policy: By phone interview.

Peter Jensen

My Own Training
Graduate, American Academy of Dramatic Arts; Hunter College theater major; studied acting with Uta Hagen, Terry Schreiber, and in two-year Meisner Program. Extensive improv training with NY Team for Theatre Sports.

My Performance Background
Running roles on *Guiding Light* and *Search for Tomorrow*. Roles Off and Off-Off Broadway, Member NY Team for Theatre Sports.

My Teaching Philosophy
If each student is treated as an individual with unique attributes and led through the correct processes in the proper environment, then each student will reach his or her highest potential and succeed.

What Inspires Me to Teach
Helping the actor craft something deeply real and original out of his or her own talent and creativity. Witnessing the student realize the playwright's intentions.

Other Important Things for Prospective Students to Know
I believe the best coaches need to have a profound understanding of acting and be experienced directors in order to craft the best monologues and auditions. My fifteen years of teaching and directing experience enables me to do just that.

How I Would Describe the Art of Acting
Through a deep understanding of self, others, and the art of acting, the actor is able to enter into and live through the psychological, emotional and physical life of the character.

What I Look for When I Interview a Prospective Student
A student who is serious, open, and shows talent. Someone who loves the work and works hard.

The Kind of Student Who Gets the Most Working with Me
Students that are willing to bring their own personal point of view to the work. Students who are willing to risk and be vulnerable.

The Facts
Years Teaching: 16
Studios: American Academy of Dramatic Arts, 120 Madison Avenue, New York, NY 10016
Phone: home (212) 982-4620
work (212) 686-9244 (ext. 335)
E-mail: BPRLJenson@aol.com

Pjensen@NYAADA.org
Web Site: www.AADA.org
Private Coaching: Yes, $50 per hour
Admission Policy: Interview.

Rachel Jones

My Own Training

Studied with Howard Meyer for many years; studied Meisner Technique with Greg Zittel and privately with Mona Fultz. Attended St. Edwards University in Austin, Texas.

My Performance Background

I have performed in the Broadway and national tour of *Madame Butterfly*. I have worked as a principal in film. I have also worked in soaps and commercials. I was a member of Avalon Repertory in New York City for many years. I am currently a member of Axial Theatre in Westchester, where I work as an actor and a director. I most recently performed as Hannah in *All That's Fair* at the Colleen Dewhurst Theater at Northern Westchester Center for the Arts.

My Teaching Philosophy

I really believe in helping a student develop at his or her own pace. I feel it is really important to create an atmosphere that is nurturing and provides the student with the freedom to explore, make discoveries, and make mistakes. I encourage students to view their classwork as rehearsals culminating in a finished piece. Much of learning how to act is learning how to rehearse and how to build a craft and a character.

What Inspires Me to Teach

For me, teaching feels like a complete circle, a giving back of the knowledge I have had the privilege of gathering over my lifetime as an actor. It is incredibly gratifying to help others discover the artist within themselves, to watch the work evolve, grow, take flight.

Other Important Things for Prospective Students to Know

I like hard workers! I like students to take a proactive role in their own development, to work on pieces that inspire them, and to take risks.

How I Would Describe the Art of Acting

Acting is the art of living truthfully under imaginary circumstances. We always begin with our own emotional instrument, investigating ourselves and what makes us tick. Then we learn how to build on that premise into character work.

What I Look for When I Interview a Prospective Student

I look for a student who has the desire to learn, a student who will bring commitment and tenacity to the learning process. I place students according to my sense of their level of experience. Most begin in my beginning class, moving into the advanced class as they are ready.

The Kind of Student Who Gets the Most Working with Me

I feel there is no one prototypical student and that I am able to give to each person on an individual basis. I suppose a student who is willing to examine his or herself fully and work with his or her own instrument would be the student who would ultimately benefit the most.

The Facts

Years Teaching: 3
Address: 11 Fox Ridge Road, Armonk, NY 10504
Studios: Howard Meyer Acting Program
Northern Westchester Center for the Arts
Connecticut Conservatory for the Performing Arts
Phone: home (914) 273-8940
office (914) 234-4288
Howard Meyer Acting (914) 962-8828
Fax: (914) 273-7970
E-mail: actoroon@hotmail.com
Private Coaching: Yes, $75 per hour
Admission Policy: I place most students in my beginning/intermediate class; if a student's experience indicates he or she needs to be in an advanced class, we begin there.

Classes

Beginning Technique and Scene Study for Young Actors (ages 10–14)
Fee: $375 for 12 weeks
Schedule: Mon., 5–7 PM
Beginning/Intermediate Technique and Scene Study for Adults
Fee: $375 for 12 weeks
Schedule: Mon., 7:30–10:30 PM

Karen Kohlhaas

My Own Training

New York University undergraduate study in drama: David Mamet, William H. Macy; Stella Adler Conservatory.

My Performance Background

I'm an Off-Broadway theater director (Atlantic, Public, Second Stage) who started as an actor in plays with the Atlantic Theater Co. (founding member) and in Mamet's first movies. I have been a director since 1993.

My Teaching Philosophy

I am a longtime teacher of Practical Aesthetics. I give equal weight in monologue classes to developing the actors' directorial sense so that they are conscious of the physical story they are presenting to the audience.

What Inspires Me to Teach

The desire to be a part of preserving, inspiring, and developing the highest standards of stage acting so that old and new plays are given the best possible performances for their audiences. Also, the incredible fulfillment of seeing actors develop, discover, and express themselves.

Other Important Things for Prospective Students to Know

Author of *The Monologue Audition: A Practical Guide for Actors*.

How I Would Describe the Art of Acting

The actor is the transmitter of the conscious and the unconscious truths of the story to the audience.

What I Look for When I Interview a Prospective Student

Actors with some previous training and experience who want to work on monologues in a group setting. Actors who want to empower themselves in monologue and other auditions, who are willing to work hard and treat their own and others' work with respect.

The Kind of Student Who Gets the Most Working with Me

Actors who see acting and auditioning as a way of reaching other human beings with stories they want to tell, not just a way to self-promote. Actors who love working on great writing.

The Facts

Years Teaching: 15
Address: c/o Atlantic Acting School
453 W. 16th Street
New York, NY 10011
Phone: (212) 252-4200
E-mail: monologuesKarenK@aol.com
Web Site: www.monologueaudition.com
Private Coaching: No
Admission Policy: Based on interview; not an appropriate first class for beginning actors.

Classes

Level 1 Monologue Workshop
Fee: $425
Schedule: See Web site.
Level 2 Monologue Workshop
For previous students only; also scene study through Atlantic Acting School full-time programs (www.atlantictheater.org).

Deena Levy

My Own Training

Experimental Theatre Wing, New York University; Emerson College; two-year training with William Esper; Kate McGregor Stewart; Actors Movement Studio; Banff School of Fine Arts.

My Performance Background

In the Boom Boom Room, Off Broadway. Performed, wrote, and produced numerous original works in collaboration with such artists as Anne Bogart, Nicky Silver, Richard Lagravanes.

My Teaching Philosophy

What is it about you that works? When you're in, you're in and when you're out, you're in. In other words: When you are slick and brilliant, it's great. When you're blocked, self-conscious, and uncoordinated — it's human!

What Inspires Me to Teach

Teaching and then witnessing the actor come to understand and know how to truly use technique. "The Breakout," being in that place where all that exists is the present moment.

Other Important Things for Prospective Students to Know

I choose teaching over acting. What makes you passionate about acting; that amazing desire to be creative — that's what fills me when I teach.

How I Would Describe the Art of Acting

A combination of precision and instinct — shadow and light. All the elements somehow merge and then the heart opens.

What I Look for When I Interview a Prospective Student

Commitment, a burning desire to learn, no pressure, and maybe a couple of laughs.

The Kind of Student Who Gets the Most Working with Me

The kind that really wants to go for it.

The Facts

Years Teaching: 14
Address: 215 W. 20th Street, #2W
New York, NY 10011
Phone: (212) 340-1084
E-mail: deenalab@aol.com
Private Coaching: Yes, $75 per hour

Classes

Ongoing Classes (all end with showcase)
Fee: $220 per month each (four classes)
Schedule: Mon., 6:30–10:30 PM;
Tues., 7–11 PM; Wed., 11:30 AM–
4:00 PM; Thurs., 6–10 PM
More Than Acting: Weekend Workshop (limited to 10; call for info.)
Fee: $425
Schedule: Sat., 10 AM–6 PM;
Sun., 10 AM–7 PM
Voice and Movement
Fee: $285
Schedule: 10-week sessions, twice a year
On Camera Commercial Workshop
Fee: $275
Schedule: Twice a year with casting director Terry Berland

Bernice Loren

My Own Training

Graduate, Dramatic Workshop of the New School for Social Research. Stanislavski system and numerous other approaches. Further studies in voice and speech, singing, dance, pe-riod styles and movement, yoga, t'ai chi ch'uan, and other movement systems.

My Performance Background

Forty to fifty roles Off Broadway and in resident theaters and stock companies; some radio and TV. Also directed over thirty plays.

My Teaching Philosophy

Teaching is giving and sharing all one has learned in a way that leads students to discover (rather than my handing down rules) artistic truths and mastery of the so-called techni-cal skills as part and parcel of the creative process.

What Inspires Me to Teach

A conviction that working out of a single creative source and consistent principles behind acting, voice/speech, and movement/dance leads to richer, more alive, as well as more truthful, expressive, meaningful, and memorable theater.

Other Important Things for Prospective Students to Know

Acting is a heightening or distillation of behavior, a purveyor of truth, and revelation of spirit. As a result, cre-ativity, form, content, and commu-nication are totally interdependent.

What I Look for When I Interview a Prospective Student

One who is open to learning and willing to investigate possibilities that may be quite different from pre-vious experience or from precon-ceptions of what acting is.

The Facts

Years Teaching: 33
Address: 350 W. 55th Street
New York, NY 10019
Studio: Expressions
Phone: (212) 586-8604
Private Coaching: Yes, $35 for
90 minutes

Classes

Foundations (group)
Fee: $25 per class
Development (group)
Fee: $25 per class
Advanced Study (group)
Fee: $25 per class
Performance Workshop (group)
Fee: $25 per class

Jodie Lynne McClintock

My Own Training

BA in acting, speech, and English, Westminster College; Yale/Oxford: British American Drama Academy; the Royal Shakespeare Company; and the Actors Center. Privately, my greatest mentors have been Earle Gister, Robert Smith, Leon Katz, and Patsy Rodenburg.

My Performance Background

Broadway and Off Broadway, London's West End, Israel's National Theatre, guest artist with the Royal Shakespeare Company, *Showtime,* PBS's *American Playhouse,* and regional theaters.

My Teaching Philosophy

I believe in empowering actors. As a working actor myself, I am in a unique position to guide my clients as they create their own methodology and build their careers. Because of my strong background in British technique, my mission is to meld the British reverence for text with the vitality of the American actor to make the script active.

What Inspires Me to Teach

The next best thing to acting myself is enabling someone else to do so and sharing in his or her success whatever form that might take. How thrilling to breathe life into others.

Other Important Things for Prospective Students to Know

I do both classes and private coaching sessions here at my studio in Queens. Private coaching is in monologue selections (classical and contemporary) and polishing, cold reading, role preparation, with a speciality in general auditions for graduate schools or overseas acting programs.

How I Would Describe the Art of Acting

With the text as the skeleton, our job is to flesh out and breathe life into the character as defined by the playwright, to provide the actions inherent in the words using ourselves as the canvas or medium in a truthful, graceful manner.

What I Look for When I Interview a Prospective Student

I look for a client who is engaged, curious, committed; someone who desires to exercise their imagination with unflagging energy.

The Kind of Student Who Gets the Most Working with Me

Someone who is open-minded and flexible as we explore innumerable possibilities in solving a moment, is willing to rehearse outside class, and comes prepared; someone with a specific goal.

The Facts

Years Teaching: 21
Address: 49-01 39th Avenue
Sunnyside, NY 11104-1007
Phone: (718) 476-2590
Fax: (718) 505-3733
E-mail: jlmcclintock@hotmail.com
Web site: www.jodiemcclintock.com
Private Coaching: Yes, $75 per hour
Admission Policy: Telephone interview for private coaching. For classes: Sample Class day once a year for auditing. Admission by interview/audition.

Classes

Shakespeare Introductory: Sonnets, Soliloquies, and Text
Fee: Call for fee.
Schedule: 5 weeks, 3 hours per week
Shakespeare on Film: Scene Study with Monologues
Fee: Call for fee.
Schedule: Class usually runs in conjunction with Shakespeare Introductory.
Intermediate Shakespeare: Scene Study and Monologues
Schedule: 8–12 weeks, 4–5 hours per week
Advanced Shakespeare: Playing with Passion Into Performance
Schedule: 10–12 weeks, 4–5 hours per week. This class is conducted like a rep company in rehearsal for several rotating Shakespeare productions.

New Classes: Shakespeare Sundays and Monologue Mondays
Go to Web site or call for details.

Howard Meyer

My Own Training

Two years of Meisner training with Ron Stetson; sensory work with Mimi Turque, Karen Wohl; voice with Chuck Jones; advanced technique and scene study with Michael Howard, Caymichael Patten.

My Performance Background

Playwright, director, and actor whose work has appeared Off Broadway and at regional theaters, including New York Theatre Workshop, Manhattan Theatre Club, The Playwright's Center, The Schoolhouse, Fleetwood Stage, and Axial Theatre.

My Teaching Philosophy

I believe that acting is both an art and a craft. My task is to inspire creativity as well as impart tools that eventually form a repeatable craft. I accomplish this through group exercises, individual exercises, and scene study.

What Inspires Me to Teach

Having participated and continuing to participate in the unforgettable and magical moments of transformation of my students. Also, looking back, I note with gratitude the part I play in my students' evolution.

Other Important Things for Prospective Students to Know

When students choose me, they are selecting a theater artist actively engaged in his own creative process. I am the artistic director of the Axial Theatre, as well as a working playwright, actor, and director.

How I Would Describe the Art of Acting
The full activation of one's emotional, imagined, and physical life in the service of the character and world of the play.

What I Look for When I Interview a Prospective Student
The courage to dedicate focused time and careful attention to the work of artistic discovery.

The Kind of Student Who Gets the Most Working with Me
The student who takes the pursuit of his or her artistic evolution seriously and embraces the patient and steady nature of the process.

The Facts
Years Teaching: 13
Address: 1305 White Hill Road
Yorktown Heights, NY 10598
Studios: Howard Meyer's
Acting Program
Phone: (914) 962-8828
E-mail: hmaxial@aol.com
Web Site: www.hmacting.org
Private Coaching: Yes, $85 per hour
Admission Policy: Interview.

Classes
Advanced Technique/Scene Study
Fee: $145 per month, or $175 for 5-week month
Schedule: Wed., 7:30–11 PM
Playwriting Workshop
Fee: $395 for 12-week session
Schedule: Tues., 7:30–9:30 PM

Robin Morse

My Own Training
Meisner Technique with William Esper; singing performance with Carole D'Andrea; Shakespeare with Patsy Rodenburg.

My Performance Background
Acting debut at age seventeen, starring opposite Chita Rivera and Donald O'Conner in the Broadway musical *Bring Back Birdie*. Recent: in original company of John Guare's *Six Degrees of Separation* and Athol Fugard's *My Children! My Africa!* at Washington's Arena Stage (nomination for Best Actress, Helen Hayes Award). Recent television appearance: *Law and Order SVU*.

My Teaching Philosophy
For real growth to occur, I believe it is imperative that an actor has a safe and supportive environment in which to work. I also feel strongly about encouraging actors to not only focus on their art, but to develop an interest and a point of view about the world around them as a way of informing their art.

What Inspires Me to Teach
Being able to give back all that I have learned.

Other Important Things for Prospective Students to Know
I accept all levels of experience and training, and each student receives personal one-on-one instruction every week. I will help you choose material that is right for you, interpret text, and free you up so you can work at your highest potential.

How I Would Describe the Art of Acting

Learning to behave truthfully in imaginary circumstances.

What I Look for When I Interview a Prospective Student

Apart from talent, someone who understands about process, has a certain amount of self-awareness, and is enthusiastic about learning. In addition, the student needs to have had some prior training.

The Kind of Student Who Gets the Most Working with Me

One who is open, who is willing to find out more about who they are through their work, and who is ready to play and get messy.

The Facts

Years Teaching: 8
Address: 353 W. 39th Street, #304
New York, NY 10018
Studios: Private and Atlantic Theatre Company/NYU Undergraduate Program
Phone: (212) 352-4024
Fax: (212) 927-3887
E-mail: robingus@earthlink.net
Private Coaching: Yes, $75 per hour
Admission Policy: After a student audits the class and expresses an interest in joining,a personal interview will be set up.

Classes

Acting: Monologue and Scene Study
Fee: $200 per month
Schedule: Tues., 2–5 PM
Singing Performance
Fee: $200 per month
Schedule: Tues., 11–2 PM

John Charles Murphy

My Own Training

Michael Chekhov Center, courses in actor training; Completion Diploma, Ecole Jacques Lecoq, Paris; MA, theater and dance, University of Colorado, Boulder; BA, English and speech, Creighton University, Omaha, Nebraska.

My Performance Background

Mummenschanz, Worldwide, Italian television and commercials, Off-Off Broadway, Colorado Caravan/Overland Stage Co., Boulder, Colorado.

My Teaching Philosophy

To demonstrate that movement is at the heart of the actor's instinct. Through movement one can release body and mind, and in so doing rediscover innate creativity and spontaneity.

What Inspires Me to Teach

When students utilize their abilities, having achieved an inspiration or breakthrough, it verifies that the instruction is serving its purpose: students can and do learn the art of acting through proper structure and guidance.

Other Important Things for Prospective Students to Know

One of my main goals as a teacher is to create an environment that encourages the free exchange of images, thoughts, or ideas.

How I Would Describe the Art of Acting

The art of acting, in its widest sense, is the communication of thoughts, feelings, behavior, or character in an authentic way. Acting of this caliber is compelling to watch because it has the capacity to transform the reality of each spectator.

What I Look for When I Interview a Prospective Student

Authenticity, spontaneity, curiosity, courage, willingness to risk, to explore, and to not know, desire, enthusiasm, mental balance, ability to listen, ability to observe and to see, sense of awareness, and an openness to be actively involved in the experience of life.

The Kind of Student Who Gets the Most Working with Me

Students who are curious, who are genuinely interested in deriving insight from their awareness of and their participation in the wonders of nature and of life.

The Facts

Years Teaching: 26
Address: 230 W. 82nd Street, #D4
New York, NY 10024
Studios: New School University
Marymount Manhattan College
C.U.N.Y, New York City Technical College, Private Studio
Phone: (212) 501-2357
E-mail: goplayou@yahoo.com
Private Coaching: Yes, $75 per hour
Admission Policy: Short interview.

Classes

Freeing Body Expression
Fee: $350
Schedule: 24 contact hours

Improvisation
Fee: $450
Schedule: 30–36 contact hours

Interior Clown
Fee: $400
Schedule: 30 contact hours

Buffoon
Fee: $450
Schedule: 30–33 contact hours

Storytelling
Fee: $450
Schedule: 30–36 contact hours

Character and Scene Studies
Fee: $ 350
Schedule: 24 contact hours

Elements of Creativity
Fee: $400

Joe Perce

My Own Training
AA Drama (Miami Dade), American Academy of Dramatic Arts, Gene Frankel Theater, Olinda Tuturro (Meisner), Improvisation (Del Close).

My Performance Background
1987 CLEO Award Winner for Best Male Performer in a commercial; twenty-three years of improvisational comedy with The First Amendment, Chicago City Limits, Comedy Mind Spill, Comedy Olympics. Voted best Improvisational Comic of 1989 by *Backstage* and *Good Day NY.* Many Off Broadway and regional theaters. Film productions include *Black Rain, The Hidden, Bum Rap,* and *Don't Mess with My Sister.* TV: *The Bodyguards, Law and Order, The Equalizer,* Nickelodeon, MTV, Comedy Central, *The David Suskind Show*, and ABC's *After School Special.*

My Teaching Philosophy
Take risks.

What Inspires Me to Teach
The students and watching them grow as they discover confidence within themselves and the art.

Other Important Things for Prospective Students to Know
I want my students to constantly be challenging themselves and have lots of fun doing so. My classes are hands on and on your feet, so get ready to work.

How I Would Describe the Art of Acting
Being in the moment, spontaneity, commitment, and listening are a few of the things I emphasize. With improvisation, you are actor, director, and writer all rolled into one.

What I Look for When I Interview a Prospective Student
Creativity, listening skills, ensemble playing.

The Kind of Student Who Gets the Most Working with Me
One who wants to discover and explore within him- or herself all colors of his or her acting and improvisation; one that comes to class to work.

The Facts
Phone: (212) 645-0030
Web site: TheImprovWrkshp@aol.com

Classes
Joe is currently teaching "Improvisational Comedy" and "he Comedy Workshop" at the School for Film & Television: (212) 645-0030.

Jack Poggi

My Own Training
Ph.D., drama and theater, Columbia University; acting: Uta Hagan, Mira Rostova; movement: Lloyd Williamson.

My Performance Background
Performed over one hundred roles in New York City and in regional theater throughout the country. Frequent performer on both daytime and prime-time television.

My Teaching Philosophy
I encourage my students to tap into their special gift, I help them to find or create an ideal role for themselves, and I show them how to dissolve the fears and other obstacles that block true expression.

What Inspires Me to Teach
Seeing students break through their inhibitions and find joy in their work.

Other Important Things for Prospective Students to Know
I am the author of *The Monologue Workshop*.

How I Would Describe the Art of Acting
The spontaneous expression of true feeling that illuminates the world we live in.

What I Look for When I Interview a Prospective Student
Enthusiasm, energy, humor, commitment.

The Kind of Student Who Gets the Most Working with Me
The one who wants it the most and is willing to work the hardest.

The Facts
Years Teaching: 41
Address: 880 W. 181st Street., Apt. 4B
New York, NY 10033
Studio: Actors Connection
630 Ninth Avenue, Suite 1410
New York, NY 10036
Phone: (212) 928-6882
(212) 382-3535 (service)
E-mail: Jackpoggi@aol.com
Private Coaching: Yes, $60 per hour or four sessions for $200
Admission Policy: I require at least one year of basic acting training plus evidence of commitment to complete the work.

Classes
Monologue Workshop
Fee: $250
Schedule: Six consecutive Mons., or Sats. for three hours

A. M. Raychel

My Own Training
Drama degree, Marquette University; New York Institute of Technology: TV direction, production; acting/directing technique: Uta Hagan, Lee Strasberg.

My Performance Background
New York–based Off Broadway director/teacher. Producing/artistic director (TSI established 1980). Taught acting and directing at The New School, Baruch College, and NYU.

My Teaching Philosophy
Talent is raw material. Only through specific technique can constant quality be achieved: "How you read is how you will play."

What Inspires Me to Teach
Helping actors hone their acting craft helps me hone my directing skills and fulfills my desires to direct and produce quality productions.

Other Important Things for Prospective Students to Know
I believe discipline and commitment are essential to professional longevity.

How I Would Describe the Art of Acting
When you cease to "act" and become synonymous with the character's life. This is achieved by step-by-step technique: A conscious technique to reach/access the subconscious.

What I Look for When I Interview a Prospective Student
Have strong purpose and desire to perfect the specifics of craft.

The Kind of Student Who Gets the Most Working with Me
Students who enjoy challenges as a way of life. Students who actively participate in theater productions.

The Facts
Years Teaching: 22
Address: 750 Eighth Avenue,
Suite 200
New York, NY 10036
Studio: The Theatre-Studio, Inc
Phone: (212) 719-0500
Fax: (212) 719-0537
E-mail: Arayche@attglobal.net

Web Site: www.Theatrestudio.org
Private Coaching: Yes, $250 for 90 minutes
Admission Policy: Fax or e-mail letter of interest: Why you want to act; what your goals are.

Classes
Improvisational Reading Techniques
Fee: $350 for 12 weeks
Schedule: Mon., 5–8 PM, year-round
Scene Study and Acting Exercises
Fee: $350 for 12 weeks
Schedule: Thurs., 5–8 PM, year-round
Full Acting Program
Fee: $600 for 12 weeks
Schedule: Mon. and Thurs., year-round. (Note: "Full Acting Program" students have the option to participate regularly in new one-act plays presented year-round.)

Katheryn Rossetter

My Own Training
Private Study in New York City with Ernie Martin, Barbara Poitier, and Doug Moston; vocal study with Leon Kurzer.

My Performance Background
Twenty years of Broadway, Off Broadway, film, TV, and comedy cabaret. I continue to perform in all areas and musical theater.

My Teaching Philosophy
I combine the techniques of Stanislavski and Meisner to guide my students to a fluid, organic, emotional truth and a moment-to-moment reality. The training will sustain them throughout their careers.

What Inspires Me to Teach
The hunger and enthusiasm of my students inspires me to teach and share my wisdom. Also, a desire to plumb the depths of creativity and further the art of acting.

Other Important Things for Prospective Students to Know
I teach each individual to find his or her unique truth. Class is structured to provide a safe place to try, fail, try again, learn, and ultimately triumph.

How I Would Describe the Art of Acting
The art is to illuminate and reflect human behavior. To extend human understanding in collaboration with the writer and director. The actor must be fearless in taking emotional risks and seek to answer questions that most of the world is trying to avoid.

What I Look for When I Interview a Prospective Student
I look for commitment and desire above all else. Since I teach all levels, beginner to professional, I do not require an audition.

The Kind of Student Who Gets the Most Working with Me
A student who is disciplined, dedicated, intellectually curious, and emotionally fearless, as well as imaginative and resourceful will enjoy and thrive in my class.

The Facts
Years Teaching: 8
Address: 325 W. 45th Street, #207
New York, NY 10036

Studios: Teach independently and also at NYU continuing education
Phone: (212) 946-5135
E-mail: NYKass@aol.com
Web Site: www.kathrynrossetter.com
Private Coaching: Yes, $70 per hour

Classes
Beginner/Intermediate
Fee: Call for fee and details.
One-Person Show Workshop
Schedule: 10-week sessions.
Fee: Call for fee and details.

Ken Schatz

My Own Training
At Circle in the Square/NYU Tisch School of the Arts, my teachers included Alan Langdon, Elizabeth Browning, Jacqueline Brookes, Terese Hayden, Andrea Haring. Peter DeLorenzo, Jon Sperry, Shelley Wyant, and many artists from NYU's Experimental Theatre Wing. I've studied privately with many teachers and directors, including Augusto Boal, Kristin Linklater, Randolyn Zinn, and Bill Reed, and am certified by Moni Yakim in Physical Technique.

My Performance Background
Acting credits include *Finding Graceland* with Harvey Keitel and Bridget Fonda, Todd Haynes's film *Poison*, the Obie-winning *Crowbar* and *Bad Penny* with End Garde Arts, *Sesame Street*, and performances with Blue Light, Willow Cabin, John Montgomery, Gorilla Rep., and Bread and Puppet theater companies. Voice-over credits include MTV's *Daria*

and Cartoon Network's series *Sheep in the Big City.*

My Teaching Philosophy
The right tool for the right job. I combine many different approaches, styles, and techniques to equip professional actors with the creative vocabulary, tools, and skills they need to do their best.

What Inspires Me to Teach
Every moment of discovery in class, rehearsal, performance, and in life — goofy or poignant — inspires me to teach and inspires me to learn. I am fascinated by human decision, behavior, style, strategy, challenge, and action.

Other Important Things for Prospective Students to Know
Coaching credits include Tim Blake Nelson's "The Grey Zone," *Cop Land, There's Something About Mary, Shadrach,* and "Spin City." I have administered several acting training programs for NYU Tisch School of the Arts and am the former associate director of Circle in the Square Theatre School.

How I Would Describe the Art of Acting
Acting is exploration and articulation — making physical, vocal, mental, emotional, and spiritual connections and choices to create character and communicate story. Most of all, it is a glorious opportunity.

What I Look for When I Interview a Prospective Student
This student, the people and experiences of our class, and me — would we learn from and teach each other?

I evaluate actors by professional standards of talent, experience, intelligence, enthusiasm, commitment, and potential, but above all, I look for a hunger for the work.

The Kind of Student Who Gets the Most Working with Me

The student interested not just in "being an actor" but in acting — the student who seeks his or her own real courage, genius, depth, and sense of fun and who sees those qualities in others will always have a home in the work we do together.

The Facts

Years Teaching: 13
Address: ACTORTEC
106 Hicks Street, #4A
Brooklyn, NY 11201
Phone: (718) 625-8372
(212) 307-0388 (Circle in the Square Theatre School)
E-mail: Ken@actortec.com
Web Site: www.actortec.com
Private Coaching: Yes, $100 per hour
Admission Policy: Admission to classes is by audition. To assure a safe, concentrated working environment for all students, auditing is not permitted. Class size is limited. No audition is required for a first private coaching session.

Classes

Audition Monologue Lab
Fee: $160
Schedule: Sun., 10 AM–6 PM
Improvisation
Fee: $420
Schedule: Eight Weds., 2–5 PM or 7–10 PM

Physical Acting
Fee: $420
Schedule: Eight weeks, Tues. and Thurs., 3:30–5:00 PM or 7–8:30 PM
Scene Study
Fee: $420
Schedule: Eight Mons., 2–5 PM or 7–10 PM
Speech and Dialect Salon
Fee: $420
Schedule: Eight Sats. 10 AM–12 PM, plus individual tutorials
Voice
Fee: $420
Schedule: Eight weeks, Mon. and Wed., 10:30 AM–12 PM

Louis Scheeder

My Own Training

Columbia University School of the Arts: James Ray, Jenny Egan.

My Performance Background

My background is as a director on Broadway, Off Broadway, Off-Off Broadway, and at regional theaters in the United States and Canada. Also worked as an assistant director at the Royal Shakespeare Company.

My Teaching Philosophy

If you are open and accessible, I will commit myself to your growth as an actor. Every student has a different learning curve.

What Inspires Me to Teach

A belief that performance can actually make a difference in how we see the world. The sheer magic and unpredictability of live performance inspires me.

Other Important Things for Prospective Students to Know

I put a great deal of thought and energy into class. I expect as much of the student. I am also the coauthor (with Shane Ann Younts) of *All the Words on Stage: The Complete Pronunciation Dictionary for the Plays of William Shakespeare*.

How I Would Describe the Art of Acting

The ideal goal is the creation of "thought in action." The presentation of a play text in an emotional, kinetic, and forceful present. All characters in plays are living, thinking, active beings who don't know what will happen next.

What I Look for When I Interview a Prospective Student

Someone who is open to nonlinear thinking. Someone who can embrace contradictions and therefore embrace human action.

The Kind of Student Who Gets the Most Working with Me

One who is motivated and willing to work specifically and in minute detail. One who will follow the body and not the brain.

The Facts

Years Teaching: 18
Address: 7 Stuyvesant Oval, #9D
New York, NY 10009
Studios: The Classical Studio Department of Drama, Tisch School of the Arts
Phone: (212) 614-9131
E-mail: louis.scheeder@nyu.edu
Private Coaching: Yes.
Admission Policy: By interview and, ideally, recommendation.

Classes

Contemporary and Classical **(cotaught with Darci Picoult)**
Fee: $385 for 10-week session
Schedule: Mon., 6–9 PM
Shakespeare
Fee: $295
Schedule: Mon., 2–5 PM

Pamela Scott

My Own Training

Graduate, Eastern Michigan University, American Academy of Dramatic Arts; over ten years assisting acting coach Sandra Seacat.

My Performance Background

Joseph Papp's Public Theatre, West Bank Downstairs Theatre, The Irish Arts Center, HERE with PS NBC, Pulse Ensemble Theatre, Duo Theatre, and film (*Ten Benny*).

My Teaching Philosophy

To create a safe, nurturing, energized environment for actors to take chances and risks. Working from an emotionally honest, physically energized, and creatively full place.

What Inspires Me to Teach

Love of the work. My students inspire me on a daily basis: watching them learn to trust and grow within their craft and their instrument, watching them realize they are enough.

Other Important Things for Prospective Students to Know

I believe with structure comes freedom, but I also believe in flexibility and going with the flow. I'm a storyteller and playwright. I love teaching and have a great time.

How I Would Describe the Art of Acting
Delving into the depths of our souls and awareness to discover who we are, who we become and how we can get what we want within the given circumstances of the play.

What I Look for When I Interview a Prospective Student
An openness and willingness to learn. Acting isn't an exact science and needs to be explored with an open mind and a willingness to trust.

The Kind of Student Who Gets the Most Working with Me
The kind that are open to learning and are willing to be challenged in a positive way and to hear honest but compassionate feedback.

The Facts
Years Teaching: 6 years
Address: AADA 120 Madison Avenue
New York, NY 10016 or
The School for Film & Television
39 W. 19th Street
New York, NY
Phone: (212) 541-7600
E-mail: Pamannscott@hotmail.com
Private Coaching: Yes, $75 per hour
Admission Policy: Interview with me and audition.

Classes
Monologues and Cold Reading Skills
Fee: $35–$45 per class
Schedule: TBA
Scene Study
Fee: $35–$45 per class
Schedule: TBA

Lunch Live: Performance Opportunity
Fee: $600

Judith Searcy

My Own Training
BA/ASU, MFA, acting/directing at UNC-G; postgraduate studies at Columbia University, University of London. New York: Terry Schreiber, Alice Spivak, Joan See.

My Performance Background
I've worked as a writer, director, actor, and improviser in New York City for almost twenty years. I was a principal New York City mainstage cast member of Chicago City Limits for ten years. I have also improvised with members of all the major improvisational troupes in NY and around the world in various clubs and venues. My stage and screen credits include the title role in the award-winning short film *Marge*, featured appearances on cable's *Off the Cuff*, *Comedy Central*, *The Today Show*, and *Good Day New York*. In addition to directing several original plays Off-Off Broadway, I have directed, written, and appeared in scores of industrial shows and videos.

My Teaching Philosophy
Process first! I believe in being as present with my students as possible because that's what I'm asking them to do with me. My goal is always to honor where they are in their work and help them to increase their comfort zone by supporting them in creative risk taking.

What Inspires Me to Teach

Seeing the lights go on. I believe the work I do in improvisation is important to people's lives as well as their acting techniques. A good improviser goes beyond the literal and can see possibilities where other people only see limits. This changes lives as well as careers.

Other Important Things for Prospective Students to Know

I am currently chairperson of the Improv/Comedy faculty at The School for Film & Television in New York, I am also the cofounder of CTS, a company that teaches workshops in creative thinking, presentation skills, and team building for corporate clients.

How I Would Describe the Art of Acting

It's like an archeological dig. Any good acting process unearths treasures you didn't even know you had. Being truly present and learning to listen actively with your whole body will lead you to inventive, moment-to-moment work that makes the great actors great.

What I Look for When I Interview a Prospective Student

I look for a willingness to participate fully, even if you are scared, and a motivation to try it without judging yourself. If you just want to be entertained, buy tickets to a show.

The Kind of Student Who Gets the Most Working with Me

Students of all levels who are looking for more spontaneity and presence in their work and who are willing to trust the process.

The Facts

Phone: (212) 645-0030 ext.197 (The School for Film & Television)
E-mail: JESearcy@aol.com
Private Coaching: Yes, fees on request

Classes

Improvisation. 1
Basics.
Improvisation. 2
Advanced improvisation.
Improvisation. 3
Performance improvisation, culminating in showcase.
Intro to Comedy
An on-camera comedy basics class—finding your comic persona.

Jacqueline Segal

My Own Training

BA, theater arts major, Bennington College; masters classes in directing and screenwriting, Hunter College. After college I studied a total of eight years with: Bill Hickey, Larry Arrick, Michael Gazzo.

My Performance Background

Off Broadway in the fifties and sixties with the ANTA Theatre Group and the St. Marks Theatre Group.

My Teaching Philosophy

Class is about opening the doors that got shut during the growing-up years, getting in touch with the places in us that we don't use so that we can use them in our acting. My classes are about exploration and creativity — not about competitions.

What Inspires Me to Teach

I think I was always meant to teach acting. The ways in which we learn to use ourselves as good actors is endlessly interesting to me. It forces me to learn and to grow — to put my money where my mouth is.

Other Important Things for Prospective Students to Know

I treat this craft with utmost respect, and I expect the same from my students. If they work with me, it will be about craft and not career.

How I Would Describe the Art of Acting

Since acting is about life, we have an endless opportunity to grow. We are the only art form in which the self is the instrument, so there is no other art form like it. It is about service: service to the playwright, to fellow actors, and to the audience.

What I Look for When I Interview a Prospective Student

The first thing is to find out why he or she wants to study acting. After that — and I always meet with and talk with perspective students — it's a gut feeling about that person.

The Kind of Student Who Gets the Most Working with Me

People who want to learn because they love the craft. I don't judge talent. People always surprise me in that area.

The Facts

Years Teaching: 22
Studio: I teach privately at a space I rent at the Bank St. Theatre.
Phone: (212) 683-9428
Fax: Same number.
Private Coaching: Yes, $100 per hour
Admission: It's all based on meeting with students.

Class
Basic technique/Scene study
Fee: $150 per month
Schedule: Mon., 6–9 PM
Onstage/Offstage Workshop
Fee: $150
Schedule: 10 AM–6 PM (call for days)

Lynette Sheldon

My Own Training
Stella Adler: three-year graduate program; Michael Howard: two years; Larry Moss: two years; Milton Katselas: summer programs, The Ensemble Theatre: and Byron Syron: three years (Sydney, Australia).

My Performance Background
Feature films, television series, soaps, regional theater, commercials, stock at Lincoln Center.

My Teaching Philosophy
I believe in nurturing and developing the actor's talent, imagination and heart; in training actors to pursue the truth with courage and humanity through solid technique based on Stanislavski's, Stella Adler's, and Meisner's teachings.

What Inspires Me to Teach
What inspires me is an actor's desire to learn the craft and to grow beyond their wildest imagination; to see the possibilities and raw talent in an actor and cultivate that talent into confidence, craft and artistry.

Other Important Things for Prospective Students to Know
I began studying and acting as a teen in Australia and then moved to New York and have since worked successfully in theater, film, and television for twenty years. I have studied Tai Chi, the Alexander Technique, Bioenergetics, and breath work, which influence my teaching approach, and developed my own technique, which encompasses solid acting craft together with body, mind, heart, and soul — and the business of acting.

How I Would Describe the Art of Acting
It is the magic that happens when we aim to live truthfully in all circumstances, moment to moment in any art form. Acting is that elusive human balance of vulnerability with courage, humor with boldness, simplicity within complexities.

What I Look for When I Interview a Prospective Student
Willingness, the desire to learn, a sense of humor, and commitment to the craft.

The Kind of Student Who Gets the Most Working with Me
The student who has already decided he or she wants to be a working actor and is totally committed to becoming the best-trained actor he or she can possibly be.

The Facts
Years Teaching: 14
Address: Lynette Sheldon Actors Studio, New York, NY and Sydney, Australia
Phone: (212) 477-0171
(917) 748-1006 (West Coast)
E-mail: lsactorstudio@hotmail.com

Web Sites: www.lynettesheldon.com
www.lsactorstudio.com
Private Coaching: Yes
Admission Policy: By interview and
working audit.

Classes
Master Class (technique, scene
study, character development and
script analysis)
Fee: $200 and up per month
Beginner/Intermediate
(technique and improvisation)
Fee: $190 per month
Weekend Audition Intensives
Fee: $300 per weekend
Schedule: Every 6 weeks, all day Sat.
and Sun.

Lynn Singer

My Own Training
BA, literature, film, theater. Studio
training with Uta Hagen, Liz Dixon,
Alice Hermes.

My Performance Background
Off Broadway and Off-Off Broadway, film, television, and many
voice-overs.

My Teaching Philosophy
To create an atmosphere of great
support and trust so brilliance can
show up.

What Inspires Me to Teach
I have never not taught. Holding and
honoring creativity can heal us.

Other Important Things for
Prospective Students to Know
Twenty years of body work (bioenergetics, yoga) support my teaching

How I Would Describe the
Art of Acting
"Hold the mirror up to nature."

What I Look for When I
Interview a Prospective Student
Someone struggling with themselves
to find what they really need.

The Kind of Student Who
Gets the Most Working with Me
Willing to risk and go deep.

The Facts
Years Teaching: 27
Address: 201 W. 16th Street
New York, NY 10011
Studios: T. Schreiber Studio and private
Phone: (212) 242-3297
E-mail: LGSVoice@earthlink.net
Web site: www.lsvoiceworks.com
Private Coaching: Yes, $100 per hour
Admission Policy: Interview and/or
recommendation.

Classes
Acting
Fee: $190 per month
Schedule: Mon., 6:30–10:30 PM;
WED., 1–5 PM
Voice: Beginning
Call for details.
Voice: Advanced
Fee: $360 for 10 weeks
Schedule: Tues., 6–8 PM

Tom Soter

My Own Training
Seven years at Chicago City Limits.
Twenty years as improviser.

My Performance Background
Three years with NY improv squad.
Ten years as host/producer/performer
in Sunday Night Improv Jam.

My Teaching Philosophy
Anyone can improvise if he or she is given proper support and guidance.

What Inspires Me to Teach
I love helping people create.

Other Important Things for Prospective Students to Know
I am a writer (published two books). I have been teaching since 1987.

How I Would Describe the Art of Acting
Improv should be fun — otherwise why do it?

What I Look for When I Interview a Prospective Student
A willingness to listen and learn.

The Kind of Student Who Gets the Most Working with Me
One who listens and drops his ego.

The Facts
Years Teaching: 18
Address: 1264 Amsterdam Avenue, 3B
New York, NY 10027
Studio: Center Stage
48 W. 21st Street
Phone: (212) 353-7716
Fax: (212) 254-6745
E-mail: tsoter@habitatmag.com
Web Site: www.tomsoter.com
Private Coaching: No
Admission Policy: Open, except for performance class, by audition.

Classes
Improv for Everyone
Fees: $20 per class or $150 for 10
Schedule: Tues., 7–9 PM
Improv for Performance
Fee: $350
Schedule: Call.

Beginning Improv
Fee: $20 per class or $150 for 10
Schedule: Call.

Jeffrey D. Stocker

My Own Training
Attended Otterbein College and University of Akron. Directed over thirty short videos and over one hundred stage productions and readings here in New York City. Member of Academy of TV Arts and Sciences.

My Performance Background
I have performed professionally on stage and television for over thirty-five years and have directed in New York City and the tri-state area since 1978.

My Teaching Philosophy
Good acting is good reading: actors must read cold copy well to succeed in today's market.

What Inspires Me to Teach
The actors themselves: I love to watch their talents develop.

Other Important Things for Prospective Students to Know
I am a professional director as well as a coach for both stage and screen.

How I Would Describe the Art of Acting
The art of make-believe. Acting is like magic: magicians must perform the same trick over and over and convince the audience the magic is real each time — so does the actor when working.

Caroline Thomas'
Total Theatre Lab

Integrated Acting Process

Monologues* Voice & Speech* Audition Coaching*
Teen & Adult* Scene Study* Private & Group Classes*
Showcases

Liz Lewis (Casting Director) "Interesting place for new actors. The shows I saw were really excellent - good, strong acting."

Alicia Minshiew - (Kendall, All My Children) "Caroline Thomas encouraged me to get to know my true self, and to use my whole self for my acting."

Zoe Saldana (Pirates of the Caribbean, Crossroads, Drumline) "I always recommend Caroline's class whenever anybody asks me,"

cttheatre@aol.com   www.totaltheatrelab.com   212-799-4224

What I Look for When I Interview a Prospective Student

Desire to learn; desire to have me as their coach.

The Kind of Student Who Gets the Most Working with Me

Working actors, actors who are already going on auditions who can use my cold-reading technique. Also, the untrained actor that has no theater/overacting bad habits.

The Facts

Years Teaching: 25
Address: 90 Lexington Avenue,
Suite 1H
New York, NY 10016
Studios: Film Acting Studio
Phone: (212) 725-3437
E-mail: Studio-90-LEXS@prodigy.net
Web Site: www.filmactingstudio.com
Private Coaching: Yes, $100 per hour
Admission Policy: All sessions are ongoing and are paid in advance. All are on-camera, and the actor receives a copy of work.

Classes

Private Session On-Camera
Fee: $375 for 5 one-hour sessions
Schedule: Ongoing
Scene Study On-Camera
Fee: $325 for 5 one-hour sessions
Schedule: Ongoing
Readers' Theater Workshop
Fee: $500 for 10 two-hour sessions
Schedule: Ongoing
Theater Workshop
Fee: $650 for 12 two-hour sessions,
performance at National Arts Club
Schedule: Ongoing

Caroline Thomas

My Own Training

Graduated from R.A.D.A. in London; studied two years with Mordecai Lawner from the Neighborhood

Playhouse; studied Method Acting with Edward Greer; studied voice/movement workshops with Grotowski and Andre Gregory.

My Performance Background
Off Broadway and regional theater.

My Teaching Philosophy
I have developed the Integrated Acting Process, which combines aspects of Meisner, Method, Grotowski's voice and movement, and R.A.D.A. speech and characterization with my own ideas. I provide a flexible technique that actors can adapt to their personal acting and career needs.

What Inspires Me to Teach
I am fulfilled by watching the students develop. I listen as attentively to them as they listen to me and learn how to better teach them from observing what they need. They, in turn, learn that acting is an art form, not just a series of skills.

Other Important Things for Prospective Students to Know
I have written a chapter, "Breathe Before You Act," for Movement for Actors (Allworth Press, 2002). I love Shakespeare and teach it in my voice/speech class. I write scenes and plays from student improvisations and direct them — as well as published works — in student showcases.

How I Would Describe the Art of Acting
To be totally oneself on the inside and endless versions of oneself and others on the outside.

What I Look for When I Interview a Prospective Student
I look for openness and the determination to work hard and the ability to engage in a process and not focus on results.

The Kind of Student Who Gets the Most Working with Me
I have rigorously avoided having any particular *type* of student, but the ones who benefit most listen and do their homework as consistently as possible. They maintain their individuality while accepting and integrating correction and specific criticism.

The Facts
Years Teaching: 23
Address: Total Theatre Lab
118 W. 79th Street, Suite 12A
New York, NY 10024
Studio: Shetler Studios
250 W. 54th Street, Suite 1212
New York, NY 10019
Phone: (212) 799-4224
Fax: (212) 595-9770
E-mail: cttheatre@aol.com
Web Site: www.totaltheatrelab.com
Private Coaching: Yes, $75 per hour. $65 or fee by arrangement for students enrolled in group classes.
Admission Policy: By interview. Students are encouraged to audit before enrolling (no charge).

Classes
(Note: 1 class, $150; 2 classes, $260; 3 classes, $300)
Sensory/Monologue (Beginner)
Fee: $150 (if taken alone)
Schedule: Tues., 5–7 PM

Improvisation/Scene Study
(Beginner)
Fee: $150 (if taken alone)
Schedule: Tues., 7–10:30 PM
Sensory/Monologue
(Intermediate/Advanced)
Fee: $150
Schedule: Wed., 5–7 PM
Improvisation/Scene Study
(Intermediate/Advance)
Fee: $150
Schedule: Wed., 7–10:30 PM
Voice/Speech/Spoken Poetry
Fee: $150
Schedule: Fri., 10:30 AM–12:30 PM

Steven Thornburg

My Own Training
Stella Adler Conservatory (Adler privately and in classes); Herbert Berghof classes; MA plus Ed.D, Columbia University; MFA, film and television, NYU Tisch.

My Performance Background
Twenty-five years experience with contemporary and classical plays. Recent: Musical comedy/dance revues and work with Tony Award–winning Glines.

My Teaching Philosophy
Text-based environment is provided to grow in a process of repetition and to confirm a method, if desired.

What Inspires Me to Teach
Twofold: (1) My work with historic teachers such as Stella and Herbert; (2) My own students when I see them blossom.

Other Important Things for Prospective Students to Know
Author of the plays: *Sammy and Three Roads Home*, and author of *Tao of Acting: A Spiritual Approach to Success.*

How I Would Describe the Art of Acting
When the actor makes it look easy or when he or she fools the audience into believing in the character and story.

What I Look for When I Interview a Prospective Student
One who has talent as an ensemble team player and without a selfish ego. One who has a sense of humor.

The Kind of Student Who Gets the Most Working with Me
The playful kind who is open to occasional exercises or games to unleash spontaneity and imagination.

The Facts
Years Teaching: 21
Address: 30-458 75th Street
East Elmhurst, NY 11370
Studio: Shetler 54 Studios and
Raw Space Studios
Phone: (718) 505-6110
E-mail: Ffcset@aol.com
Web Site: www.spotlighton.org
Private Coaching: Yes, $50 per hour
Admission Policy: Interview and/or audition for advanced classes. Open door (with probationary period) for beginner classes.

Classes
Acting Technique, Advanced
Fee: $200 for 12 weeks
Schedule: Mon., 6–9 PM

Acting Technique, Beginning
Fee: $200 for 12 weeks
Schedule: Sun., 4–7 PM

Karen Porter White

My Own Training
BA, Webster College, St. Louis; MO American Conservatory Theatre; Scene study: Terry Schreiber, Jill Andre, and Joanna Beckson; Meisner Technique: Phil Gushee; audition and scene Study: Michael Shurtleff.

My Performance Background
Children's theater, regional stock, Off and Off-Off Broadway.

My Teaching Philosophy
Enlighten, Empower, Encourage.

What Inspires Me to Teach
Too many good actors audition badly! Michael Shurtleff's Twelve Audition Guideposts provide a practical blueprint for auditioning, no matter what the actor's technique is (or isn't); it's very rewarding to see an actor "get it."

Other Important Things for Prospective Students to Know
Each session consists of twelve classes; students must be punctual; everyone works twice every class.

How I Would Describe the Art of Acting
We are the storytellers of our society; it's our responsibility to tell the stories clearly and entertainingly.

What I Look for When I Interview a Prospective Student
A vivid imagination, willingness to explore, and respect for the art and craft of the theater.

The Kind of Student Who Gets the Most Working with Me
Someone who has a vivid imagination and willingness to explore, and has the ability to take the work seriously (although it's fun), but not themselves.

The Facts
Years Teaching: 8
Address: 410 E. 6th Street, #16B
New York, NY 10009
Studios: Private classes (6–8 students) usually at Shetler or CAP 21
Phone: (212) 252-2713 (voice mail)
Fax: (212) 677-8134
E-mail: KPWsdt@att.net
Private Coaching: Yes, $60 per hour
Admission Policy: Interviews; recommendations.

Classes
Michael Shurtleff's Audition Guideposts
Fee: $600 for 12 classes
Schedule: Mon., 6–10 PM

Lynn Winters

My Own Training
BS, voice, Arizona State University and Mansfield University; HB Studios, Chicago City Limits.

My Performance Background
Multimedia, MYC stage; plays and musicals; television; soaps and commercials, night clubs; film and print.

My Teaching Philosophy
The Winter technique is based on

Stanislavski principles combined with using organic human nature as tools to stimulate emotion. Our honest emotional connection dictates our voice inflection and our physicality.

What Inspires Me to Teach

I love to teach acting because it is all about truth. It is the only vocation in this world that is applauded and rewarded with truth as its goal.

Other Important Things for Prospective Students to Know

I believe that creativity can blossom only in a safe environment. I am the only one who gives feedback, not the other students. I encourage my students to listen to their own inner voices and not to the voices of their neighbors.

How I Would Describe the Art of Acting

In the art for of acting, the whole human is the paint, the canvas, the artist. We, as actors, are re-creating the whole, three-dimensional human by using the organic design of human nature as tools.

What I Look for When I Interview a Prospective Student

I do not believe in auditioning students. It is not my place to judge creativity. It is my job to bring out my students' creative acting talent and guide them to be the best they can be.

The Kind of Student Who Gets the Most Working with Me

The student who has the passionate desire to dig under the surface of the words. The student who is deep, dedicated, and brave enough to do the work of a true actor.

The Facts

Years Teaching: Over 20
Address: 21 Bleecker Street, New York, NY 10014
Studios: Lynn Winters Studio of Acting and Voice, New York City and Port Washington, NY
Phone: (212) 636-9829
Private Coaching: Yes, $75 per hour; career counseling, $75 per hour
Admission Policy: Adults only, open admission

Classes

Private Acting Sessions
Fee: $65 per hour (with annual Showcase and Champagne Reception in New York City)
Acting Audition Workshop
Fee: $150 for 5-hour workshop
Schedule: One day, 5 hours

Walt Witcover

My Own Training

BA, speech and drama, 1946, Cornell University; MA, dramatic production, 1947; American Theatre Wing, NY, 1947–1950; Lee Strasburg Acting Class: 1950–1953; Actors Studio Directors Unit: 1955–1969; Uta Hagen 1960–1961.

My Performance Background

Off Broadway, 1947–1953; artist-in-residence, Stratford, 1948; Summer Stock.

My Teaching Philosophy

"I am as if." First, continuing to live onstage as Stanislavski says, to free the student to live here and now as if there and then.

What Inspires Me to Teach
Intelligent, open-minded students.

Other Important Things for Prospective Students to Know
Process, better than product; the question is the answer; the problem is the solution.

How I Would Describe the Art of Acting
Real immediate experience and behavior in imaginary circumstances

What I Look for When I Interview a Prospective Student
Intelligence, open mind, maturity, patience, seriousness, sense of truth, honesty.

The Kind of Student Who Gets the Most Working with Me
A serious, questioning student ready to learn a process; patient, self-disciplined.

The Facts
Years Teaching: 50
Studio: Witcover Acting Studio
40 W. 22nd Street
New York, NY 10010
Phone: (212) 691-4367
Fax: (212) 989-7274
E-mail: Witcover@gig.net
Web Site: www.Witcover.org
Private Coaching: Yes, $65 per hour
Admission Policy: By interview only.

Classes
Private Session (one on one)
Fee: $300 for 5 sessions
(1 hr., 15 mins.)
Schedule: To be arranged,
1 to 3 classes per week
Partner Sessions (two per class)
Fee: $250 for 5 sessions
(2 hrs.)
Schedule: To be arranged,
1 private, 1 partner class weekly

TWO

Getting Schooled

2. ACTING SCHOOLS

Mrs. Anne Jillian's Spotlight On: The Meisner Intensive Training Program

Along with acting, directing, and writing best-selling acting books on the Meisner technique, Larry Silverberg has been running his professional acting program, The Meisner Intensive Training Program, for the past seventeen years (read more about Silverberg in Section A: *Act New York*'s Master Teachers). This rigorous, nine-month program is one of the very few places in the world where you can learn the Meisner approach from a teacher who got the work directly from the source, Sanford Meisner.

The training program meets two nights a week for four hours per class. As if the class work weren't demanding enough, there are heavy requirements on working outside class in rehearsals with partners. This is clearly not a class for anyone who has a casual interest in acting: This is a place for absolutely serious-minded students; it is a place for students ready to work very, very hard.

Students' comments about the class are often powerful and deeply felt, such as, "This has been the peak experience of my life"; "This class has given me the greatest treasures I have ever re-ceived"; "I have experienced my acting soar to places I had only dreamed of"; "This class was the toughest, most personally demanding thing I have put myself through, and I learned more than I ever thought possible."

You have to move quickly to get into one of Silverberg's classes. He only offers three classes a year, and the spots go fast. There is the nine-month program, which begins every September, his summer six-week program, which begins in early July, and the Film Acting Intensive, which meets for ten full days at various times during the year.

Silverberg's Film Acting Intensive is a very exciting new class. This

55

program meets from early in the morning until the early evening for ten days. In this boot-camp-type intensive, students' days are filled with classes in advanced elements of character work, point-of-view exercises, physical impediment techniques, and in-depth character improvisations.

All this hard work eventually leads to the creation of a short feature film in which the students are the stars. Silverberg has the finest guest teachers working alongside him, and the film project is directed by an award-winning filmmaker. After the film is shot and edited, students and their guests attend a screening of the production. Each student leaves the class with a DVD of the film for his or her own use.

If you want to study in any of Silverberg's classes, our advice is to get on the waiting list early and get yourself an interview.

The Meisner Intensive Training Program
(212) 462-3005
www.actorscraft. com

Josh's Spotlight On: The School for Film & Television

You go and buy a *Back Stage* paper and start looking for an acting school. You see all the flashy ads that talk about how they can teach you everything you need to know. With so many choices, how do you go about choosing the right school? *Act New York* is here to help!

Of course, you want a place with the course work you want to study and where you can get the most for your money. Well, all classes are not created equal. You should compare class hours as well as price. The folks at The School for Film & Television (SFT) told us that this is one area that really sets them apart from other schools offering similar classes. In most cases, SFT is less expensive per hour. Compare SFT's class maximum of twelve students (in most three-hour classes) to other two-hour classes with twenty-student maximums. There is also no membership fee at SFT.

When you add the SFT faculty (who's bios speak for themselves at www.filmandtelevision.

com) to this mix, you can see why SFT is one of the premier places for anyone seriously studying acting. Also, SFT is the home base for Larry Silverberg's world-renowned Meisner Intensive Training Program. If you want to study with Larry, SFT is the only place you can do it.

The school was proud to tell us that it is accredited. College credits are given for successful course completion. SFT offers course work with real goals for skill development and with guaranteed policies regarding tuition. National leaders in actor training have praised the faculty for their programs.

As we perused SFT's list of student accomplishments, we saw that students have done principal work in: *The Gilmore Girls, The Hughleys, Ed, OZ, The Sopranos, Soul Food, ER, Providence, West Wing, The X Files, Law and Order, Law and Order: Special Victims Unit, Crossing Jordan, Days of Our Lives, Melrose Place, Earth: Final Conflict, The Beat, The Education of Max Bickford, Guiding Light, Saturday Night Live, Whacked, Where's Angelo, The*

Father, The Son, True Vinyl, and well over a thousand commercials. SFT summed it up this way, "While some view television and film as entertainment, we see it as our yearbook." Their motto is "Results you can act on!"

The School for Film & Television
39 W. 19th Street,
12th Floor
New York, NY
(212) 645-0030
www.filmandtelevision.com

Other Acting Schools

Actors Connection
630 Ninth Avenue (bet. 44th and 45th Sts.)
New York, NY 10036
(212) 977-6666
(212) 765-4274
E-mail: contactus@actors connection.com
www.actorsconnection.com

Actors Conservatory
750 Eighth Avenue,
Room 400–401
New York, NY 10036
(212) 764-0543
www.actorsconservatory.org

Actors Institute
159 W. 25th Street,
9th Floor
New York, NY 10001
(212) 924-8888
www.tairesources.com

Actors Movement Studio
302 W. 37th Street
New York, NY 10018
(212) 736-3309
E-mail: ams@actorsmovement studio.com

www.actorsmovement studio.com

Actors Workshop
65 W. 55th Street
New York, NY 10019
(212) 757-2835

American Academy of Dramatic Arts
120 Madison Avenue
New York, NY 10016
(212) 686-9244
1-800-463-8990
www.aada.org

American Musical and Dramatic Academy
2109 Broadway
New York, NY 10023
(212) 787-5300
1-800-367-7908
Fax: (212) 799-4623
E-mail: info@amda.edu
www.amda.edu

Atlantic Theatre Company
453 W. 16th Street
New York, NY 10011
(212) 691-5919
Fax: (212) 691-6280
E-mail: admissions@ atlantictheater.org
www.atlantictheater.org

Cap 21 (studios)
18 W. 18th Street, 6th Floor
New York, NY 10011
(212) 807-0202
Fax: (212) 807-0166
www.cap21.org

Caymichael Patten Studio
211 W. 61st Street
New York, NY 10023
(212) 765-7021 (also fax)
E-mail: info@cpattenstudio. com
www.cpattenstudio.com

Circle in the Square Theatre School
1633 Broadway
New York, NY 10019

(212) 307-0388
E-mail: circleinthesquare@ att.net
www.circlesquare.org

Creative Acting Company
122 W. 26th Street,
Suite 1102
New York, NY 10001
(212) 352-2103
Fax: (212) 352-2076
www.creativeacting.com

Endeavor Studios
19 W. 21st Street
New York, NY 10010
(212) 645-2641

Gene Frankel Studio
24 Bond Street, Suite 1102
New York, NY 10001
(212) 777-1767
E-mail: info@genefrankel. com
www.genefrankel.com

Gertrude Stein Reparatory Theatre
15 W. 26th Street,
2nd Floor
New York, NY 10010
(212) 725-0436
Fax: (212) 725-7267
E-mail: info@gertstein.org
www.gertstein.org

Harlem Theatre Co.
473 W. 150th Street
New York, NY 10031
(212) 281-0130

HB Studios, Inc.
120 Bank Street
New York, NY 10014
(212) 675-2370
www.hbstudio.org

HERE Arts Center
145 Sixth Avenue (bet. Spring and Broome Sts.)
New York, NY 10013
(212) 647-0202
Fax: (212) 647-0257
E-mail: info@here.org
www.here.org

Kimball Studio
60 E. 13th Street, 3W
New York, NY 10003
(212) 929-1984
(212) 260-9335
E-mail: Kelly@kimballstudio.
com
www.kimballstudio.com

**Larry Silverberg's
Meisner Intensive
Training Program,
The School for Film &
Television
30 W. 24th Street
New York, NY 10011
(212) 462-3005
www.actorscraft.com**

Lee Strasberg Institute
115 E. 15th Street
New York, NY 10003
(212) 533-5500
Fax: (212) 473-1727
E-mail: theleeny@aol.com
www.newyork-strasberg.com

**Michael Howard
Studios**
152 W. 25th Street
New York, NY 10001
(212) 645-1525
Fax: (212) 645-9159
E-mail: info@michaelhoward
studios.com
www.MichaelHoward
Studios.com

**Neighborhood
Playhouse School of
the Theatre**
340 E. 54th Street
New York, NY 10022
Fax: (212) 906-9051
E-mail: info@the-neiplay.org
www.the-neiplay.org

New Actors Workshop
259 W. 30th Street,
2nd Floor
New York, NY 10001
(212) 947-1310
1-800-947-1318
Fax: (212) 947-9729
E-mail: newactorsw@aol.com
www.newactorsworkshop.
com

**New York Film
Academy**
100 E. 17th Street
New York, NY 10003
(212) 674-4300
Fax: (212) 477-1414
E-mail: film@nyfa.com
www.nyfa.com

Penny Templeton Studio
261 W. 35th Street,
Suite 304
New York, NY 10001
(212) 643-2614
Fax: (212) 643-2615
E-mail: pts158@penny
templetonstudio.com
www.pennytempletonstudio.
com

**The School for Film &
Television**
39 W. 19th Street,
12th Floor
New York, NY 10011
(212) 645-0030
1-888-645-0030
Fax: (212) 645-0039
E-mail: jsee@sft.edu
www.filmandtelevision.com

**Stella Adler
Studio of Acting**
31 W, 27th Street, 3rd Floor
New York, NY 10001
(212) 689-0087
1-800-270-6775
Fax: (212) 689-6110
E-mail: info@stellaadler.com
www.stellaadler.com

T. Schreiber Studio
151 W. 26th Street,
7th Floor
New York, NY 10001
(212) 741-0209
Fax: (212) 741-0948
E-mail: info@t-s-s.org
www.t-s-s.org

The Theatre Studio
750 Eighth Avenue,
Suite 200
New York, NY 10036
(212) 719-0500

TVI Actors Studio
Actor's Equity Building
165 W. 46th Street,
Suite 509
New York, NY 10036
(212) 302-1900
1-800-884-2772
Fax: (212) 302-1926
www.tvistudios.com

Weist-Barron
35 W. 45th Street, 6th Floor
New York, NY 10036
(212) 840-7025
E-mail: wbacting@weist
barron.com
www.weistbarron.com

William Esper Studios
261 W. 35th Street
New York, NY 10001
(212) 904-1350
E-mail: info@esperstudio.com
www.esperstudio. com

3.
AUDITION AND
MONOLOGUE
TECHNIQUE

Liz's Spotlight On: Auditioning with Acting Coach Ruth Nerken

Liz sat down with Ruth Nerken to explore the wide world of auditions.

LB: Why is an audition class necessary in your eyes?

RN: Most people admit to being either igno-rant of what to ex-pect at an audition or scared of auditioning. If they are nervous about auditioning, class provides them a weekly chance to go through the audition process and then to analyze their technique as well as their own demeanor. Acting is acting. It's all about acting, but certainly acting for the camera is different than auditioning for the camera.

LB: OK, let's talk about that. How is auditioning for the camera different?

RN: Actors need to learn how to make things happen in the very tiny space that is allowed. I shouldn't even use the word *space* — they have to make everything happen from a mark. When you get the job, if the scene takes place on a beach, they'll put you on a beach. It's better than theater in terms of helping you fulfill the reality of where you are. But at an audition, you don't get the beach, you don't get the wind, you don't get the surf. You have to stand there and make me believe you're standing on the beach talking to somebody. If it says that the character would be walking, there's nothing you can do about that except perhaps do several little, minor adjustments in your body to give a sense of freedom and space, but you can't move from that mark.

LB: What do you think is essential for an actor to know about auditioning in general?

RN: Be on time. Every casting director, the majority, "late actors" are their biggest complaint. Also, be comfortable asking questions, but don't manufacture them. Some people think they look smarter if they ask a question. If that's the reason, inevitably the question turns out to be questionable. If you can, find out how the casting director tends to set up her auditions. Do they use a stool? Are you on a little platform? Is there a camera or is it across the desk?

LB: How does the actor find these things out?

RN: That's when you talk to your audition coach or your friends in the business. I always suggest actors rehearse for the audition sitting on a stool, standing, as well as across a desk, so that you're comfortable with any eventuality. One thing I promise you, there is going to be a surprise. The casting people might have "the reader" jump over a whole series of lines and just give you your cue line, so be prepared for that as well.

LB: What common mistakes are made during auditions that you see time and time again?

RN: Being overly humble, you know, "Thank you, thank you, thank you so much for seeing me." Other mistakes include apologizing for a bad choice and stopping auditions in the middle. If you stop the audition right at the beginning, it's easier for them to deal with. But if you go halfway through and then say "Can I start again?," the answer's going to be "No just continue." So don't even bother asking. Simply find your bearings and continue. Also, you must get good at script handling.

LB: What does that mean?

RN: That means, when you are not speaking, listen to your partner, do not be reading your next lines getting ready for your cue.

LB: So what you are saying is to really "be" with your partner?

RN: Yes, be present to your partner. You must remember that when the casting staff reviews the tape, nothing else is going to be on that monitor except your face. So if you're spending half the time looking down at the script, that's what they see. It's going to be more about behavior than saying the right words. We are assuming that you are literate.

Now about props, only use them when you really can't do the scene without it. For instance, if there's a line where the other character says, "Let me light that for you," you probably should have a cigarette. Not that you should smoke it, but you should have a cigarette. But there's one script I give out where the woman bumps into a man and says, "I'm so sorry." The stage directions say that she takes out a tissue and starts wiping down his vest. You can't do that because there's no one to do it to. Your reader is twelve feet away from you, right?

LB: And don't be afraid to have the script in hand?

RN: You should always have the script in hand at the first audition whether you know the lines or not. I've actually gone around asking casting directors what is preferred, and that's what the majority say. Even if you've memorized, because then it still looks like you're still ready to grow. The book *The Camera Smart Actor* by Richard Brestoff will tell you everything you can expect to happen on a set.

LB: Assuming an actor does or feels like he or she has made a mistake, what can be done?

RN: It depends on the mistake. If it's something that happens during the acting of the audition — if you're in the middle of the script and you make a mistake — stay concentrated, stay in character, and fix the mistake. That's perfectly reasonable and very professional. If you absolutely must say anything, say it with a sense of humor so you don't look like you're horrified by this mistake — "No big deal, I'm going to take it from here."

LB: How should an actor prepare for an audition?

RN: You may pick up a script and go, "I know exactly what I want to do with this." If not, don't be afraid to use a coach. And then, if you have time, read the whole script and do your script analysis. Then practice the scene every possible way that you can. Allison Janney who's on *West Wing* said the one thing she was missing in preparing for auditions was a sparring partner. She wanted someone to do the lines with. So that's something you can always do with a friend who's an actor.

LB: And on the issue of callbacks?

RN: For the callback, it's understood that you know the text and are willing to make choices. It's really important for the callback that you take the same choices and improve on them, getting deeper into the character.

Ruth Nerken
The School for
Film & Television
(212) 645-0030.

Audition Training

Actors Advent
(212) 627-0854
Offers workshops in audition technique, scenes, and monologues.

Actors Connection
630 Ninth Avenue, Suite 1410 (bet. 44th and 45th Sts.)
New York, NY 10036
(212) 977-6666
(212) 765-4274
E-mail: contactus@actors connection.com
www.actorsconnection.com
Offers workshops in monologues and auditioning.

The Film Acting Studio
90 Lexington Avenue, Suite 1H
New York, NY 10016
(212) 725-3437
E-mail: studio-90-lexs@ prodigy.net
www.filmacting studio.com

TVI Actors Studio
Actor's Equity Building
165 W. 46th Street, Suite 509
New York, NY 10036
(212) 302-1900
1-800-884-2772
Fax: (212) 302-1926
www.tvistudios.com
Offers workshops in monologues and auditioning, career consulting, and marketing services.

Weist-Barron
35 W. 45th Street, 6th Floor
New York, NY 10036
(212) 840-7025
E-mail: wbacting@weist barron.com

www.weistbarronacting.com
Offers classes in monologue research and performance and cold reading.

Audition and Monologue Coaches

Betsy Capes/ Capes Coaching
(646) 274-1514
Fax: 646-2741523
E-mail: info@capesco.com
www.capesco.com
Audition coach. Specializes in private coaching for actors for upcoming auditions or to help clarify their career goals. Capes has worked at Manhattan Theatre Club as casting assistant, The Public Theatre, Binder Casting, and The Roundabout Theatre Company.

Robert Dagny
(212) 371-8258
www.actorsaudition coaching.com
Private coaching. Creator of the "The Performers Audition Package."
(See Section B: Qualified Coaches.)

Laurie Eliscu
1-800-774-9430
(914) 720-9896
E-mail: laurieeliscu@aol.com
Private coaching, small classes. Also a director. Founded Hudson River Repertory Company, Inc.

Michael Goldstrom
(212) 252-4546
E-mail: michael@goldstrom. com
www.goldstrom.com
Scenes, monologue, and audition coaching. Graduate of Juilliard, LAMDA, and Columbia. Shakespeare to contemporary. Private and classes. All levels, all ages.

Maria Greco
630 Ninth Avenue
New York, NY 10036
(212) 247-2011
E-mail: castings@mariagreco casting.com
www.mariagrecocasting.com
Acting for camera. Year-round classes, children's classes.

Paul Harman
(212) 252-4767
E-mail: paulharman@mind spring.com
www.auditionsuccess.com
Offers Musical Theatre Audition Technique. Class is six weeks and kept small so everyone works every week. Also teaches private lessons.

Kymberly Harris
(347) 276-2936
E-mail: kymlharris@aol.com
www.bway.net/~fresh
Monologue and audition coach. Auditioning technique; career advancement; scene study; method acting; audition preparation for theater, film, and television
(See Section B: Qualified Coaches.)

James Jennings
(212) 581-3044
Method technique, scene study, monologues. Beginner to advanced.

Karen Kohlhaas
(212) 252-4200
E-mail: Karen@monologue audition.com
www.monologueaudition. com
Private classes in monologues
(See Section B: Qualified Coaches.)

William Martin
(212) 724-1548
E-mail: wgmartinjr@aol.com
Private coaching monologues and scene study us-

ing contemporary, classic, and Shakespearean works.

Jack Poggi
(212) 928-6882
E-mail: jp.actor@verizon.net
Author of *Monologue Workshop*. Helps actors find material and coaches them accordingly. Private coaching. Also teaches a six-week monologue workshop at Actors Connection (AC). Call Jack or AC for next available class. (See Section B: Qualified Coaches.)

Lois Raebeck
(718) 624-8145
E-mail: loisraebeck@aol.com
Private coach. Helps conquer stage fright and with difficulties of memorizing. Only takes students who have completed previous class work or training.

Ken Schatz
(718) 625-8372
www.kenschatz. com/actortec.html
Teaches a monologue lab, privately or at Circle in the Square Theater.
(See Section B: Qualified Coaches.)

Pamela Scott
(212) 567-0857
E-mail: pamannscott@hotmail.com
Teacher/coach. Beginning to advanced acting technique and scene study. Coach monologues and audition scenes. All levels, all ages. (See Section B: Qualified Coaches.)

Karen Porter White
(212) 252-2713 (voice mail)
E-mail: kpwsdt@att.net
Teaches Michael Shurtleff''s *Audition Guideposts*. Private classes (six to eight students) (See Section B: Qualified Coaches.)

Florence Winston
(212) 541-7600 (answering service)
E-mail: wynn@qis.net
Teacher/coach. Alternative conservatory. In-depth, ongoing study of text and character. Private work combined with group work through study of classical and contemporary monologue scenes and one-act plays.

Prudence Wright-Holmes
(917) 723-0164
(212) 864-6525
E-mail: prudenceholmes@hotmail.com
Teaches privately and at The New School. (See Section B: Qualified Coaches.)

Tammy Jacobs
(212) 721-6964
Fax: (212) 721-6964
E-mail: itstotammy@aol.com
Teacher/coach.

4. COMEDY AND IMPROV CLUBS AND SCHOOLS

Clubs

Check *Ross Reports* to see which clubs have open-mike night.

Boston Comedy Club
82 W. 3rd Street (at 6th Ave.)
New York, NY 10012
(212) 477-1000
E-mail: info@bostoncomedyclub.com
www.bostoncomedyclub.com

Caroline's Comedy Club
1626 Broadway
(bet. 49th and 50th Sts.)
New York, NY 10019
(212) 757-4100

Fax: (212) 956-0197
E-mail: contact@carolines.com
www.carolines.com

Chicago City Limits
1105 First Avenue
(at 61st St.)
New York, NY 10021
1-888-5233
E-mail: info@chicagocitylimits.com
www.chicagocitylimits.com

Comedy Cellar
117 MacDougal Street (bet. W. 3rd and Bleecker Sts.)
New York, NY 10012
(212) 254-3480
www.comedycellar.com

Comic Strip Live
1568 Second Avenue (bet. 81st and 82nd Sts.)
New York, NY 10028
(212) 861-9386
E-mail: info@comicstriplive.com
www.comicstrip live.com

Dangerfield's
1118 First Avenue (at 61st St.)
New York, NY 10021
(212) 593-1650
www.dangerfields.com

Gladys' Comedy Room at Hamburger Harry's
145 W. 45th Street (Broadway and 6th Ave.)
New York, NY 10036
(212) 832-1762
(212) 840-0566
www.gladyscomedyroom.com

Gotham Comedy Club
34 W. 22nd Street
(bet. 5th and 6th Aves.)
New York, NY 10010
(212) 367-9000
(212) 367-9003
E-mail: info@gothamcomedyclub.com
www.gothamcomedyclub.com

HA! Comedy Club NYC
369 W. 46th Street
New York, NY 10036
(212) 977-3884
www.hacomedynyc.com
Email: info@hanyc.com

**The New York
Comedy Club**
241 E. 24th St. (at 3rd Ave.)
New York, NY 10010
(212) 696-5233
www.newyorkcomedyclub.
com
Email: Linda@newyorkcome-
dyclub.com

Rosie's Turn
55 Grove Street
New York, NY 10014
(212) 366-5438
E-mail: webmaster@
rosesturn.com
www.rosesturn.com

Stand-Up New York
236 W. 78th Street (at
Amsterdam Ave.)
New York, NY 10024
(212) 595-0850
E-mail: ncimato@standup
ny.com
www.standupny.com

Upright Citizens Brigade
307 W. 26th Street (bet. 6th
and 7th Sts.)
New York, NY 10001
(212) 366-9176
Fax: (212) 366-9231
E-mail: info@ucbt.net
www.ucbtheater.com

Uptown Comedy Club
2290 12th Avenue
New York, NY 10027
(212) 981-1200
(212) 590-2570
Fax: (212) 590-2572
E-mail: contactohm@aol.com
www.ohm1.com/uptown.htm

Schools

**American
Comedy Institute**
481 Eighth Avenue, Suite
736
New York, NY 10001
(212) 247-5555
E-mail: info@comedy
institute.com
www.comedyinstitute.com
One-year professional comedy program and workshops.

Comic Strip Live
1568 Second Avenue (bet.
81st and 82nd Sts.)
New York, NY 10028
(212) 861-9386
E-mail: info@comicstriplive.
com
www.comicstriplive.com
Offers an eight-week stand-
up comedy workshop.

Armando Diaz
(212) 586-3575
E-mail: Armando@armando
diaz.com
www.Armandodiaz.com
Offers classes in improv
and sketch writing. Works
with beginners through
advanced.

**The New York
Comedy Club**
241 E. 24th Street (at 3rd
Ave.)
New York, NY 10010
(212) 696-5233
E-mail: classes@newyork
comedyclub.com
www.newyorkcomedyclub.
com

**New York
Comedy School**
(212) 712-6381
Stand-up comedy. Private
coaching and classes with
showcase.

Tom Soter
48 W. 21st Street
New York, NY 10010
(212) 316-4916

E-mail: tsoter@habitatmag.
com
www.tomsoter.com
Improv class.

Stand-Up New York
236 West 78th Street (at
Amsterdam Ave.)
New York, NY 10024
(212) 595-0850
E-mail: classes@standupny.
com
www.standupny.com

Upright Citizens Brigade
307 W. 26th Street
New York, NY 10001
E-mail: classes@ucbt.net
www.ucbt.net
Long form improv and sketch
comedy.

5. DANCE SCHOOLS

Classes are mainly on a
single-visit basis and
not set up as a year-
round commitment.
Check Web sites for
monthly class offerings.

**Alvin Ailey American
Dance Center**
211 W. 61st Street,
3rd Floor (bet. West End
[11th] and Amsterdam [10th]
Aves.)
New York, NY 10023
(212) 767-0940
Fax: (212) 767-0625
E-mail: info@alvinailey.org
www.alvinailey.org
Classes taught: Ballet, modern, Horton, ballroom, gymnastics, Dunham, body conditioning, tap, and more.

**Arthur Murray
Dance Studio**
677 Fifth Avenue, 4th Floor
(bet. 53rd and 54th Sts.)
New York, NY 10022
(212) 593-1633
E-mail: info@arthurmurray
nyc.com

www.arthurmurraynyc.com
Classes taught: Fox trot, waltz, rumba, samba, cha-cha, line dancing, swing, disco, nightclub. Rehearsal space rental available.

Ballet Arts at City Center
130 W. 56th Street
(bet. 6th and 7th Aves.)
New York, NY 10019
(212) 582-3350
E-mail: info@balart.com
www.balart.com
Classes taught: Jazz, music theater, voice, modern, tap.

Ballroom on Fifth
319 Fifth Avenue, 4th Floor
(at 32nd St.)
New York, NY 10016
(212) 532-6232
www.ballroomonfifth.com
Classes taught: Ballroom, mambo, merengue, stepping, swing, tango, waltz, and more.

Broadway Dance Center
221 W. 57th Street (bet. Broadway and 7th Ave.)
New York, NY 10019
(212) 582-9304
Fax: (212) 977-2202
E-mail: info@bwydance.com
www.broadwaydancecenter.com
Classes taught: Tap, jazz, ballet, modern, hip hop, house, theater performance, voice, yoga, stretch, tumbling, belly dance, pilates, and more.

Dance New York, Inc.
237 W. 54th Street,
3rd Floor (bet. Broadway and 8th Ave.)
New York, NY 10019
(212) 246-5797
E-mail: info@dancenewyork.com
www.dancenewyork.com
Classes taught: Salsa, cha-cha, merengue samba, mam-

bo, tango, rumba, fox trot, quickstep, swing, Viennese waltz, waltz.

Gelabert Studios
255 W. 86th Street (at Broadway)
New York, NY 10024
(212) 874-7188
www.gelabertstudios
gallery.com
Classes taught: Ballet, specialize in prevention of injury through proper technique. Class size limited: ten to twelve students.

International Ballet Dance Center at Lindt Studio
250 W. 57th Street (at Broadway)
New York, NY 10019
(212) 974-1150
(212) 974-1158
www.lindtballet.com
Classes taught: Ballet, facial gymnastics, body conditioning, mambo, fango. Rehearsal space rental available.

Isadora Duncan Dance Foundation/Lori Belilove & Company
141 W. 57th Street (bet. 6th and 7th Aves.)
New York, NY 10001
(212) 691-5040
E-mail: info@isadoraduncan.org
www.isadoraduncan.org
Classes taught: Duncan technique, modern, ballet. Teachings, intensives, productions.

Joffrey Ballet School
434 Sixth Avenue (at Broadway)
New York, NY 10011
(212) 254-8520
Fax: (212) 614-0148
www.joffreyballetschool.com
Classes taught: Ballet.

Martha Graham School of Contemporary Dance
316 E. 63rd Street (bet. 1st and 2nd Aves.)
New York, NY 10021
(212) 838-5886
Fax: (212) 838-0339
E-mail: info@marthagraham
dance.org
www.marthagrahamdance.
org
Classes taught: Martha Graham technique, ballet, yoga, pilates, workshops. Rehearsal space rental available.

The New Champions Dance Studio
257 W. 39th Street, 14th Floor (bet. 7th and 8th Aves.)
New York, NY 10018
(212) 307-7707
E-mail: championsdance
studio@hotmail.com
www.champions dance.com
Classes taught: Cha-cha, disco, fox trot, rumba, Latin/salsa, swing, tango, waltz. Rehearsal space rental and more.

New Dance Group
254 W. 47th Street (bet. Broadway and 8th Ave.)
New York, NY 10036
(212) 719-2733
Fax: (212) 719-0457
E-mail: rickschussel@ndg.org
www.ndg.org
Classes taught: Tap, jazz, ballet, modern, hip-hop, international styles, swing, acting, music, pilates, and more.

New York Conservatory of Dance
30 E. 31st Street (bet. Madison and Park Aves.)
New York, NY 10016
(212) 725-2855
E-mail: nycod@earthlink.net
http://home.earthlink.net
\~nycod
Classes taught: Ballet. Rehearsal space rental available.

Peridance

132 Fourth Avenue,
2nd Floor (bet. 12th and
13th Sts.)
New York, NY 10003
(212) 505-0886
Fax: (212) 674-2239
E-mail: info@peridance.com
www.Peridance.com
Classes taught: Ballet, tap,
jazz, modern, hip-hop, theatre dance, karate, and
more.

Sandra Cameron Dance Center, Inc.

199 Lafayette Street (bet.
Kenmare and Broome Sts.)
New York, NY 10012
(212) 431-1825
E-mail: info@sandra
cameron.com
www.sandracameron.com
Classes taught: Ballroom,
Latin, hustle, Argentine Tango, salsa. Group classes and
private lessons and rehearsal
rental space available.

STEPS

2121 Broadway
(bet. 74th and 75th Sts.)
New York, NY 10023
(212) 874-2410
Fax: (212) 787-2449
E-mail: info@stepsnyc.com
www.stepsnyc.com
Classes taught: Ballet, tap,
hip-hop, jazz, modern, street,
swing, ethnic, theater/
character, acting, music,
yoga, pilates. (Also has The
Barre Café and Boutique.)
School at STEPS for children
ages two to seventeen: (212)
874-2410, ext. 20.

West Side Dance Project

357 W. 36th Street, 3rd
Floor (bet. 8th and 9th Aves.)
New York, NY 10018
(212) 563-6781
E-mail: info@joria
productions.com
www.westsidedanceproject.
com

Classes taught: Classical ballet, music theatre, jazz, tap,
and more.

You Should Be Dancing . . . !

412 Eighth Avenue,
4th Floor (bet. 30th and
31st Sts.)
New York, NY 10001
(212) 244-0011
Fax: (212) 868-3281
E-mail: info@youshould
bedancing.net
www.youshouldbedancing.
net
Classes taught: Salsa, swing,
tango, Argentine tango, hip-
hop, merengue, rumba, cha-
cha, waltz, Viennese waltz,
fox trot, belly-dancing.
Space available.

6. SINGING TEACHERS AND COACHES

In New York, there is a
difference between a
teacher and a coach. A
teacher will teach you
to sing, whereas a
coach, for the more ex-
perienced, will help you
to prepare for auditions
and work on and build
your repertoire. Most
are teachers as well as
coaches, but some are
specific. Here is a list of
only a handful of the
hundreds of teachers in
New York. Check *Back
Stage* and *Show Busi-
ness Weekly*; ask
around and try people
out until you find
someone you feel you
can grow from.

Breck Alan

(212) 979-1277
E-mail: breck@breckalan. com
www.bodysinging.com
Styles: Rock/pop, jazz,
Broadway. All levels.
Teacher and coach: vocal
mechanics/technique and
song styling. Call for fees.

Nathan Andersen

(212) 582-6765
E-mail: jederengel@hotmail.
com
www.voicelessonsNY.com

Andres Andrade

(212) 539-3561
E-mail: andradeten@aol.com
Styles: Classical musical theater, jazz, pop. Teacher. All
levels. Call for fees.

Barbara Bliss

(212) 799-3424
E-mail: Barbara@barbara
bliss.com
www.barbarabliss.com
Styles: Broadway, opera,
pop. Primarily technique;
willing to coach. All levels.
Call for fees.

Liz Caplan

(212) 645-9369
1-866-SING-OUT
E-mail: Liz@LizCaplan.com
www.LizCaplan.com
Styles: Broadway, pop, rock.
Teacher and coach. Begin-
ners through professionals.
Call for fees.

Russell Daisey

(212) 663-7598 or
(917) 662-1421
Styles: Broadway, pop, jazz,
classical. All levels. Currently
teaches at Columbia University; formerly taught at Circle
in the Square and NYU. Call
for fees.

Maria Fattore

(646) 732-1077
E-mail: maria@mariafattore.
com

www.mariafattore.com
Styles: all. Teacher and
coach. All levels: children
under thirteen only taken if
under professional management or involved in a professional activity, such as Metropolitan Opera Children's
Chorus or Harlem Boys
Choir. Call for fees.

Leslie Giammanco
(212) 543-2244
E-mail: leslie@leslie
giammanco.com
www.lesliegiammanco.com
Styles: Broadway, pop, classical, jazz. Vocal technician
and coach. All levels. Call
for fees.

Effie Jansen
(212) 860-8422
Styles: Pop, R&B, rock,
gospel, jazz, Broadway.
Teacher and coach. Helps
prepare for demo record-
ings. Helps write music. Also
teaches piano. Call for fees.

Jay Kerr
(212) 582-5118
E-mail: jay@jaykerr.com
www.jaykerr.com
Styles: Broadway, pop, jazz,
cabaret. Teacher and coach.
All levels; beginners welcome. Call for fees.

Michael Kingsley
(212) 787-4975
Styles: Broadway, pop, R&B,
rock, voice-overs, demos.
Teacher and coach. Call for
fees.

Robin Morse
(212) 352-4024
E-mail: robingus@earthlink.
com
Offers in-studio and
private lessons. Teaches
monologue and scene study
and singing performance
classes. (See Section B:
Qualified Coaches.)

Mary L. Rodgers
(212) 873-6931
Styles: Musical theater (bel
canto). Vocal technique: beginners to intermediate. Vocal coaching: all levels. Call
for fees.

Neil Semer
(212) 265-6454
E-mail: neilsemer@aol.com
www.neilsemer.com
Styles: All. Teacher and
coach. All levels. Call for
fees.

Lynn Starling
(212) 245-5939
E-mail: LstarlingVoice@
aol.com
Styles: Broadway, cabaret.
Teacher and coach. All levels. Call for fees.

7. VOICE, DICTION, AND VOICE-OVER TECHNIQUE

Voice and Diction

Baruch College
Continuing and Professional
Studies
One Bernard Baruch Way
Box B1-116
New York, NY 10010
(646) 312-5000
Fax: 646-312-5101
E-mail: caps@baruch.cuny.
edu
http://caps.baruch.cuny.edu/
programs/esl.htm
Public speaking, voice and
diction, accent reduction, ad-
vanced communication, and
fluency.

Thom Garvey
(212) 696-7822
www.speakingeffectively.com
Vocal/speech coaching, ac-

cent reduction, dialect training, vocal strengthening.
Call for fees and more information.

**The Great Voice
Company, Inc.**
616 East Palisade Avenue
Englewood Cliffs, NJ 07632
1-800-333-8108
(201) 541-8595
Fax: (201) 541-8608
E-mail: info@greatvoice.com
www.greatvoice.com
Training division provides
workshops, books, and
tapes for businesspeople
who want to improve their
voice and presentation skills.
Specialized training is also
provided for those who want
to become professional
voice-over artists.

**Doug Honorof, Ph.D.
(Verberations LLC)**
(917) 696-3633
E-mail: dialectdoug@yahoo.
com
www.dialectdoug.com
Yale-trained accent and
dialect/dialogue coach.
Metro-NYC area; on loca-
tion. Dialect and language
research for on-camera and
stage productions. Voice-
over direction. Credit
cards/PayPal accepted.

**Lemond Language
Consulting**
6 W. 18th Street, 4B
New York, NY 10011
(212) 206-3900
Fax: (212) 243-3966
E-mail: info@lemond
language.com
www.lemondlanguage.com
The foundation of the accent
reduction program is based
on a clear understanding of
the rhythm and music of English. Lemond therefore em-
ploys music as one of its
tools for teaching accurate
pronunciation. Accurate

rhythm, intonation, and correct sound production are learned through the reading of limericks, tongue twisters, and repetition drills. Other trainings that can assist the non-native English speaker include presentation skills English skills.

Marci Meikle
(212) 758-7464
E-mail: marcelle10022@
aol.com
Teaches accent reduction, diction, 26 different dialects, various regional American dialects, and a general American dialect through strengthening and positioning of the tongue and its surrounding muscles.

New York Speech Improvement Services
253 W. 16th Street
New York, NY 10011
(212) 242-8435
1-800-SPEAKWELL
E-mail: samspeech@aol.com
www.nyspeech.com
Accent elimination, specialty dialects, and accents for actors and professional speech and improvement for public speakers. NYS licensed speech pathologists. Individual and small group classes. Admission by interview; evaluation at no charge. By appointment only.

Olsen Speech & Language Improvement Center
347 Fifth Avenue, Suite 1406 (bet. 33rd and 34th Sts.)
New York, NY 10016
(212) 951-3844
(866) 675-4222
E-mail: speechinfo@
olsenspeech.com
www.olsenspeech.com
Accent reduction, learn any accent, the actor's voice,

voice and diction. We find people's true voices and help them to project beautifully and magnetically.

Judith Pollak, M.A., C.C.C.
(212) 362-6714
(917) 494-2811
E-mail: JudithJae@aol.com
Improve voice production and reduce foreign and regional accents. Call for fees and more information.

Power for Communications
118 W. 79th Street
New York, NY 10024
(212) 595-1733
Fax: (212) 724-9172
E-mail: dcrt@mindspring.com
www.arthurreel. com
Speech Improvement, accent correction, acting for non-actors. Private and group classes.

Verberations LLC
134 W. 26th Street, Suite 606
New York, NY 10001
(646) 638-0787
1-800-485-6124
Fax: (646) 638-0266
E-mail: queries@
verberations.com
www.verberations.com
Dialect coaching for stage and screen, voice-overs, demos and training programs geared toward actors.

Voice-overs

The Art of Voice
(212) 517-8616
E-mail: steveharris@aol.com
Complete voice-over instruction, talent cultivation, demo reel services, techniques, and marketing strategies for all aspiring voice-over artists.

David Zema, Inc. Voice of Success Programs
135 W. 26th Street
New York, NY 10001
(212) 675-4978
Fax: (212) 271-3295
E-mail: davidzema@aol.com
www.davidzema.com
Voice-over techniques and training include: audition skills on microphone, studio recording sessions, opening vocal range and stylistic variety. Students are encouraged to make choices and take risks.

Edge Studio
307 Seventh Avenue, Suite 1007
New York, NY 10001
(212) 868-3343
1-888-321-3343
E-mail: info@edgestudio.com
www.edgestudio.com
Voice-over training, demo production, casting. Private and small groups. Specializes in workshops.

Ruth Franklin
(212) 496-9696
Fax: (212) 496-9696
Has 50,000 national voice-over credits to her name. Teaches a master class in NY and LA. Class is small, and an audition is required. Eight-week class offers something new every week, including various types of voice-over and marketing plans.

Shut-Up & Talk
(212) 262-2622
630 Ninth Avenue, Suite 1410 (located in Actors Connection)
New York, NY 10036
E-mail: info@shutupandtalk. com
www.shutupandtalk.com
Specialize in voice-over training in Spanish and English. Professional voice-over

studio. In-studio coaching, professionally mixed and produced demos.

T.J.'s Voices
(212) 465-8050
www.workinginshowbiz.com/tj.html
Voice-over training. Small groups. Agent attends last class. Receive a free marketing kit.

To conclude the class section, here are a few words from Mickey Pantano about a new class she offers called The Celebrated Self.

The Celebrated Self

In my work I have discovered that actors are a unique breed — rare, intriguing, and questioning with strengths, idiosyncrasies, and quirks. I've noticed that the most successful actors are able to break out of a mold. They think bigger than life, which has a big impact on their career. Working actors continually renew, cultivate, and rediscover what inspires them and motivates them.

Too often, actors offer a watered-down version of themselves to try and be what others want. I ask the question: Do you cover up the passion, the fire, the spark of what makes you who you truly are? Why would you do that when these are the very things that inspired you to act in the first place?

I work with actors to develop a provocative, compelling way to market themselves, designed around who they really are so that they evolve and learn to cultivate their self-expression. I work with them as individuals to boldly position themselves as unique, one of a kind.

The Celebrated Self offers classes on body and image training for actors who are ready to break the rules, be daring, evocative, spontaneous, and themselves.

For more information call: (212) 539-8486

THREE

getting the job

8. TALENT AGENTS

Key
S = SAG
A = AFTRA,
E = Equity
W = Writers' Guild of America
D = Directors' Guild of America

About Artists Agency, Inc.
1650 Broadway #1406
New York, NY 10019
(212) 581-1857
S A E
Represents actors for all areas, especially upcoming and established stand-up comics and comedic character actors and actresses for film, TV, and theater. Interviews by appointment only. Don't phone or visit. Accepts photos/résumés and videotapes by mail only.

Abrams Artists Agency
275 Seventh Avenue,
26th Floor
New York, NY 10001
(646) 486-4600
S A E
Agents: Harry Abrams (owner); Neal Altman (SAE) (sr. vice president.); Robert Altermann (SAE) (vice president); Tracey-Lynn Goldblum (SAE) (vice president); Billy Serow (SAE) (voice-over commercials); J.J. Adler, Jonathan Saul (SAE) (voice-overs and promos); Alison Quartin (SAE), Amy Mazur (AE) (on-camera commercials); Genine Esposito (print); Mary Guzowski (commercial print); Mark Turner (SAE) (hosting); Richard Fisher (SAE); Jill McGrath (SAE); Paul Reisman (SAE) (film, TV, theater). Children, teens, and young adults: Ellen Gilbert (SAE) (film, TV, and theater); Dina Bogner (film, TV and theater); Bonnie Shumofsky (SAE) (commercials); Heather Finn (SAE) (print); Vincent DeVito (SAE) (business affairs). Literary Department:

Maura Teitelbaum (W). Don't phone or visit.

Access Talent, Inc.
37 E. 28th Street, Suite 500
New York, NY 10016
(212) 684-7795
www.accesstalent.com
S A
Agents: Linda Weaver (owner); Chas Cowing (owner); Todd Kijanka (agent); Roger Becker (studio manager); Pam Lewy (assistant); Marge Tate (talent payment). This office handles all aspects of voice-over representation. Please submit your voice-over materials on compact disc only.

Acme Talent & Literary
875 Sixth Avenue,
Suite 2108
New York, NY 10001
(212) 328-0388
S A E W
Agents: Adam Lieblein (owner) (SAEW); Eileen Haves (SAE) (commercials, industrials, voice-overs); Nina Shreiber (adult theatricial,

film, TV), Leo Bookman (WD) (literary for film, TV, theater). Select list of all types or all areas of film, TV, theater, musical theater, and beauty. Accepts photos, résumés by mail only. Referrals from Casting Directors required. Please no drop-ins or unsolicited phone calls or faxes.

Agency for the Performing Arts, Inc.
485 Madison Avenue, 13th Floor
New York, NY 10022
(212) 582-1500
S A E W
Agents: Harvey Litwin (CFO); Caroline Daughters; Maryanne Rubacky; Mark Schlegel. All types for all areas; no children or directors. Don't send video or audiotapes. Bicoastal.

Agents for the Arts, Inc.
203 W. 23rd Street, 3rd Floor
New York, NY 10011
(212) 229-2562
S A E
Agents: Carole J. Russo (SAE); H. Shep Pamplin (SAE). All types for all areas. Interviews by appointment only. Photos/résumés by mail only. Voice-over and videotapes by request only. Don't phone or visit.

American International Talent Agency
303 W. 42nd Street, Suite 608
New York, NY 10036
(212) 245-8888
S A E
Agents: Wanza King (SAE); Claretta King (SAE). All types for all areas, including children (five and up). Interviews by appointment only. No drop-ins. We are not accepting photos and résumés until further notice.

Andreadis Talent Agency, Inc.
119 W. 57th Street, Suite 711
New York, NY 10019
(212) 315-0303
S A E
Agents: Barbara Andreadis (owner). All types, including children, for all areas. Accepts photos and résumés by mail only. No unsolicited tapes. Interviews are by appointment only. Don't phone or visit.

Ann Steele Agency
330 W. 42nd Street, 18th Floor
New York, NY 10036
(212) 629-9112
S A E
Agents: Ann Steele (owner). Represents union talent for film, theater, and TV. Interviews and auditions are by invitation only. Please do not phone, visit, or send tapes. Signed clients only. No freelance. New clients by referral only. Does not open unsolicited mail.

Ann Wright Representatives
165 W. 46th Street, Suite 1105
New York, NY 10036
(212) 764-6770
S A E W
Agents: Ann Wright (owner) (voice-overs, on-camera, commercials, theater, and films); Dan Wright (director Literary Department). Mail photos and résumés. Please don't phone or visit. Interviews by appointment only.

Archer King, Ltd.
317 W. 46th Street, Suite 3A
New York, NY 10036
(212) 765-3103
E-mail: akingltd@yahoo.com
S A E W

All types for theater, TV, and movies (no commercials or voice-overs).

Arcieri & Associates, Inc.
305 Madison Avenue, Suite 2315
New York, NY 10165
(212) 286-1700
Fax: (212) 286-1110
E-mail: talent@arcieritalent.com
www.arcieritalent.com
S A
Agents: Steven Arcieri (SA) (commercials and voice-overs); Carmen Marrufo (SA) (Hand Models); Noel Short (SA) (commercials and voice-overs). Represents celebrity and noncelebrity artists as well as hand, leg, and body-part models for television and radio commercials, network promotions, documentary narration, animation, movie trailers, audio books, industrials, new media, and print. Please do not phone, fax, or visit. Accepts voice-over, demo CDs and tapes, photos, modeling cards by mail. Attends showcases and accepts showcase invitations.

The Artists Group East
1650 Broadway, Suite 610
New York, NY 10019
(212) 586-1452
S A E
Agents: Robert Malcolm (owner); Cynthia Katz (owner); Daniel Grunes (SAE). All types for film, theater, and TV. Also represents teens sixteen and over.

Associated Booking Corporation
1995 Broadway, Suite 501
New York, NY 10023
(212) 874-2400
Fax: (212) 769-3649

E-mail: info@abcbooking.
com
www.abcbooking.com
S A E
Agent: Oscar Cohen (president); Jody Wenig; Paul La-Monica; Paul Horton, Michael Boheim, and Lisa Cohen (marketing). Represent singers and recording artists for major recording events.

Atlas Talent Agency, Inc.
36 W. 44th Street,
Suite 1000
New York, NY, 10036
(212) 730-4500
Fax: (212) 730-5820
E-mail: info@atlastalent.com
www.atlastalent.com
S A E
Agents: John Wasser (SAE); Lisa Marber-Rich (SAE); John Hossenlopp (SAE); Ian Lesser (SAE); Marilyn McAleer (SAE); Lynn Eriksen (SA); Rachel Sackheim-Petrella (SA); Michael Guy (SA); Melissa Rollins (SA). Actors/actresses, broadcasters, comedians, narrators, and spokespersons for commercials, industrials, voice-overs, promos, narrations, animation, and broadcasting. Interviews by appointment only. Accepts photos, résumés, and tapes by mail only. Attends showcases. Don't phone, fax, or visit.

Babs Zimmerman Productions, Inc. (Agency)
305 E. 86th Street
New York, NY 10028
(212) 348-7203
E
All types for all areas. No children or models. Interviews are by appointment only. No demo voice-overs. Will accept professional singing tapes. Will submit for film and TV also.

Barry-Haft-Brown Artists Agency (B-H-B)
165 W. 46th Street,
Suite 908
New York, NY 10036
(212) 869-9310
S A E
Agents: Bob Barry (owner); John Camillieri. All types for all areas except commercials. No children. Accepts photos and résumés. Don't phone.

Bauman, Redanty & Shaul
250 W. 57h Street,
Suite 2223
New York, NY 10107
(212) 757-0098
S A E
Agents: Mark Redanty (SAE); Charles Bodner (SAE); Tim Marshall (SAE). All types for all areas. No commercials, no voice-overs, no children. Don't phone. Does not take mailed submissions.

Bernard Leibhaber Agency
352 Seventh Avenue,
New York, NY 10001
(212) 631-7561
S A E
Agents: Bernard Liebhaber (owner). All types for film, TV, and theater. No commercials. No children. Pictures and résumés received by mail will be given respectful consideration. Phone calls, visits, and tapes are not welcome.

The Bethel Agency
311 W. 43rd Street,
Suite 602
New York, NY 10036
(212) 664-0455
Fax: (212) 664-0462
S A E
Agent: Lewis R. Chambers (owner). All types for all areas. No children at the present time. Photos and résumés

by mail only. Interviews are by appointment only. Please do not phone or visit.

Beverly Anderson
1501 Broadway, Suite 2008
New York, NY 10036
(212) 944-7773
S A E
Agent: Beverly Anderson (owner). Theater, film, and TV. Talent must have strong credits. No children or babies. Interviews are by appointment only. Photos and résumés are accepted by mail only. No tapes accepted. Absolutely no phone calls or visits.

bloc nyc
41 E. 11th Street, 11th Floor
New York, NY 10003
(212) 905-6236
www.blocagency.com
S E
Agents: David Crombie (head of agency) (SA); David Krasner (SAE); Alison Clark (dance). Represents actors of all types for TV, film, and theater. Dance department represents professionals only for commercials, TV, film, music videos, and musical theater. No visits. Interviews are by appointment only. Accepts photos and résumés by mail only. Accepts choreography videotapes only by mail.

Blue Ridge Entertainment
41 Union Square West,
Suite 809
New York, NY 10003
(646) 638-1745
S A E
Agents: Tony Cloer (SAE). All types, except children, for all areas. No commercials or voice-overs. Photos and résumés are accepted by mail only. Do not send tapes. Do not phone.

Bret Adams, Ltd.
448 W. 44th Street
New York, NY 10036
(212) 765-5630
S A E
Agents: Bret Adams (owner)
(writers and directors; some
actors); Margi Rountree,
(partner) (SAE) (actors only);
Bruce Ostler (partner) (SAE)
(writers and directors only);
Ken Melamed (partner)
(SAE) (actors only); Melissa
Hardy (writers and direc-
tors). All types for all areas
except commercials and children. Also represents directors, choreographers, designers, and conductors.
Interviews by appointment
only. Please don't phone, fax
or visit. Accepts photos and
résumés by mail only. No unsolicited tapes. Attends
showcases; accepts show-
case invitations.

Bruce Levy Agency
311 W. 43rd Street,
Suite 602
New York, NY 10036
(212) 262-6845
S A E
Agents: Bruce Levy (owner).
All types for all areas (film,
commercials, TV, theater, industrials, and commercial
print). Leading women and
men, character actors and
special, offbeat, unusual talent. Do not seal envelopes
when sending photos and résumés. Please do not phone
or visit.

Carry Company
49 W. 46th Street, 4th Floor
New York, NY 10036
(212) 768-2793
Fax: (212) 768-2713
S A E W
Agents: Sharon Carry (own-
er); Jessica Fley; Amanda
Keith (assistant). Actors for
TV, film, commercials. All
types: stand-up comedians,

ethnic and character types,
choreographers, and musical
theater performers. Interviews by appointment only.
No phone calls or visits.

**Carson-Adler
Agency, Inc.**
250 W. 57th Street,
Suite 2030
New York, NY 10107
(212) 307-1882
S A E
Agents: Nancy Carson (owner) (children through early
twenties-legit); Bonnie Deros-
ki (S) (babies through teens:
commercials); Shirley Faison
(SA) (babies through young
adults). Interviews by appointment only. Mail photos
and résumés. Babies and
children snapshots OK.

**The Carson Adler
Organization, Ltd.**
234 West 44th Street,
Suite 902
New York, NY 10036
(212) 221-1517
S A E
Agents: Steve Carson (owner) (film, TV, theater, commercials); Barry Kolker (partner) (SAE); Sabrina
Deschenes (partner) (com-
mercials) (S); Jenevieve
Brewer (print department).
All types for all areas including children's department,
starting with babies. Mail
photos. Interviews are by appointment only. Audio and
videotapes by request only.
Absolutely no phone calls or
visits.

**Classic Model &
Talent**
213 W. 35th Street,
10th Floor
New York, NY 10001
(212) 947-8080
Fax: (212) 947-8088
www.classicagency.com

E-mail: info@classicagency.
com
Agents: Ruth Winig (vice
president); Mary Depetris
(director of TV/film). All
types for all areas in New
York and New Jersey vicini-
ties. Mail photos, comp
cards, and résumés (not returned) to attention of New
Talent.

Coleman-Rosenberg
155 E. 55th Street, Suite 5D
New York, NY 10022
(212) 838-0734
S E
Agents: Deborah Coleman
(SE). Theater, TV, movies; all
types, music directors. No
commercials, models, or children. Interviews by appointment only. Don't phone or
visit. Not accepting any new
clients.

**Columbia Artists
Management, Inc.**
165 W. 57th Street
New York, NY 10019
(212) 841-9500
Fax: (212) 841-9744
E-mail: info@cami.com
www.cami.com
A
Classical music musicians
only.

**Cornerstone Talent
Agency, Inc.**
37 W. 20th Street,
Suite 1108
New York, NY 10011
(212) 807-8344
E-mail: DayStarSing@aol.com
S A E
Agents: Steve Stone (SAE);
Mark Schlegel (SAE); Shan-
non Kelly (associate). Actors,
comedians, and singers; all
types for animated series/
features, CD-ROMs and interactive, film, soaps, theater,
and TV. No commercials,
voice-overs, models, or children. Accepts photos by mail

only. Don't phone, fax, visit, or send videotapes. Interviews by appointment only.

Cunningham, Escott, Dipene & Associates

257 Park Avenue South, Suite 900
New York, NY 10011
(212) 477-1666
S A E

Agents: T.J. Escott (president). On-camera: Ken Slevin (exec. vice president) (SA); Carrie Morgan (SA); David P. Cash (SA). Beauty: Jill Reiling (SA); Samantha Berliner (S) (represents models for commercial endorsements, TV, and film). Voice-overs: Sharon Bierut (SA); Anita Reilly (SA); Billy Collura (SA). Promos: Donna Mancino (SA); Nate Zeitz; Jenny Lee (SA). Children and teens (for legit commercial and print): Halle Madia (S); Leslie Zaslower (S); Mara Glauberg (SE). Print (adults): Stephanie Bellarosa. Print (youth): Lori Amster. Exclusive signed client agency for all types including young people, models for TV and radio commercials and related areas. Videotapes and audiotapes/CDs may not be returnable. CED New York is now accepting voice-over demos for commercials, promos and station affiliate/ imaging via the Internet. Please send links to Web sites or mp3 files only to NYVOICES.

Don Buchwald & Associates

10 E. 44th Street
New York, NY 10017
(212) 867-1200
Fax: (212) 867-1070
www.buchwald.com
S A E W

Agents: Don Buchwald (owner); Richard Basch (business affairs attorney) (SAE). The-ater, TV, film: Joanne Nici (SAE); Ricki Olshan (SAE); Rachel Sheedy (SAE); David Williams (SAE); Hannah Roth (SAE). Youth: Victoria Kress (SAE); Missey Dweck (SAE). Commercials: David Elliott (SA); Robin Starr (SA); Steven Kaye (SA); Scott Linder SA); Michael Raymen (SA); Robyn Stecher (SA), Katherine Ryan (SA); Jason Marks (SA); Maura Maloney (SA); Stewart Nacht (SA); Seth Goldberg (commercial celebrity agent); Robin Steinfeld (commercial promo agent). Broadcasting: David Katz (SA). Actors and actresses, children (five to twelve), teens (thirteen to eighteen), and young adults for TV and radio commercials, theater, and film; directors, screenplay writers, radio and TV personalities.

Dorothy Palmer Talent Agency, Inc.

235 W. 56th Street, Suite 24K
New York, NY 10019
(212) 765-4280
S W

Excellent actors and actresses, broadcasters, comedians, dancers, singers, models, TV hosts/hostesses, narrators, voice-over specialists, and spokespersons; senior citizens, all ethnicities and ages, unusual and specialty acts, etc., for film, soaps, TV, commercials, industrials, infomercials, voice-overs, TV hosting, print, special events. TV hosts should send videotapes as well as pictures and résumés. All others should mail pictures and résumés only. No deliveries, visits, or calls. Will not work with anyone who visits or calls; just mail pictures and résumés. Literary department specializes in established writers of independent films.

Welcomes serious investors to call Dorothy Palmer regarding production of these films. A high-fashion department is now being added for movies, TV, commercials, and print. High-fashion men and women should mail pictures and résumés ASAP and write "high-fashion" on envelope.

Douglas, Gorman, Rothacker & Wilhelm, Inc. (DGRW)

1501 Broadway, Suite 703
New York, NY 10036
(212) 382-2000
S A E

Agents: Flo Rothacker (owner); Jim Wilhelm (owner); Michelle Gerard (SAE); Josh Pultz (SAE). All types for theater, TV, and film. No children or voice-overs. Pictures and résumés accepted by mail only. Please do not phone or visit. No unsolicited tapes.

Dulcina Eisen Associated

154 E. 61st Street
New York, NY 10021
(212) 355-6617
S A E

Agents: Dulcina Eisen (owner); Barry P. Katz (SAE); Margaret Emory (SAE). All types for theater, TV, film. No children. No unsolicited mail unless performing in New York or through recommendations. No open interviews. Don't phone or visit.

Duva-Flack Associates, Inc.

200 W. 57th Street, Suite 1008
New York, NY 10019
(212) 957-9600
S A E

Agents: Robert Duva (owner); Elin Flack (owner); Richard Fisher (SAE); Kimberly Coffiner (SAE). Actors for film, theater, and TV. Also represents directors, writers, designers, choreographers. No commercials or children. Mail photos and résumés. Interviews by appointment only. Video/audio tapes by request only. No phone calls please.

Eastern Talent Alliance, Inc.
1501 Broadway, Suite 404
New York, NY 10036
(212) 220-9888
S A E
Agents: Allen Flannagan (owner); Carole Davis (owners). Theater, TV, film. No commercials, no children. Not accepting any new clients or submissions at this time. Don't phone or visit.

Electric Talent, Inc.
172-13 Hillside Avenue,.
Suite 202
Jamaica Estates, NY 11432
(718) 883-1940
E-mail: elecrtrictalent@aol.com
A
Agent: Robert Persad (A). All types for all areas: TV, movies, print, and commercials. Send picture and résumé by mail only. Tapes will not be returned. No visits.

EWCR and Associates
311 W. 43rd Street,
Suite 304
New York, NY 10036
(212) 586-9110
S A E
Agents: Gary Epstein (owner); Randi Ross (SAE) (children and young adults); Renee Panichelli (SAE). All types, ages for all areas. No commercials. No unsolicited video or audiotapes. Don't phone, visit, or drop off pictures. Bicoastal.

Fifi Oscard Agency, Inc.
110 W. 40th Street,
Suite 1601
New York, NY 10018
(212) 764-1100
A E W D
Agents: Fifi Oscard (AE) (owner); Carmen La Via (E), Peter Sawyer; Francis DelDuca (E); Kevin McShane; Julien Rouleau; Cathleen Ihasz. All types for all areas, including children for films, TV, print, and commercials.

Flaunt Model & Talent, Inc.
114 E. 32nd Street, #501
New York, NY 10016
(212) 679-9011
E-mail: flauntmodels@earthlink.net
S A
Agents: Gene Roseman (A) (president); Lisa Stern; Millie Kelly; Lena Baylor. Models (male and female, no children) for high fashion, commercial, petite, plus sizes, parts. Also represents actors/actresses, athletes, dance performers, ethnic/foreign types, seniors and spokespersons for commercials, industrials, infomercials, CD-ROMs, and interactive, music videos, and print advertising. Composites and headshots by mail only. We do not do voice-overs. Please do not phone or visit.

Fresh Faces Agency, Inc.
2911 Carnation Avenue,
Baldwin, NY 11510-4402
(516) 223-0034
Fax: (516) 379-0353
E-mail: ffAgent@aol.com
www.freshfacesagency.com
S A E
Agents: Aggie Gold (owner); Jamie Gold (assistant). Actors, actresses, and children (five and up) for all areas except print and voice-overs.

Do not visit. Interviews by appointment only.

Frontier Booking International, Inc. (FBI)
1560 Broadway, Suite 1110
New York, NY 10036
(212) 221-0220
S A E
Agents: John Shea (SAE) (commercials, hosts, and legit); Heather Finn (SA) (commercials and voice-overs). All types for all areas from three years to early thirties. Pictures and résumés are accepted by mail only. Interviews are by appointment only. Don't phone.

The Gage Group
315 W. 57th Street,
Suite 408
New York, NY 10019
(212) 541-5250
S A E
Agents: Martin Gage (owner-L.A.); Philip Adelman (SAE); Steven Unger (SAE); Wendie Relkin Adelman (SAE) (commercials/soap operas). Actors for all areas. No babies or children. No unsolicited tapes. Don't phone or fax. Bicoastal.

Garber Talent Agency
2 Pennsylvania Plaza,
Suite 1910
New York, NY,10121
(212) 292-4910
S A E
Agents: Karen S. Garber (owner); Mark Fleischman (SAE). All types for all areas. Highest caliber dancers and actors. No children. No unsolicited tapes. Mail without return address will not be opened. Don't phone or visit.

Generation TV
20 W. 20th Street, #1008
New York, NY 10011
(646) 230-9491
S A

Agents: Patti Fleischer (owner); Dina Torre (SA) (commercials); Melanie Diaz (legit). Represents children, teens, early twenties (no adults) for commercials, industrials, and voice-overs. Don't phone or fax or visit. Accepts photos and résumés by mail only.

The Gersh Agency New York, Inc.
41 Madison Avenue, 33rd Floor
New York, NY 10010
(212) 997-1818
S A E
Agents: Rhonda Price (vice president); Stephen Hirsh (vice president); Bill Butler (SAE) (vice president); Lindsay Porter (SAE); Jennifer Konowal (SAE); Sally Ware (SAE); Jason Gutman; Randi Goldstein. Literary department: Scott Yoselow (WD); Peter Hagan (WD); John Buzzetti; Mike Lubin; Kara Baker-Young (D); Peter Franklin. All types for theater, film, and TV. Don't phone or visit.

Gilla Roos
16 W. 22nd Street, 3rd Floor
New York, NY 10010
(212) 727-7820
Fax: (212) 727-7833
E-mail: droos@gillaroos.com
www.gillaroos.com
S A
Agents: David Roos (owner); Marv Josephson (SAE) (adults: theater, film, TV); Ellen Manning (SA) (adults: commercials, industrials); Jason Bercy (S) (kids, teens, young adults: commercials, film, TV); Ramona Pitera (S) (commercial print). All types for all areas: theater, film, TV, commercials; actors, models, children/babies division. Interviews by appointment only.

Ginger Dicce Talent Agency
56 W. 45th Street, Suite 1100
New York, NY 10036
(212) 869-9650
S A E
Agents: Ginger Dicce (owner). Commercials, films, soaps, voice-overs, and industrials. Interviews by appointment only. Photos and résumés by mail only. No tapes or CDs accepted. Don't phone or visit.

Greer Lange Associates, Inc.
3 Bala Plaza West, Suite 201
Bala Cynwyd, PA 19004
(610) 747-0300
E-mail: info@greerlange.com; résumé@greerlange.com
www.greerlange.com
S A E
Agents: Greer Lange; Linda Gagliardi; Janine Jones (new talent). Actors/actresses, ethnic/foreign types, hand and body-part models (female and male), narrators, seniors (mature), spokespersons for CD-ROMS and interactive, promotions, commercials, films, industrials, infomercials, print advertising, theater, TV, voice-overs. Interviews by appointment only. Accepts photos and résumés by mailand email only. Accepts tapes and demos by mail only. *All talent must be willing and able to audition and work in the Philadelphia area.*

GWA (G. Williams Agency)
525 S. 4th Street, #365
Philadelphia, PA 19147
(215) 627-9533
S A E
Agents: Gail Williams (owner/TV and film); Jason Lewis (theater and commercials);

Lauren Leonard (new talent). Actors and actresses, including children and teens (thirteen to nineteen); comedians, dance performers, ethnic/foreign types, narrators, seniors, singers, spokespersons. Teens and young adults for all areas except animated series/features, informercials, music videos and sound recordings, and promotional announcements. Don't phone, fax, or visit. Interviews by appointment only. Accepts photos and résumés by mail only. Audio, videotapes upon request only, and will not be returned.

Hanns Wolteers International, Inc.
10 W. 37th Street, 3rd Floor
New York, NY 10018
(212) 714-0100
E-mail: HannsW@aol.com
S E
Agents: Oliver Mahrdt (owner). TV, commercials, movies; actors, actresses, and offbeat, unusual types; directors, writers, producers, and variety acts. No models or kids. Also has a language department that specializes in foreign languages. Please don't phone or visit. No unsolicited video/audio tapes, scripts, or screenplays. Interested in native foreign language actor/actresses and character actors with strong credits.

Harden-Curtis Associates
850 Seventh Avenue, Suite 405
New York, NY 10019
(212) 977-8502
S A E
Agents: Mary Harden 9owner); Nancy Curtis (owner); Diane Riley (SAE); Michael Kirsten (SAE). All types for

all areas. No children, commercials, or voice-overs. Photos and résumés by mail only. Do not send tapes. Do not phone or visit.

Hartig-Hilepo Agency, Ltd.
156 Fifth Avenue,
Suite 1018
New York, NY 10010
(212) 929-1772
S A E
Agents: Michael Hartig (SAE); Paul Hilepo (SAE); Lauren Weiner (assistant). All types for all areas. No voice-overs. No children. Photos and résuméd by mail only. No phone calls. No visits.

Henderson-Hogan Agency, Inc.
850 Seventh Avenue,
Suite 1003
New York, NY 10019
(212) 765-5190
E-mail: jhogan@henderson-hogan.comS A E
Agents: Jerry Hogan (SAE); George Lutsch (SAE); Heather Overton (assistant). Legit/theatrical only; no commercials, voice-overs or print. No children under twelve. All types. Interviews by appointment only. No tapes accepted.

H.W.A. Talent Representatives
220 E. 23rd Street, #400
New York, NY 10010
(212) 889-0800
S A E
Agents: Craig Holzberg (SAE); Benjamin E. Klein (assistant); Michael Gasparro (associate agent and assistant); Byrony Williams (assistant). Youth department: Sheryl Lefkoe (SAE). Film, TV, and theater for adults sixteen and up: Diana Doussant (SAE); Jay Kane (SAE); Paty Woo (SAE) (LA). Business af-

fairs: Nellie Gonzalez. On-camera commercials, commercial print, voice-overs, industrials; adults and children; daytime drama and musical theater for adults. Photos and résumés accepted. Do not send unsolicited videotapes. Interviews by appointment only. Please don't phone or visit.

Independent Artists Agency
159 W. 25th Street,
Suite 1011
New York, NY 10001
(646) 486-3332
S A E
Agents: Jack Menashe (SAE) (owner) (theatrical); Jessica Noujaim (associate). Represents actors, actresses, models (for acting), and singers for animated series, CD-ROMs, and interactive, films, soaps, theater, and TV. Please no phone calls or visits. Interviews by appointment only. Accepts photos and résumés by mail only. No unsolicited tapes.

Ingber & Associates
274 Madison Avenue,
Suite 1104
New York, NY 10016
(212) 889-9450
S A E
Agents: Carole R. Ingber (owner); Tracy B. Freeman (SA) (on maternity leave); Amy E. Davidson (SA). Represents actors and actresses for commercials (on-camera and voice-over), industrials, and promos. No children's division. Photos and résumés accepted. Interviews by appointment only. Audio cassettes and videotapes are not returnable. Please don't phone or visit.

Innovative Artists Talent & Literary Agency
235 Park Avenue South,
7th Floor
New York, NY 10003
(212) 253-6900
S A E
Agents: Richie Jackson (SAE); Gary Gersh (SAE); Allison Levy (SAE); Lisa Liebermen (SAE); Suzette Vazquez (SAE); Eddie Mercado (SAE); Jana Kogen (SAE) (young talent); Sue King (SAE); Michael Shera (SAE); Jennifer Jackino (SAE) (on-camera); Barbara Coleman (SAE) (young talent/on-camera); Maury DiMauro (SAE); Ross Haime (SAE); Nipa Parikh (SAE); Melissa Cardona (SAE) (beauty); Debra Sherry (SAE); Allen G. Duncan (E) (voice-over); Shari Hoffman (voice-over/promos); Lola Richardson (SAE) (commercials; business affairs). Film, theater, TV, beauty, voice-over, broadcast, commercials. Absolutely no visits or phone calls.

Innovative at Ford Models
142 Greene Street, 4th Floor
New York, NY 10012
(212) 219-6190
S
Agents: Melissa Cardona; Barbara Feinstein; Alison Luscombe (E) (commercial and theatrical). Models (male and female) for film, TV, theater, and commercials. Photos and résumés accepted by mail. Absolutely no visits or phone calls.

International Creative Management
40 W. 57th Street
New York, NY 10019
(212) 556-5600
S A E W AGMA
Agents: Boaty Boatwright (SAE) (theater, motion

pictures). Film: Sam Cohn; Paul Martino; Andrea Eastman. Celebrity endorsements: Lisa Roina (SA); Gordon Corte (SA); Helen T. Shabason (E). Music: Christianne Weiss (AE). All types for all areas through many subagents. I.C.M. Commercials: Phil Sutfin; Tara Boragine; David Coakley; David Evans. Actors for on-camera and voice-over commercials. Tapes are accepted but not returnable.

Jim Flynn Agency
208 W. 30th Street,
Suite 401
New York, NY 10001
(212) 868-1068
S A E W
Agent: Jim Flynn (owner). Theater, TV, and film. No children. Please don't call and please don't stop by.

Jordan, Gill & Dornbaum, Inc.
1133 Broadway, Suite 623
New York, NY 10010
(212) 463-8455
S A E
Agents: Robin Dornbaum (owner); Jeffrey J. Gill (owner); David McDermott (owner) (commercials); Jan Jarret (SAE) (head, Legit Department). Represents children and young adults (to age thirty), actors/actresses and dancers for commercials, voice-overs, soaps, television, film, and theater. Photos and résumés accepted by mail only. Interviews are by appointment only. Don't phone or visit.

Judy Boals, Inc.
208 W. 30th Street,
Suite 401
New York, NY 10001
(212) 868-0924
E-mail: jboals@earthlink.net
S A E W

Agents: Judy Boals. Represents actors and actresses for all types of work. Do not phone, fax, or visit. Industry referral only. Interviews by appointment only. Accepts photos and résumés by mail only. Attends showcases.

Kazarian/Spencer & Associates, Inc.
162 W. 56th Street,
Suite 307
New York, NY 10019
(212) 582-7572
S A E
Agents: Cynthia Kazarian (president); Pamela Spencer (exec. vice president); Riley Day (vice president/general manager); Victoria Morris (director); Lori Swift (agent); Beth Rosner (agent). Actors/actresses sixteen and over for film, TV, theater. Accepts photos and résumés by mail only. No videotapes. Don't phone or visit.

Kerin-Goldberg & Associates
155 E. 55th Street, Suite 5D
New York, NY 10022
(212) 838-7373
S A E
Agents: Charles Kerin (owner); Ellison K. Goldberg (owner); Ronald Ross (SAE); Donald Birge (SAE). Actors for all areas. No commercials. Interviews by appointment only. Photos and résumés are accepted by mail. Don't phone or visit.

Kivi Martin Agency (KMA)
11 Broadway, Suite 1101
New York, NY 10004
(212) 581-4610
S A

Kolstein Talent Agency
85 C Lafayette Avenue,
New York, NY 10901
(845) 357-8301
S A E

Agents: Naomi Kolstein (SA) (owner). All types of actors all ages for all areas. Photos and résumés accepted by mail only. Please no phone calls or unscheduled visits.

The Krasny Office, Inc.
1501 Broadway, Suite 1303
New York, NY 10036
(212) 730-8160
S A E
Agents: Gary Krasny (owner); B. Lynne Jebens (SAE); Christine Iobst (SAE); Norma Eisenbaum (SA) (commercials and voice-overs). All types/ages, including comedians, for all areas: TV, film, theater. No children. No drop-ins. Pictures and résumés are accepted by mail.

Lally Talent Agency, LLC (LTA)
630 Ninth Avenue, #800
New York, NY 10036
(212) 974-8718
S A E
Agents: Dale R. Lally, Stephen Laviska (SAE) (owners); Barry Axelrod (assistant). Actors for TV, theater, and film. No children, commercials, voice-overs, and print. Pictures and résumés are accepted by mail only. Audio/video tapes are not accepted or returned. No phone calls or visits.

The Lantz Office
200 W. 57th Street,
Suite 503
New York, NY 10019
(212) 586-0200
Fax: (212) 262-6659
A E
Agent: Robert Lantz. Only represents writers and directors for film and stage. Does not accept headshots or résumés.

L.B.H. Associates
LM 2/24
1 Lincoln Plaza, Suite 30V
New York, NY 10023
(212) 501-8936
A
Big bands and jazz attractions; vocalists, Broadway-type musical talent.

Lionel Larner, Ltd.
119 W. 57th Street,
Suite 1412
New York, NY 10019
(212) 246-3105
S A E
Agent: Lionel Larner (owner). All types for all areas including stars. No models, children, or commercials. No phone calls, please. Interviews are by appointment only.

Leading Artists, Inc.
145 W. 45th Street,
Suite 1204
New York, NY 10036
(212) 391-4545
S A E
Agents: Dianne Busch (SAE); Mark Upchurch (SAE); Stacy Baer (SAE). Assistants: Jamie Jacobs; Beth Boisi. All types for all areas. No commercials, models, or children. No voice-over tapes accepted. No phone calls.

The Luedtke Agency
1674 Broadway, Suite 7A
New York, NY 10019
(212) 765-9564
(212) 581-0803 Commercial Divison
S A E W
Agents: Penny Luedtke (owner) (legit/literary). Commercial division: Annette Paparelle; Mary Haggerty (on-camera and voice-over commercials). All types of actors and actresses for all areas. Also represents directors and writers. No children. Photos and résumés

are accepted by mail only. Don't phone or visit.

Mary Anne Claro
Talent Agency, Inc.
1513 W. Passyunk Avenue
Philadephia, PA 19145
(215) 465-7788
Fax: (215) 465-2747
www.clarotalent.com
S A E
Agent: Mary Anne Claro. Actors/Actresses, children and teens (four years and up), spokespersons for commercials, films, industrials, soaps, TV. Please no phone calls. Interviews by appointment only. Please send photo and résumé by mail only. Only video tapes accepted.

The Meg Pantera
Agency, Inc.
1501 Broadway, Suite 1508
New York, NY 10036
(212) 278-8366
Fax: (212) 278-8367
S A E
Agents: Meg Pantera (SAE). Represents all ethnicities. Actors and actresses, dance performers, ethnic and foreign types, performers with disabilities, seniors, singers for films, soaps, theater, and TV. Don't phone, fax, or visit. Accepts photos and résumés by mail only. Accepts tapes only by request. Attends showcases.

Michael Amato Agency
1650 Broadway, Room 307
New York, NY 10019
(212) 247-4456 - 7
S A E W
Talent and literary agent. All types for all areas: celebrities, athletes, ethnics, children (five and up), teens, character actors, radio announcers; models, print work. Also maintains a Latin file. Send photos and résumés.

Models on the Move &
Talent Agency
1200 Route 70,
Barclay Towers, Suite 6
Cherry Hill, NJ 08034
(856) 667-1060
S A
Agents: Lucy King. Agency works with all ages and ethnicities. Actors, voice-over talent, dancers, models, entertainers, character actors. Babies through mature adults for TV, commercials, feature film, industrials, music videos, soaps, spokespeople, voice-overs, videos, fashion, print, and theater. Seeking all talent: Caucasian, Asian, African-American, Indian, Hispanic, and mixed racial; children through mature adults. Talent should be willing to travel to auditions, appointments, and bookings. Agency accepts voice-over tapes and videos. Please do not fax. Send supply of headshots and or comp cards, résumés with self-addressed stamped envelope for response. Union and nonunion. Interviews by appointment only. Also looking for more child actors ages one to fourteen, as well as models and model types and promotional talent. Always looking for new talent.

Nicolosi & Co., Inc.
150 W. 25th Street,
Suite 1200
New York, NY 10001
(212) 633-1010
S A E
Agents: Jeanne Nicolosi (owner); John Woodward (SAE); Russell Gregory (SAE). All types for all areas. No commercials. No voice-overs. Interviews by appointment only. Don't phone, visit or send videotapes.

Nouvelle Talent Management, Inc.
20 Bethune Street, #5A
New York, NY 10014
(212) 352-2712
S A
Agent: Toni Sipka. All types for all areas. Send photo and résumé by mail. No phone calls or visits. Interviews by appointment only.

Omnipop, Inc. Talent Agency
55 W. Old Country Road
Hicksville, NY 11801
(516) 937-6011
E-mail: omni@omnipop.com
www.omnipop.com
S A E
Agents: Tom Ingegno (owner); Bruce Smith (SA) (LA). Omnipop continues to expand its talent base to include trained, experienced dramatic actors, building on its established reputation for representing strong comedic actors. Accepts photos, résumés, and videotapes by mail only. Videotapes returned only if an SASE is enclosed. Attends showcases.

Oppenheim-Christie Associates, Ltd.
13 E. 37th Street, 7th Floor
New York, NY 10016
(212) 213-4330
S A E
Agents: H. Shap Pamplin (SAE) (owner). All types for all areas: TV, film, theater, commercials, industrials, voice-overs, and print. Submit photos, résumés, and tapes by mail. Interviews are by appointment only. Audio and videotapes are not returnable. Absolutely no phone calls or visits.

Paradigm
500 Fifth Avenue,
37th Floor
New York, NY 10110
(212) 703-7540
S A E
Agents: Clifford Stevens; Richard Schmenner (SAE); Sarah Fargo (SAE); Roseanne Quezada (SAE). On-camera commercials: Doug Kesten (SA); Stayce Mayer (SA); Vanessa Gringer (SA). Models for on-camera commercial endorsements; voice-overs (accepts voice-over tapes): Jeb Bernstein (SA); Olivia Catt (SA); Edward Batchelor (SA). Promos: Vickie Barroso (SA). All types for all areas. No children. Mail photos and résumés. No videotapes, visits, or phone calls.

Peggy Hadley Enterprises, Ltd.
250 W. 57th Street,
Suite 2317
New York, NY 10107
(212) 246-2166
S A E
Agents: Peggy Hadley (owner). All types for all areas except commercials. Accepts photos and résumés. No models or children. Don't phone or visit.

People New York, Inc.
137 Varick Street, Suite 402
New York, NY 10013
(212) 206-3700
www.idmodels.com
S
Agents: Paolo Zampolli (owner); Jose Pinto (subagent). Actors/actresses, models, infomercials, music videos, and TV. Do not visit; no drop-ins. Accepts photos, résumés, and tapes (audio/video) by mail only; please send to above address, Attn: New talent and Jose Pinto.

Peter Beilin Agency, Inc.
230 Park Avenue, Suite 200
New York, NY 10169
(212) 949-9119
S A
Agent: Peter Beilin (owner). We "keep it simple" and represent a rarified roster of extraordinarily talented professional entertainers including, but not limited to, radio, and television personalities, newscasters, sportscasters, athletes, comics and comedians, convincing illusionists, impersonators, and legitimate actors. No children and no models, mute or otherwise.

Peter Strain & Associates, Inc.
1501 Broadway, Suite 2900
New York, NY 10036
(212) 391-0380
S A E
Agents: Peter Strain (owner); Bill Timms (SAE); Bill Veloric (SAE). All types for all areas. No children. Photos and résumés are accepted by mail. Please don't phone or visit. Interviews are by appointment only.

Professional Artists
321 W. 44th Street,
Suite 605
New York, NY 10036
(212) 247-8770
S A E W
Agents: Sheldon Lubliner (owner); Marylinn Scott Murphy (owner); Kevin Hale (subagent); Jamie Fisher (assistant). All types for theater, film, and TV. Also hosts, directors, and choreographers. Photos and résumés by mail only. Don't phone or visit. Interviews by appointment only.

Radioactive Talent, Inc. (RTI)
350 Third Avenue, Box 400
New York, NY 10010 (mailing address only)
(917) 733-4700
www.radioTV.com
S A ASCAP
Agents: Kenjamin Franklin (owner). Radio DJ's, TV hosts, news reporters/anchors, singer/songwriters, foreign language talent, celebrities, comics for commercials, lectures, industrials, film animation, jingles, radio, and TV. Photos, résumés, video/audio tapes are only accepted by mail at above address. AFTRA franchised address: 240-03 Linden Boulevard, Elmont, NY 11003.

Reinhard Talent Agency, Inc.
2021 Arch Street, Suite 400
Philadelphia, PA 19103
(215) 567-2000
www.reinhardagency.com
Agents: Virginia B. Doyle (owner); Alicia J. Schwartz (SAE); Lynn Delaney (print). All types for TV, film, theater, commercials, industrials, print, runway, and makeup artists. Mail photo and résumés. Interviews by appointment only. Don't phone or visit. No audio/video-tapes accepted.

The Richard Astor Agency
250 W. 57th Street, #2014
New York, NY 10107
(212) 581-1970
S A E
Agents: Richard Astor (owner); William E. Harkins (SAE). All types for film, TV, soaps, theater. No children, models, or voice-overs. Headshots and résumés accepted. Interviews by ap-

pointment only. Don't visit without an appointment.

Schiowitz/Clay/Rose, Inc.
165 W. 46th Street,
Suite 1210
New York, NY 10036
(212) 840-6787
S A E
Agents: Josh Schiowitz (owner LA/NY) (SAE); Teresa Wolf (SAE); Kevin Thompson (SAE). Actors/actresses for films, theater, TV, and soaps. No commercials or voice-overs. Interviews by appointment only. No drop-ins. Accepts photos and résumés by mail only. Don't phone, fax, or visit.

Schuller Talent/New York Kids
276 Fifth Avenue, #204
New York, NY 10001
(212) 532-6005
S A E
Agent: Margaret Matuka (SA). Children, teenagers, young adults for modeling and TV. All ethnic groups. Photos and résumés accepted. Pictures, videotapes, and voice-over tapes are not returnable. Also has beauty division.

Silver, Massetti & East, Ltd.
145 W. 45th Street,
Suite 1204
New York, NY 10036
(212) 391-4545
S A E
Agents: Monty Silver (owner); Dianne Busch (SAE), Mark Upchurch (SAE), Stacy Baer (E). Assistants: Irakli Gaprin, Jaine Jacobs. All types for all areas. No commercials, models, or children. No voice-over tapes accepted. No phone calls. Bicoastal.

Stanley Kaplan Talent
139 Fulton Street, Room 503
New York, NY 10038
(212) 385-4400
S A E
Agents: Stanley Kaplan. All types for all areas including children, teenagers, and seniors. Interviews by appointment only. When submitting photos, please send multiple photos.

Stone-Manners Agency
900 Broadway, Suite 803
New York, NY 10003
(212) 505-1400
S A E
Agents: Tim Stone. Actors/actresses for films, soaps, theater, and TV. Interviews by appointment only. Accepts photos and résumés by mail only. Don't phone, fax, or visit.

Talent House Agency
311 W. 43rd Street,
Suite 602
New York, NY 10036
(212) 957-5220
E
Agents: Dave Bennett (vice president)) (E). Actors/actresses for theater, films, industrials, and TV; music theater performers with strong credits for Broadway. Do not phone, fax, or visit. Interviews are by appointment only. Photos, résumés, and tapes (video) are accepted by mail only. By referral only. No unsolicited e-mails or faxes.

Talent Network Group
111 E. 22nd Street,
3rd Floor
New York, NY 10010
(212) 995-7325
A
Agents: Maureen Lanagan; Bill Iannone. Actors/actresses, athletes, ethnic/foreign types, models (male and fe-

male), spokespersons, teens (thirteen to nineteen), young adults for commercials, films, music videos, soaps, TV. Don't phone, fax, or visit. Interviews by appointment only. Accepts photos, résumés, and tapes (audio/video) by mail only.

Talent Representatives
20 E. 53rd Street, #2A
New York, NY 10022
(212) 752-1835
S A E W
Agents: Honey Raider (owner (SA); Kelly Stark (assistant). All types for all areas. No babies or children. Interviews are by appointment only. No unsolicited manuscripts or phone calls. No sealed envelopes.

Tamar Wolbrom, Inc.
130 W. 42nd Street,
Suite 707
New York, NY 10036
(212) 398-4595
www.tamarw.com
S A
Agent: Tamar Wolbrom (SA) (owner). Represents actors/actresses, comedians, ethnic/foreign types, language specialists, narrators, and spokespersons for animated series/features, commercials, industrials, sound recordings, and promotional announcements and voiceovers. No children's department. CDs, photos, and résumés accepted by mail only. No videotapes, visits, or phone calls.

Top Cat Talent Agency, Inc.
1140 Broadway, Suite 701
New York, NY 10001
E-mail: topcattalent@hotmail.com
S
Agents: Sheldon S. Zimet (owner/agent); Anthony Schi-

ano (subagent). Represents actors, actresses, athletes, children (five to twelve), comedians, dance performers, ethnic/foreign types, models, narrators, seniors (mature), spokespersons and teens (thirteen to nineteen), young adult for CD-ROMs and interactive, commercials, industrials, infomercials, music videos, print advertising, and voice-overs. Don't phone, fax, or visit. Interviews by appointment only. Accepts photos and résumés by appointment only. Works only with managers.

Veronica Goodman Agency
34 North Black Horse Pike
Runnemede, NJ 08078
(856) 795-3133
Fax: (856) 228-7662
S A E
Agents: Veronica Goodman (owner); Tracey McKensie (African-American file); Tiffany DeAngelis (high-fashion male and female models for print, runway, and commercials); Paul DeAngelis (children: three to eleven). All types; union and nonunion; twelve years to adult. Encourages identical, outgoing twins and triplets, children who are skilled in song and dance for stage. Seeking new entertainers, new ideas, and scripts for TV and stage. Accepts submissions of pictures with résumés by mail only. Please do not send tapes, etc., unless requested; materials will not be returned. Absolutely no drop-ins! Interviews by appointment only. Currently looking for celebrity talent through representation or individual submission for future bookings for new theater opening. Celebrities from the fifties to present all welcome.

Please send headshot and résumé with envelope marked "Celebrities."

William Morris Agency, Inc. Talent & Literary Agency
1325 Sixth Avenue
New York, NY 10019
(212) 586-5100
www.wma.com
S A E W D
Administration: Lou Weiss (chairman emeritus); Alan Kannof (COO East Coast); Wayne S. Kabak (Sr. vice president) (Co-COO NY); Cara Stein (Co-COO NY). TV: Jim Griffin; Jackie Harris; Jim Ornstein; Henry Reisch; Jon Rosen; Ken Slotnick; Conan Smith; Cara Stein; Brian Stern. Literary/books: Owen Laster; Suzanne Gluck; Jennifer Rudolph Walsh; Virginia Barber; Manie Barron; Mel Burger Berger; Joni Evans; Traci Fisher; Karen Gerwin; Jay Mandel. Lectures: Betsy Berg. Corporate consulting: Patti Kim. Motion Pictures: Kenny Goodman; Jeff Hunter; Leora Rosenberg. Theater: Peter Franklin; Jack Tantleff; David Kalodner; Biff Liff; John Santoianni; Steve Spiegel; Jeremy Katz. Commercials: Brian Dubin; Glenn Gulino; Marc Guss; Jeff Googel. Personal appearance: Kenny DiCamillo; Cara Lewis; Roland Scahill; Barbara Skydel; Susan Weaving. Please do not send unsolicited photos, credits, tapes, or scripts.

Writers & Artists Agency
19 W. 44th Street,
Suite 1410
New York, NY 10036
(212) 391-1112
S A E W
Agents: Chris Till (E); William Craver (SAE); Lynda

Wills (Literary Department). All types for all areas. No babies, commercials, or print. Don't phone or visit.

9. PERSONAL MANAGERS

Allied Artists Management
John R. Sanchez
244 Fifth Avenue,
Suite E273
New York, NY 10001
(212) 726-3125
Clients: Actors, actresses, children, teenagers, variety/comedy performers.

Alpha Centauri Management, Inc.
6 Ocean Blvd.
Keyport, NJ 07735
(908) 583-4441
Clients: Actors, comedians, directors, producers, and writers Nineteen and up. Accepts photos, résumés, and tapes by mail from SAG, AF-TRA, and EQUITY members.

A.M. Ambrosino Management
P.O. Box 307
New York, NY 10044
(212) 317-8511
Fax: (212) 579-9117
Clients: Actors, actresses, voice-over talent, directors, producers, writers, variety/comedy performers. Videotape, CDs, and treatments received weekly.

American Talent Management, Inc.
244 Fifth Avenue, Suite 503
New York, NY 10001
(212) 686-6547
Fax: (212) 686-6554
E-mail: info@amertalentmgt.com
www.amertalentmgt.com
Clients: Actors eighteen and

up. No children or models. Accepts photos, résumés, and tapes by mail from SAG, AFTRA, and Equity members.

Astral Entertainment, Inc.
377 Park Avenue South, 4th Floor
New York, NY 10016
Clients: Music performers, composers, recording artists, bands, directors, producers, and writers. Accepts photos, résumés, and tapes by mail.

Baker Management
1 Gansevoort Street
New York, NY 10014
(212) 242-8877
Clients: Actors, actresses, directors, producers, writers, variety/comedy performers.

Barmar Talent Management
P.O. Box 30927
New York, NY 10011
(212) 946-1640
Clients: Actors, actresses, children, teenagers. Audio/video tapes accepted, but will not be returned. Attends showcases. Do not phone.

Black & White Artists
29 John Street, Box 220
New York, NY 10038
(212) 571-1989
Fax: (212) 571-7301
E-mail: bwartist@earthlink.net
Clients: Actors, actresses, music performers, composers, recording artists, and bands. Accepts photos, résumés, and tapes by mail from SAG, AFTRA, and Equity members. Please fax or e-mail inquiries.

The Black Dragon Group
257 W. 137th Street, Suite 4
New York, NY 10030

(212) 694-4324
Clients: Actors, actresses, directors, producers, writers, children, teenagers, newscasters, media personalities, sports personalities, variety/comedy performers, musical performers, composers, recording artists, orchestras, bands.

Caroline's Management
1626 Broadway
New York, NY 10019
(212) 956-0101

Cary Hoffman Management
236 W. 78th Street
New York, NY 10024
(212) 873-4840
Clients: Actors, actresses, directors, producers, writers, variety/comedy performers.

Charles Rapp Enterprises, Inc.
1650 Broadway, Suite 1410
New York, NY 10019
(212) 247-6646
Fax: (212) 247-6645
E-mail: info@charlesrapp.com
www.charlesrapp.com
Clients: Actors, actresses, directors, producers, writers, variety/comedy performers, musical performers, composers, recording artists, orchestras, bands.

Coastal Entertainment Productions
32-31 35th Street
Astoria, NY 11106
(718) 728-8581
www.coastalentertainment.com
Clients: Actors, actresses, writers, variety/comedy performers.

Creative Management Group
301 W. 53rd Street, Suite 4K
New York, NY 10019

(212) 245-3250
Clients: Actors, actresses, directors, producers, writers, children. teenagers. Accepts photos/résumés by mail only. Do not phone or visit.

Creative Talent Management
91-08 172nd Street
Jamaica, New York 11432
(718) 658-0443
Clients: Actors and actresses (children to adult), newscasters, sportscasters, music performers, directors, producers, writers, comedy/variety performers. Has a foreign language department for Asian, Hispanic, Middle Eastern, Russian, African, and East Indian. Accepts photos, résumés, and tapes by mail.

Cuzzins Management
(a division of Sokol-Frankmano)
250 W. 57th Street,
Suite 1001
New York, NY 10107
(212) 765-6559
Clients: Actors and actresses, ages three to thirty. No models or babies. Accepts photos, résumés, and tapes by mail.

DCA Productions
330 W. 38th Street, #303
New York, NY 10018
(212) 245-2063
Clients: Actors, actresses, writers, variety/comedy performers, musical performers, composers, recording artists, orchestras, bands. Pictures and résumés are accepted by mail only. Tapes are accepted but not returnable.

Dee-Mura Enterprises, Inc.
269 W. Shore Drive
Massapequa, NY 11758
(516) 795-1616
Fax: (516) 795-8797
Clients: Actors, actresses, directors, producers, writers, children, teenagers, newscasters, media personalities, sports personalities, variety/comedy performers, musical performers, composers, recording artists, orchestras.

Essay Management
364 W. 46th Street
New York, NY 10036
(212) 262-3036
Fax: (212) 262-3036
E-mail: essayj@aol.com

Estelle Fusco Talent Management
72 Moriches Road
Lake Grove, NY 11755
(631) 467-7574
Clients: Actors, actresses, children, teenagers.

Fox-Albert Management Ent. Inc.
88 Central Park West
New York, NY 10023
(212) 799-9090
Clients: Actors of all types. Union only. Accepts photos, résumés, and tapes by mail.

Gerard W. Purcell Associates, Ltd. (NCOPM)
46-19 220th Place
Bayside, NY 11361
(718) 224-3616
Clients: Actors, actresses, directors, producers, writers, newscasters, media personalities, sports personalities, variety/comedy performers, musical performers, composers, recording artists, orchestras, bands, artists, authors, choreographers, photographers, set designers, costume designers. Particularly interested in composers who write poems, music, lyrics.

Gerri Mandall Management
241 W. 37th Street,
10th Floor

New York, NY 10018
(212) 719-6915
Clients: Actors, actresses, newscasters, media personalities, sports personalities.

Glasser/Black Management
283 Cedarhurst Avenue
Cedarhurst, NY 11516
(212) 947-3228
Clients: Actors, actresses.

Goldstar Talent Management
850 Seventh Avenue
New York, NY 10019
(212) 315-4429
Clients: Actors and voice-over talent ages five and up. Especially interested in ethnic, character, and commercial types. Accepts photos, résumés, and tapes by mail only.

Goodwin & McGovern Theatrical Management
8 Franklin Avenue
New Hyde Park, NY 11040
(516) 932-5310
Clients: Actors, actresses, children, teenagers (up to eighteen).

Green Key Management
251 W. 89th Street,
Suite 4-A
New York, NY 10024
(212) 874-7373
Fax: (212) 874-7963
E-mail: GreenKeyM@aol.com
www.greenkeymanagement
com
Clients: Actors, actresses, children, teenagers, newscasters, media personalities, sports, personalities, variety/comedy performers, musical performers, composers, recording artists, orchestras, bands. Accepts headshots and résumés by mail. No videos unless requested.

Harvest Talent Management (NCOPM)
132 W. 80th Street, #3F
New York, NY 10024
(212) 721-5756
www.harvesttalent.com
Clients: Children, teenagers,
young adults. Absolutely no
drop-ins. Do not phone.

Herbosch Management
1035 Park Avenue
New York, NY 10028
(212) 534-6558
Fax: (212) 534-5944
Clients: Actors ages twenty
and up. Works with both
union and nonunion talent.
Currently interested in ethnic,
commercial, and character
types. Accepts photos, résumés, and tapes by mail
only.

The Holding Company
230 West End Avenue,
Suite 1A
New York, NY 10023
(212) 362-1788
Clients: Not seeking new
clients at this time. Actors
and comedy performers.
Does not look at tapes. Will
arrange audition for The
Comic Strip.

Ingrid French Management (IFM)
Contact: Ingrid French
928 Broadway, Suite 302
New York, NY 10010
(646) 602-0653
Fax: (646) 602-0720
E-mail: fren743@aol.com
www.ifmmodels.com
Clients: Actors, actresses,
children, teenagers. Photos
and résumés are accepted
by mail.

Jeff Sussman Management
2840 Broadway. Suite 282
New York, NY 10025
(212) 663-0004

Not accepting submissions.
Not accepting new clients.

J-Mitchell Management
440 Park Avenue South,
11th Floor
New York, NY 10016
(212) 679-3550
Clients: Actors, actresses,
writers, children, teenagers.

Josselyne Herman & Associates
250 W. 57th Street,
#1913A
New York, NY 10107
(212) 974-3300
E-mail: info@jherman
associates.com
www.jhermanassociates.com
Clients: Actors, actresses, directors, producers, writers.

Joyce Chase Management (NCOPM)
2 Fifth Avenue
New York, NY 10011
(212) 473-1234
Clients: Actors, actresses.
Résumés and headshots
accepted from SAG and
Equity members only.

Kanner/Esposito Entertainment
30 W. 74th Street,
Penthouse 1
New York, NY 10023
(212) 496-8175
Clients: Actors, actresses,
directors, producers, writers,
comedy/variety performers.
Accepts photos/résumés and
tapes by mail only.

Kanner Management
3515 Henry Hudson
Parkway, Suite 12D
Riverdale, NY 10463
(718) 549-4009
Clients: Actors fifteen and
up. Also Broadway caliber
singers and dancers. Ac-
cepts photos, résumés, and
tapes by mail only.

KAP Talent Management
PMB 223,
540 W. Boston Post Road
Mamaroneck, NY 10543
(914) 833-1007
Clients: Children and
teenagers (ages five to sixteen). No phone calls. Mail
pictures and résumés only.

Lloyd Kolmer Management Co.
65 W. 55th Street
New York, NY 10019
(212) 582-4735
Clients: Actors, actresses,
newscasters, media personalities, sports personalities.

Lambert & Gentile Associates
888 Eighth Avenue
New York, NY 10019
(212) 315-0754
Clients: Actors, actresses,
children, teenagers, musical
performers, composers.
recording artists, orchestras,
bands.

The Lyons Group
505 Sixth Avenue, Suite
12A
New York, NY 10018
(212) 239-3539
E-mail: newfaces@lyons
groupny.com
www.lyonsgroupny.com
Clients: Actors, actresses,
children, teenagers, sports
personalities (athletes).

Michael Katz Talent Management
P.O. Box 1925
Cathedral Station
New York, NY 10025
(212) 316-2492
Clients: Actors, actresses.
Represents all types in all
areas, Accepts materials. No
phone calls.

**Michele Donay Talent
Management**
76 W. 86th Street
New York, NY 10024
(212) 769-0924
Clients: Children. Management for TV commercials,
feature films, television,
soaps, series, movies.

**Multi-Ethnic Talent
Management**
415 E. 52nd Street, #6DA
New York, NY 10022
(212) 832-2668
Fax: (212) 754-5033
E-mail: joansil@aol.com
Clients: Actors, actresses.
Absolutely no phone calls
before or after sending pic-
ture with a stapled résumé.
One picture only; do not
seal envelope.

New York Talent
(718) 268-0641
Clients: Children (ages up to
seventeen). Call for additional information.

Pearl Management
1650 Broadway, Suite 508
New York, NY 10019
(212) 399-7224
Clients: Actors, actresses.
Looking for experienced serious actors with credits
and/or younger (eighteen to
twenty-four) actors with a
great look; very talented actors, a prerequisite. Work in
TV, film, theater, commercials, voice-overs, etc.

**Persona Management
(NCOPM)**
40 E. 9th Street, Apt. 11J
New York, NY 10003
(212) 674-7078
www.persona@nyc.rr.com
Clients: Children, young
adults (infants to twenty-five).
No phone calls. Send photos
and résumés.

**Premiere East
Management**
64 Fulton Street
New York, NY 10038
(212) 233-2450
Clients: Children, teenagers
(eight to eighteen). Records,
commercials, singers,
dancers, rappers, special
ability, musical performers.
Submissions accepted.

Ramos Management
49 W. 9th Street, 5B
New York, NY 10011
(212) 473-2610
Clients: Actors, actresses.

**Ravelo Artists
Management (RAM)**
484 W. 43rd Street, Suite
10-C
New York, NY 10036
(212) 695-9101
Fax: (646) 219-4285
E-mail: hravelo@ramtalent.
com
www.ramtalent.com
Clients: High-end boutique
talent management agency
specializing in established
and emerging actors. All areas; children to adults; all
types. No visits or phone
calls. Accepts tapes upon request.

**Richard Ornstein &
Associates**
P.O. Box 1
Freeport, NY 11520
(516) 623-8888
Fax: (516) 623-8891Clients:
Clients: Actors, actresses,
newscasters, media personalities, sports personalities,
musical performers, com-
posers, recording artists,
orchestras, bands. Representing Joe Franklin, Jack
LaLanne, Captain Lou Al-
bano, Freddie Scott, Whitey
Ford, "Wildman" Jack Arm-
strong, and other celebrities,
including police officers and
firefighters.

**Richard Rosenwald
Associates**
300 W. 55th Street
New York, NY 10019
(212) 245-4515
Clients: Actors, actresses,
teenagers, directors, producers, writers.

RKS Management, Ltd.
975 Park Avenue. Suite 10C
New York, NY 10028
(212) 717-2716
Clients: Actors, actresses,
children, teenagers, for print,
stage, TV, commercials,
voice-overs. Primarily works
with ages four to twenty-five
from all parts of the country.

**Roger Paul
Management**
1650 Broadway, Suite 705
New York, NY 10019
(212) 262-0008
E-mail: espellman126@
aol.com
rogerpaulmgmt@aol.com
Clients: Actors, actresses,
writers, variety/comedy performers. Interested in clients
who are driven and easy to
work with.

Rosalee Productions
137 W. 78th Street, Garden
New York, NY 10024
(212) 877-5538
Clients: Actors, actresses,
teenagers, directors, producers, writers.

**Rosella Olson
Management**
319 W. 105th Street, #1F
New York, NY 10025
(212) 864-0336
Clients: Actors, actresses,
variety/comedy performers.

Sinclair Management
95 Christopher Street,
Suite 6F
New York, NY 10014
(212) 366-9400
E-mail: jlesley@nyc.rr.com-

Clients: Actors, actresses, children, teenagers. May send pictures and résumés. Do not stop by.

SK Talent (NCOPM)
P.O. Box 728
Tenafly, NJ 07670
(212) 252-4997
Clients: Actors, actresses, children, teenagers, variety/comedy performers. Offbeat types, twins, triplets (babies to adults). Photos and résumés accepted. No phone calls.

Steinberg Talent Management Group
1560 Broadway, Suite 405
New York, NY 10036
(212) 582-7589
Fax: (212) 843-3480
E-mail: info@steinbergtalent.com
www.steinbertalent.com
Clients: Actors, actresses., directors, producers, writers, newscasters, media personalities, sports personalities, variety/comedy performers. Specializes in comedic talent for film, TV, and commercials.

Suzelle Enterprises
853 Seventh Avenue
New York, NY 10019
(212) 397-2047
www.avotaynu.com/suzelle
Clients: Actors, actresses, children, teenagers, newscasters, media personalities, sports personalities, musical performers, composers, recording artists, orchestras, bands. Office in Los Angeles (310) 358-3191; office in Mexico City 011-52-5-523-3604.

Tannen's Talent and Model Management
77 Tarrytown Road
White Plains, NY 10607
(914) 946-0900

E-mail: newfaces@tannenstalent.com
www.tannestalent.com
Clients: Actors, actresses, (infants to young adults).

Terrific Talent Associates, Inc. (TTA)
419 Park Avenue South, Suite 1009
New York, NY 10016
(212) 689-2800
Clients: Actors, actresses, children, teenagers.

THJ Management
405 E. 54th Street
New York, NY 10022
Clients: Actors, actresses, directors, producers with and media personalities. Prefer at least one industry referral. Seeking established actors, particularly those with Meisner backgrounds, who wish to make career changes and adjustments, television/movie actors who seek a return to theater or want to redirect their careers, and successful theater actors who wish to do movies and television.

TMT Entertainment Group
648 Broadway, Suite 1002
New York, NY 10012
(212) 477-6047
Clients: Actors, actresses, writers.

Vesta Talent Services
460 Second Avenue, Suite 11F
New York, NY 10016
(212) 685-7151
Clients: Actors and actresses, ages seventeen and up. Specializes in actors with disabilities.

Winter's Kids
33 Cedar Lane
Ossining, NY 10562
(914) 941-6063

Clients: Actors, actresses, children, teenagers.

World Music Source
(917) 771-9959
www.worldmusicsource.com
Clients: Recording artists.

Young Talent, Inc.
P.O. Box 10530
Hartsdale, NY 10530
1-800-947-4950
Clients: Actors, actresses, children, teenagers, young adults. Specializes in commercials, prime-time TV, films, soap operas, print ads, Broadway theater.

10. CASTING DIRECTORS

AAA Voice Casting
123 W. 18th Street, 7th Floor
New York, NY 10011
(212) 675-3240
E-mail: AAAVoiceCasting@aol.com
Casting directors: Carole Murray Duckworth and Dan Duckworth cast voice-overs only. Commercials, animated series/features, CD-ROMs and interactive, industrials, infomercials, audio books, medical narrations. English-as-second-language projects. Particularly interested in foreign language voice-over/narrator talent; also, experienced teen and preteen voice talent. Accepts voice samples on CD or e-mail sound files only. Should have an e-mail address. AAAVoiceCasting is a division of Voice-overs Unlimited, which provides training and other voice-over services. Don't phone, fax, or visit. Interviews by appointment only. Union and nonunion.

Attends showcases; accepts showcase invitations.

ABC Primetime Casting
157 Columbus Avenue,
2nd Floor
New York, NY 10023
Casting directors: Rosalie Joseph (C.S.A.) (vice president of casting), Marci Phillips (director of casting), Janet Murphy Butler (director of casting), and Geoffrey Soffer (coordinator of casting) cast for ABC Television. Accept photo, résumés, and demos by mail only. Also attends showcases. Interviews are by appointment only. Don't phone, fax, or visit.

Abigail McGrath, Inc.
484 W. 43rd Street,
Suite 37-S
New York, NY 10036
Casting directors: Abigail McGrath, Jenny Barriol (foreign projects), and Danica Rosen (assistant) cast for theater, film, TV, voice-overs. Please don't phone or visit. Photos are accepted by mail only. Absolutely no drop-ins.

Alan Filderman Casting
333 W. 39th Street, #601A
New York, NY 10018
(212) 695-6200
Casting directors: Alan Filderman (owner) and Steve Maihack (assistant) cast for theater, film, TV. Don't phone, fax, or visit.

Amerifilm Casting, Inc.
c/o Silvercup Studios
42-22 22nd Street,
Room M-104
Long Island City,
New York 11101
(646) 498-6252
www.amerifilmcasting.com.
Casting director: Meredith Jacobson Marciano (owner) casts for film, TV, music videos, industrials, print, etc.

Submit PR via mail or e-mail. If by e-mail, mail a hard copy as well. Audio/video tapes and CDs will not be returned. Do not phone, fax, or visit. Check Web site for updated casting information.

Amy Gossels Casting
1382 Third Avenue
New York, NY 10021
(212) 472-6981
Casting director: Amy Gossels (owner) casts both union and nonunion talent for commercials, film, TV, industrials, music videos, and extras. Accepts 8 by 10s for extra work by mail only. No tapes. Actors don't phone or visit.

Andrea Kurzman Casting, Inc.
122 E. 37th Street,
2nd Floor
New York, NY 10016
(212) 684-0710
Casts commercials, print advertising, film. Union and nonunion. Don't visit or phone. Accepts postcards by mail only.

Avy Kaufman Casting
180 Varick Street, 16th Floor
New York, NY 10014
Casting directors: Avy Kaufman (C.S.A.), Elizabeth Greenberg, Jessica Daniels, and Cody Beke accept photos by mail only. Don't phone, fax, or visit.

Background, Inc.
20 W. 20th Street,
Suite 228
New York, NY 10011
(212) 609-1103
www.bgroundinc.com
Casts union and nonunion background actors for commercials, films, industrials, music videos, and trailers. Not accepting new submissions at this time. Don't

phone, fax, or visit. Attends showcases.

Bernard Telsey Casting
145 W. 28th Street,
12th Floor
New York, NY 10001
(212) 868-1260
Fax: (212) 868-1261
Casting director: Bernard Telsey casts for theater, film, TV, commercials, voice-overs through agents only. Don't phone or fax. No drop-ins.

Beth Melsky Casting
928 Broadway
New York, NY 10010
(212) 505-5000
Casting directors: Beth Melsky (owner), Richard Reed (associate), Jenny Shulman, Debra Temco, Roger Del Pozo, Nancy Frigand, and Jeff Gafner (assistant) cast for commercials, TV, film, music videos. Pictures by mail only. Don't phone.

Block Casting
Box 170, 1710 First Avenue
New York, NY 10128
(212) 348-8371
E-mail: block_casting@hotmail.com
Casting director: Peter Block casts commercials, films, theater, and TV. Don't phone, fax, or visit. Interviews by appointment only. Accepts photos and résumés by mail only. Does not accept tapes (audio/video). Attends showcases and accepts showcase invitations. Union or nonunion.

Blue Man Productions
599 Broadway, 5th Floor
New York, NY 10012
(212) 226-6366
E-mail: casting@blueman.com
www.blueman.com
Casting directors: Deborah S. Burton, Anthony Sturnick (associate), and Karen Rock-

ower (assistant) cast Boston, Chicago and Las Vegas and upcoming productions for The Blue Man Group. Don't phone or visit. Accepting submissions for audition by appointment. Accepts showcase invitations and attends showcases. Indicate height, weight, and musical instruments played on résumé.

Breanna Benjamin Casting
P.O. Box 21077-PACC
New York, NY 10129
(212) 388-2347
Casting director: Breanna Benjamin (owner) casts for film, TV, theater, commercials, industrials, interactive. Only accepting pictures and résumés with return address and name labels matching postmarks. No audio or videotapes. Please don't phone, fax, or visit.

Carlton Casting
212 W. 35th Street,
2nd Floor
New York, NY 10001
(646) 473-0876
E-mail: carltoncasting@aol.com
Casting directors: Joel Carlton and Gayle Holsman Seay (owners) cast for commercials, films, industrials, music videos, print advertising, theater, and TV. Union and nonunion. Don't phone, fax, or visit. Interviews by appointment only. Accepts photos and résumés by mail only. Accepts showcase invitations.

Carol Hanzel Casting
48 W. 21st Street, 7th Floor
New York, NY 10010
(212) 242-6113
Casting directors: Carol Hanzel (casting director) and Melissa Braun (assistant) cast for commercials, theater,

voice-overs, TV, film, and industrials. Photos and résumés accepted by mail only. No unsolicited audio or videotapes. Do not phone or visit.

Caroline Sinclair Casting
c/o The Zipper Theatre
336 W. 37th Street,
2nd Floor
New York, NY 10018
Casting director: Caroline Sinclair (owner) casts for film, TV, theater, commercials, industrials. Don't phone or visit.

Casting House
443 Greenwich Street,
5th Floor
New York, NY 10013
(212) 965-9994
Casting directors: Danny Roth (partner), Michael Cohen (partner), Staci Rice (associate), and Jessica Elbert (intern) cast for all areas. Union and nonunion. Accepts photos, résumés, and tapes (audio/video) by mail only. Interviews by appointment only. Attends showcases. Don't phone or fax.

Casting Solutions
231 W. 29th Street,
Suite 601
New York, NY 10001
(212) 875-7573
Casting director: Liz Ortiz-Mackes casts commercials, films, industrials, TV, theater, print ads, and voice-overs. Union and nonunion. Accepts photos by mail only. Does not accept tapes. Attends showcases. Don't phone, fax, or visit.

CBS Entertainment
51 W. 52nd Street,
5th Floor
New York, NY 10019
Casting directors: Amy Herzig (vice president of Primetime Casting East

Coast), Andra Reeve (director of Primetime Casting East Coast), Lara Tal (talent coordinator, Primetime), Alison Rinzel-Lucido (director, daytime casting), Jodi Angstreich (assistant, daytime). Don't phone, fax, or visit.

Chantiles Vigneault Casting, Inc.
39 W. 19th Street,
12th Floor
New York, NY 10011
Casting directors: Sharon Chantiles and Jeffrey Vigneault cast all types for commercials, voice-overs, film, music videos, TV, theater, and extras. Union and nonunion work. Attends showcases. Accepts photos and tapes by mail only. Don't phone, fax, or visit.

Charles Rosen Casting, Inc.
140 W. 22nd.Street,
4th Floor
New York, NY 10011
Casting directors: Charles Rosen and Scott Wojcik cast for TV, voice-overs, commercials, film and theater, babies through seniors. Union and nonunion. Postcards and 8 by 10s accepted by mail only. Don't phone or visit. Attends showcases.

Cindi Rush Casting, Ltd.
27 W. 20th Street,
Suite 404
New York, NY 10011
Casting directors: Cindi Rush (C.S.A.) and Dyann Griego (assistant) cast films and theater. Don't phone, fax, or visit. Attends showcases; accepts showcase invitations.

Byron Crystal
41 Union Square West,
Suite 316
New York, NY 10003
Casts actors, all types, ath-

letes, teens, dancers, models, musicians, performers with disabilities, seniors for commercials, extra work, film, TV. Union and nonunion. Attends showcases. Accepts photos by mail only. When sending 8 by 10s, make sure to include a direct contact number; not just a service number.

CTP Casting
207 W. 25th Street,
6th Floor
New York, NY 10001
(212) 414-1931
Casting director: Jeff Bather casts all types for film, TV, commercials, theater, industrials, voice-overs. Full service payment department. Photos by mail only. Don't phone, fax, or visit. Do not fax photos. No unsolicited tapes.

Dave Clemmons Casting
265 W. 30th Street
New York, NY 10001
(212) 594-7434
Casting directors: Dave Clemmons, Rachel Hoffman, Rye Mullis (assistant), and Sara Schatz (assistant) cast for theater and industrials. Union and nonunion. Attends showcases; accepts showcase invitations. Unsolicited PR packets, videos, and demos not accepted.

Domenic Andreoli Casting
545 Eighth Avenue, Suite 401
New York, NY 10018
Casting director: Domenic Andreoli casts for TV film and commercials. Accepts headshots and résumés by mail only. Do not visit.

Donald Case Casting, Inc.
386 Park Avenue South,
Suite 809
New York, NY 10016
(212) 889-6555
Casting directors: Donald Case (owner), Donna Cassell, Tom Harris, Tisha Ioli (assistant), Fatima Kaba (assistant) cast all types for animated features, commercials, extras, film, industrials, infomercials, music videos, TV, theater, print advertising, voice-overs. Union and nonunion work. Attends showcases. Accepts photos by mail only. Don't phone, fax, or visit.

Donna DeSeta Casting
525 Broadway, 3rd Floor
New York, NY 10012
www.donnadesetacasting.com
Casting directors: Donna De-Seta (owner), Steve Schaefer, David Cady, and Becky Moore cast all types for commercials, film, industrials, infomercials, music videos, TV, theatre, print advertising, voice-overs, and union work. Accepts photos by mail only. Indicate SAG membership and background work on photos. Send to Lucy Baker and Lisbeth White. Don't phone, fax, or visit.

Downstairs Casting
428 Broadway, 5th Floor
New York, NY 10013
(212) 625-5638
Casting directors: Stacy Osnow, Lori Fromewick, F. Shumsey (associate), and G. Armstrong (associate) cast for "Hungry Man Production Company," principals for commercials. Don't phone, fax, or visit. Not accepting new submissions at this time. Attends showcases.

Pennie DuPont
36 Perry Street
New York, NY 10014
(212) 255-2708
E-mail: penniedup@aol.com
Cast actors for film. Accepts photos by mail only. Don't phone, fax, or visit.

Elissa Myers Casting
333 W. 52nd Street,
Suite 1008
New York, NY 10019
Casting directors: Elissa Myers, Paul Fouquet, and Jandiz Estrada (associate) cast for theater, film, TV. Don't phone or visit.

Extras Casting by Booked
9 Debrosses Street
Suite 513
New York, NY 10013
(212) 925-6010
Casting Director: Sean Powers casts extras for features, commercials, film, industrials, infomercials, music videos, print advertising, and TV. Union and non-Union. Don't visit. Accepts photos and résumés by mail only.

Sylvia Fay
71 Park Avenue
New York, NY 10016
Casting directors: Sylvia Fay, Lee Genick (associate) and Fleet Emerson (associate) cast all types and ages of actors for film, TV, commercials, industrials, and infomercials. Background casting for *Law and Order* (thirteen seasons). To register as a SAG member with the office, you must attend an open call, All open calls are listed at SAG, in *Backstage* and in *Showbiz* papers. Please no phone calls or visits.

Leonard Finger
1501 Broadway
New York, NY 10036
Casting director: Leonard
Finger casts all types for
union film, industrials, TV,
and print advertising. Accepts photos by mail only.
Don't phone or visit.

Janet Foster
3212 Cambridge Avenue
Riverdale, NY 10463
Casts principals only for theater, film, TV. No voice-over
or background artists. No
calls or visits.

**Fox Broadcasting
Company**
1211 Sixth Avenue
New York, NY 10036
(212) 556-2400
Casting directors: Amy
Christopher (executive director) and Rita Murphy (assistant).

**Gilburne & Urban
Casting**
80 Varick Street, Suite 6A
New York, NY 10013
(212) 965-0745
Casting directors: Jessica
Gilburne and Ed Urban cast
all types for theater, films,
TV, and industrials. Don't visit. Interview by appointment
only. Attends showcases. Accepts photos by mail only.
No unsolicited tapes or
reels.

**Godlove & Company
Casting**
151 W. 25th Street,
11th Floor
New York, NY 10001
(212) 627-7300
www.godlovecasting.com
Casting directors: Linda
Godlove (owner), Colleen
Patrick, Nicole Plesset, Beth
Schiff, and Todd Pieper cast
actors and models for commercials, industrials, TV,

voice-overs, and print advertising through agents. Attend
showcases. Accepts photos
by mail. Don't phone or fax.

Grant Wilfley Casting
60 Madison Avenue,
Room 1027
New York, NY 10010
(212) 695-3537
Casting directors: Grant Wilfley, Anna Maniscalco-Blasi,
Kristian Sorge, J. Sabel,
Melissa Braun, Heather Reidenbach, Leah Kaplan (assistant), Jason Bitensky (assistant), and Todd Seldman
(assistant) cast for film, TV,
commercials, and print. Principals through agents only.
Photos accepted for extra
work. New SAG members
Monday and Wednesday 10
AM to noon only. Must bring
SAG card, 8 by 10 and résumé. No phone calls. Casts
background actors for *Law
and Order: Special Victims
Unit, Law and Order, Criminal Intent, Third Watch, The
Sopranos, The Stepford
Wives,* and *Stay.*

Harriet Bass Casting
648 Broadway, #912
New York, NY 10012
(212) 598-9032
Casting directors: Harriet
Bass (owner) and Eileen
Duffy (assistant) cast actors/actresses, all types, ffor
theater, film, TV. Union only.
Don't phone, fax or visit. No
audio/video tapes. Accepts
postcards only.

Helyn Taylor Casting
140 W. 58th Street
New York, NY 10019
Casts for theater, commercials, TV, film. Photos and
résumés accepted by mail
only. Don't phone, fax, or
visit.

**Herman & Lipson
Casting, Inc.**
630 Ninth Avenue, Suite
1410
New York, NY 10036
Casting directors: Linda Lipson and Barry Shapiro cast
for film, TV, commercials, industrials, theater. Send photos and résumés by mail
only. Don't phone or visit.
Don't send tapes.

House
450 W. 15th Street,
Suite 202
New York, NY 10011
(212) 929-0200
Casting directors: Neil Meyer (partner), Brooke Thomas,
and Adam Joseph cast commercials, film, industrials, TV,
and voice-overs. Don't
phone, fax, or visit.

House Films
New York, NY 10001
(212) 645-8462
Casts CD-ROMs and interactive, commercials, extras, industrials, infomercials, and
voice-overs. Union and
nonunion. Don't phone, fax,
or visit. Accepts photos and
résumés by mail only. Specializes in Asian talent and
Chinese Mandarin voiceovers.

**Howard Schwartz
Recording/HSR NY**
420 Lexington Avenue,
Suite 1934
New York, NY 10170
(212) 687-4180
Casting director: Theresa
Kiernan casts voices for TV
and radio commercials, industrials, animation, CDROMs, and Internet through
agents only. Union. Don't
phone or fax. No drop-offs.
Don't send headshots. HSR
has fifteen studios, audio
post, and sound design.

Hughes Moss Casting, Ltd.
484 W. 43rd Street, Suite 28R
New York, NY 10036
(212) 307-6690
Casting directors: Barry Moss (C.S.A.) and Bob Kale (associate) cast for theater, TV, film. Do not phone or visit. No tapes.

Impossible Casting
122 W. 26th Street, 11th Floor
New York, NY 10001
(212) 255-3029
Casting directors: Craig Lechner (co-owner), Allen Greene (co-owner), and Chris Block (assistant) cast for film, TV, commercials, theater, voice-overs, industrials, and music videos. Don't phone or visit.

Inproduction Casting
589 8th Avenue, 20th Floor
New York, NY 10018
(212) 868-4047
www.inproductionnyc.com
Casting directors: Ross Meyerson and Liz Josefsberg cast commercials, theater, TV, and film, CD-ROMs and interactive, extras, industrials and infomercials. Don't phone, fax, or visit. Interviews by appointment only. Accepts photos, résumés, tapes (audio/video) by mail only. Attends showcases.

James Calleri Casting
416 W. 42nd Street
New York, NY 10036
(212) 564-1235
Casting directors: James Calleri, Alaine Alldaffer (associate), Mo Marshall (assistant, and Kristen Jackson (assistant) cast films, theater, and TV. Casting director for Playwright's Horizons. Please don't phone, fax, or visit.

Jay Binder Casting
321 W. 44th Street, Suite 606
New York, NY 10036
Casting directors: Jay Binder, (C.S.A.), Jack Bowdan, (C.S.A.), Mark Brandon, Laura Stanczyk (associate), Sarah Prosser (associate), and Megan E. Larche (assistant) cast actors/actresses, all types, children (eight to fourteen), teens, and dancers for film, TV, theater. Union work through agents only. Attends showcases. Don't phone, fax, or visit.

Jennifer Low Sauer Casting
c/o Keen Company
520 Eighth Avenue, Suite 328, 3rd Floor
New York, NY 10018
www.JenniferLowSauer Casting.homestead.com
Casts for theater, commercials, and film. Don't phone, fax, or visit. Accepts picture and résumé submissions by mail in October and April only. No tapes unless requested.Theater/screening/s howcase invites welcome.

Jerry Beaver & Associates Casting
484 W. 43rd Street, #19-N
New York, NY 10036
(212) 244-3600
Casting directors: Jerry Beaver (owner) and Mia Tuttavilla (casting associate) cast actors/actresses, all types, for TV, film, theater, commercials, voice-overs, and print advertising. Accepts photos by mail only. Indicate SAG membership on photos. Don't phone, fax, or visit.

Jimmy Hank Promotions
209 W. 104th Street, Suite 2H
New York, NY 10025

(212) 864-2132
E-mail: TVEXEC4U@aol.com
Casting director: Jimmy Floyd (owner) casts extras for commercials, films, TV, music videos, infomercials, industrials, and print. Also specializes in casted audiences. Union and nonunion. Current/recent casting includes Disney, Comedy Central, Oxygen Network, ESPN, CBS/Kingworld, Lifetime, MTV, VH1, PBS, Fox, Fox News, The Sundance Channel, NBC, Nickelodeon, PAX TV. Interviews by appointment only. Accepts photos and résumés by mail only. Attends showcases.

Joan Lynn Casting
39 W. 19th Street, 12th Floor
New York, NY 10011
(212) 675-5595
Casting director: Joan Lynn (owner) casts for TV, film, theater, commercials, voice-overs. Photos and résumés accepted by mail only. No tapes. Don't phone or visit.

Joanne Pasciuto, Inc.
17-08 150th Street
Whitestone, NY 11357
Casting director: Joanne Pasciuto casts for film, TV, commercials, industrials, voice-overs. Postcards only accepted by mail. Appointments through agents only. Don't phone or visit.

Jodi Collins Casting
9 Desbrosses Street, Suite 520
New York, NY 10013
Client Line: (212) 625-0115
Client Fax:(212) 625-0116
Talent Fax: (212) 982-1086 (business hours only)
Casting directors: Jodi Collins and Karla Brown cast for scripted TV, film, theater, and commercials. Emphasis

on comedic and alternative-type talent in addition to trained actors. Performance fliers/information updates: 10 AM to 6 PM, Mon. to Fri. Unsolicited mail will not be opened. Mutual consideration is appreciated and only appointments at office. No drop-ins, please.

Joel Manaloto Casting
1480 York Avenue,
4th Floor
New York, NY 10021
(212) 517-3737
Casting directors: Joel Manaloto (owner), Carrie Alton (associate), and Mark Gray (associate) cast principals for union and nonunion feature films. Attend showcases. For showcase invitations, please specify availability of industry comps, running times, and complete cast lists. Accepts submissions by mail only. List union status and availability for readings. Submissions by unsolicited callers and visitors are neither accepted nor considered.

Joey Guastella Casting
85-10 151st Avenue, #5B
Queens, NY 11414
(718) 835-6451
Casting directors: Joey Guastella (owner) and Diane Kral-Guastella (associate) are currently exploring opportunities in arts funding. Still accepting photos and résumés and play invitations by mail only and will continue to offer casting referral and consultation services for theater and musical theater. Unsolicited tapes of any kind are neither considered nor returned. Primarily interested in actors with theatrical background and training. Union and nonunion.

Joy Weber Casting
440 West End Avenue
New York, NY 10024
(845) 647-3849
Casting directors: Joy Weber (owner), Stephanie Kovacs (associate), and Carolyn Michel (assistant) cast for commercials, TV, film, theater. Casts through agents only. No general interviews. Don't phone or visit.

Judy Henderson and Associates Casting
330 W. 89th Street
New York, NY 10024
(212) 877-0225
Casting directors: Judy Henderson (C.S.A.), Doug Henderson (associate), and Lisa Donadio (associate) cast for film, theater, TV, voice-over, and on-camera commercials. Interviews through agents only. Accepts photos from union members only. No tapes accepted.

Judy Keller Casting
140 W. 22nd Street,
4th Floor
New York, NY 10011
Casting directors: Judy Keller (owner) and Nathalie de Lange (assistant) cast for commercials, voice-overs, feature films, TV, infomercials, industrials, and print. Only accepts audiotapes, not video. Don't phone or visit.

Judy Rosensteel Casting
43 W. 68th Street
New York, NY 10023
Casts for on-camera, voice-over, and radio commercials through agents only. Photos and tapes are not returned Don't phone or visit.

Kee Casting
424 Park Avenue South,
#128
New York, NY 10016

(212) 725-3775
Casting directors: Karen E. Etcoff and Bill Tripician (associate) cast for film, TV, commercials, industrials. Photos accepted from new SAG members only—indicate "SAG member" on outside of envelope. All actors will be considered for all types of roles, but please, no submissions unless you are also interested in background work. Previously registered members need only send postcards unless submitting new photo—indicate "update" on outside of envelope. Please no drop-ins or phone calls to the office.

Kelli Lerner Casting
330 W. 56th Street,
Suite 25E
New York, NY 10019
(212) 459-9293
Casting director: Kelli Lerner (owner) casts for theater, TV, film, print, CD-ROMs and interactive, and industrials. Union and nonunion. Don't phone, fax, or visit. Not accepting new submissions at this time.

Kipperman Casting, Inc.
12 W. 37th Street, 3rd Floor
New York, NY 10018
Casting directors: Jodi Kipperman (owner), Anthony Pichette, and Greg Levins cast for commercials, voice-overs, industrials, videos, theater, film, and TV. Photos and résumés by mail only. Indicate SAG membership on photos. Don't phone or visit.

Kristine Bulakowski Casting
Prince Street Station,
P.O. Box 616
New York, NY 10012
(212) 769-8550
Casting directors: Kristine Bulakowski (owner) and

Driss Tijani (associate) cast all types for all areas. Attend showcases. Accept photos by mail only. Please send two headshots and indicate union affiliations, if any, on envelope. Don't phone, fax, or visit.

Laura Richin Casting
33 Douglass Street, Suite 1
Brooklyn, NY 11231
(718) 802-9628
Casting director: Laura Richin (owner) casts for theater, film, and TV.

Liz Lewis
Casting Partners
129 W. 20th Street
New York, NY 10011
(212) 645-1500
Casting directors: Liz Lewis (owner) Stacy L. Seidel, Elizabeth Bunnell, Mary Egan, Lisa Fischoff, Vinnie Taylor, Angela Mickey, Krissy Berla (associate), Jaslyn Melichar (associate), Diakeim Lyles (assistant), Freya Krasnow (assistant), and Jacquelyn Sherry (assistant) cast for film, theater, TV, commercials, voice-overs, industrials, videos, comedy, avant-garde. Pictures and résumés by mail only. Don't phone on visit.

Liz Woodman Casting
11 Riverside Drive, #2JE
New York, NY 10023
(212) 787-3782
Casting directors: Liz Woodman and Stephanie Black (assistant) cast actors for union film, TV, theater through agents only. No children; no commercials or extras. Pictures accepted by mail only. Do not phone or visit.

Madland Casting
The Astoria Performing Arts Center
31-60 33rd Street, #B-9

Long Island City, NY 11106
(718) 274-4781
E-mail: MadlandCasting@aol.com
www.apanyc.org
Casting directors: Gina Holland and David Madore (assistant) cast actors/actresses for theater and musical theatr. Union and nonunion talent. Accepts photos, résumés and demos by mail only. E-mail correspondence preferred. Do not visit. Attends showcases.

Matthew Messinger
244 W. 72nd Street
New York, NY 10023
Casting director: Matthew Messinger casts for film, theater, TV, Internet, and interactive programming, animation, commercials, and voice-overs. Does not accept unsolicited tapes. Please don't phone, fax, or visit.

MBC Casting
325 W. 38th Street
New York, NY 10018
(212) 564-7214
Casting directors: Angela Montalbano and Jeff Barber cast for film, TV, commercials, industrials, voice-overs. No phone calls or visits. Casts through agents only.

McCorkle Casting, Ltd.
575 8th Avenue, 18th Floor
New York, NY 10018
(212) 244-3899
Casting directors: Pat McCorkle (C.S.A.), Bonnie Grisan (associate), and Rebecca A. Carfagna (assistant) cast for theater, film, TV. No audio or videotapes. Don't phone or visit.

McHale Barone
30 Irving Place, 6th Floor
New York, NY 10011
Casting directors: Lesley Freedman does boutique-style voice casting for commercials. Please do not call or mail submissions of any kind.

Merry L. Delmonte Casting & Productions, Inc.
575 Madison Avenue
New York, NY 10022
Casting director: Merry L. Delmonte (owner) casts all types for all areas except soaps and theater through agents only. Please indicate "extra work" on envelope. Don't phone, fax, or visit.

Mitchell/Rudolph Casting
440 Park Avenue South, 11th Floor
New York, NY 10016
(212) 679-3550
Casting directors: Jeff Mitchell and Jennifer Rudolph cast for films, theater, and TV. Accept photos and résumés by mail only. Please include your email and address on all submissions. Do not phone, fax, or visit.

MTV/MTV2 Talent
1515 Broadway, 25th Floor
New York, NY 10036
Casting directors: Rod Aissa (vice uresident of talent development and casting), Vinnie Potestivo (manager of talent and casting). Actors/actresses, on-air hosts, comedians may send pictures, résumés, and video demos by mail only. Attends showcases. Don't phone or visit.

MTV/TRL
1515 Broadway, 23rd Floor
New York, NY 10036
Casting director: Courtney Mullin casts actors/actresses, models and dancers for TV. Please don't phone, fax, or visit. Accepts photos and

résumés by mail only. Accepts tapes (audio/video) by mail only.

Mungioli Theatricals, Inc.
207 W. 25th Street,
6th Floor
New York, NY 10001
(212) 337-8832
Casting director: Arnold J. Mungioli (C.S.A.) (president) casts for theater, film, TV, and other projects. Please do not send tapes unless requested. Do not phone, fax, or visit without an appointment. Photos, résumés, and showcase flyers are accepted by mail.

Navarro/Bertoni and Associates
101 W. 31st Street,
Room 1707
New York, NY 10001
Fax: (212) 465-2064
E-mail: casting@navarro
bertonicasting.com
www.navarrobertonicasting.
com
Casting director: Riccardo Bertoni casts principals and background actors for TV, movies, commercials. Casts principals through agents. Send photos and résumés. Absolutely no visits. Don't phone.

Nickelodeon
1515 Broadway, 38th Floor
New York, NY 10036
Casting directors: Jill Greenberg-Sands (senior director), Melissa Chusid (director, talent and casting), Kia Riddick (casting coordinator), Alycia Kozak (assistant). Until further notice, no headshots, tapes, or demos accepted by mail. Don't phone or visit.

Nora Brennan Casting
752 West End Avenue,
Suite Mezz C
New York, NY 10025
(212) 531-1825
Casting directors: Nora Brennan casts for theater, commercials, voice-overs, films, and industrials. Accepts photos and résumés by mail only. Please do not phone, fax, or visit.

Norman Meranus Casting
201 W. 85th Street, 16-D
New York, NY 10024
Casting director: Norman Meranus casts musicals and plays in New York and regionally, as well as feature films. Accepts photos and résumés by mail only. Attends showcases. Don't phone, fax, or visit.

Steven O'Neill
30 Rockefeller Plaza,
Room 1628E
New York, NY 10112
Casts for prime-time programs, movies of the week, pilots, etc. Don't phone or visit. Accepts submissions by mail only.

Orpheus Group Casting
1600 Broadway, Suite 410
New York, NY 10019
(212) 957-6760
Fax: (212) 957-1320
Casting directors: Maria E. Nelson and Ellyn Long Marshall cast for film, theater, TV, industrials. No extras. No tapes please.

Paul Russell Casting
159 W. 25th Street,
Suite 1011
New York, NY 10001
Casts principals only for theater and film. No commercial or background/extra artists. Accepts photos and résumés for principal work only. Invitations by mail are welcome; please specify if industry comps. Do not send postcards. Do not send video/audiotapes. Do not phone, fax, or visit.

Paladino Casting
35 E. 21st Street, 2nd Floor
New York, NY 10010
(212) 228-5500
Casting director: Kristen Paladino (owner) casts for all types and all ages for commercials, films, industrials, music videos, print advertising, and extra work. Union snd nonunion. Attends showcases. Accepts photos, résumés, and tapes by mail only. Don't phone, fax, or visit.

Pomann Sound
2 W. 46th Street, #PH
New York, NY 10036
(212) 869-4161
Casting director: Jennifer Sukup casts voice-over talent for TV and radio commercials, animated series/features, CD-ROMs and interactive, and films. Union. Don't phone, fax, or visit. Interviews by appointment only. Attends showcases and produces talent demos. Not accepting headshots, résumés, or video demos at this time.

Rich Cole Casting
648 Broadway, Suite 912
New York, NY 10012
(212) 614-7130
Casting directors: Rich Cole and Bob Cline (associate) cast for theater only. Union and nonunion. Accepts photos by mail only. No audio or videotapes. Don't phone, tax, or visit.

Rossmon Casting and Talent Relations
35 W. 36th Street, 8th Floor
New York, NY 10018
(212) 279-9229
Ross. D. Mondschain (owner/casting director) and associates cast commercials, film, music videos, theater, TV, voice-overs from agent submissions. Accept postcards by mail only for SAG and non-SAG extra work. Don't phone or visit.

Rush and Super Casting, Ltd.
c/o Momentum Productions
36 W. 25th Street,
2nd Floor
New York, NY 10010
Cindi Rush (CS.A.) and Dani Super cast films, TV, theater. Don't phone, fax, or visit. Accepts photos and résumés by mail only. Attends showcases.

Brien Scott
71-10 Loubet Street
Forest Hills, NY 11375
(818) 343-3669
Casts for film, TV. Don't phone, fax, or visit. Interviews by appointment only. Accepts photos and résumés by mail only Accepts showcase invitations. Attends showcases.

Selective Casting by Carol Nadell
P.O. Box 1538
Radio City Station, NY 10101-1538
www.selectivecasting.com
Casts for industrial films, live corporate events, and interactive entertainment. Interested in talent with strong theatrical background as well as film and television experience. Also interested in foreign language speaking talent. Accepts photos and résumés by mail only. Don't

send audio- and videocassettes. Don't phone or visit.

Shane/Goldstein Casting
311 W. 43rd Street,
Suite 602
New York, NY 10036
(212) 445-0100
Casting directors: Brette Alysse and Andrea Shane cast independent film, theater, commercials and industrials.

Sidra Smith Casting
60 W. 129th Street,
Suite 7E
New York City, NY10027
(212) 831-6810
Fax: (917) 591-6559
E-mail: tellsid@aol.com
Casts for animated series/features, commercials, films, industrials, infomercials, music videos, print advertising, theatre, and TV. Union and nonunion. Interviews by appointment only. Attends showcases.

Sirius Casting
29 John Street, PMB 126
New York, NY 10038
(212) 445-3512
E-mail: siriuscasting@aol.com
Casting director: Jennifer Joy Arnett casts commercials, extras, films, industrials, infomercials, music videos, print advertising, TV. Don't visit; interviews by appointment only.

Skyrme, Lewis, & Fox Casting
459 Columbus Avenue, #164
New York, New York 10024
(212) 724-1121
Casting directors: Kimberly Skyrme, Kristine Lewis, and Jamie Fox cast all types for all areas for New York, Philadelphia, and Washington, DC. Specialty in choreography. Union or nonunion. Accepts

photos by mail only. No audio or videotapes. Please do not phone, fax, or visit.

Spike TV
1515 Broadway, 40th Floor
New York, NY 10036
Casting director: Casey Patterson (department head); no casting in the NY office.

Spotty Dog Productions
236 W. 27th Street,
6th Floor
New York, NY 10001
(212) 463-8550
Casting director: Renée Torrière casts for commercials, extras, print advertising, and TV. Don't phone, fax, or visit. Interviews by appointment only. Absolutely no submissions will be accepted. Attends showcases. Through agents only.

Stark Naked Productions
39 W. 19th Street,
12th Floor
New York, NY 10011
(212) 366-1903
E-mail: info@starknaked
productions.com
www.starknakedproductions.
com
Casting directors: Elsie Stark (owner), Joyce Batson, Elizabeth Gans (associate, R. More (associate), and C. B. Maltese (assistant/extra coordinator) cast for commercials, film, TV, industrials, theater, and voice-overs, Union and nonunion projects. Maintains flies for all types (principals and extras). Only one photo and résumé accepted by mail only. Don't phone or visit. Also available for translations, consulting, and casting for the Hispanic market. Member NYWIFT.

Stephanie Klapper Casting
122 W. 26th Street,
Suite 1104
New York, NY 10001
(646) 486-1337
Fax: (646) 486-3341
Casting directors: Stephanie Klapper and Kelly Gillespie (assistant) cast actors/actresses for union films, TV, and theater. Accepts photos by mail only. Don't phone, fax, or visit.

Strickman-Ripps, Inc.
65 North Moore Street,
Suite 3A
New York, NY 10013
(212) 966-3211
Casts all types for commercials, industrials, print, music videos, and voice-overs. Real people and professional talent. Send only one photo by mail only. Don't phone or visit.

Stuart Howard Associates, Ltd.
207 W. 25th Street,
6th Floor
New York, NY 10001
(212) 414-1544
Casting directors: Stuart Howard (C.S.A.), Amy Schecter (C.S.A.), Howard Meltzer (C.S.A.), and Paul Hardt (associate) cast for theater, film, TV (pilots, MOWs, talent searches, mini-series, soaps), and commercials. Please do not send tapes (audio or video) or CDs unless requested. Please do not phone, fax, or visit without an appointment. Photos, résumés, and showcase flyers are accepted by mail only. Please respect the office's policy.

Sue Crystal Casting
251 W. 87th Street, #26
New York, NY 10024
(212) 877-0737

Casts actors, all types, athletes, children, teenagers, comedians, dancers, models, musicians, seniors for commercials, film, industrials, TV, print advertising, voice-overs. Union and nonunion work through agents only. Accepts photos by mail only. Don't phone, fax, or visit.

Sylvia Fay and Associates
71 Park Avenue
New York, NY 10016
Casting director: Sylvia Fay, Lee Genick (associate), and Fleet Emerson (associate) cast all types and all ages of actors for film, TV, commercials, industrials, and infomercials. Background casting for *Law and Order* (thirteen seasons). To register as a SAG member with the office, you must attend an open call. All open calls are listed at SAG, in *Backstage* and in *Showbiz* papers. Please no phone calls or visits.

Theatreworks/USA
151 W. 26th Street,
7th Floor
New York, NY 10001
E-mail: information@theatreworksusa.org
www.theatreworksusa.org
Casting director: Robin D. Carus casts theater. Union and nonunion actors. Please don't phone, fax, or visit.

TNN (The National Network)
1515 Broadway, 38th Floor
New York, NY 10036
Jill Greenberg-Sands (casting director), Melissa Chusid (manager, casting), Kia Riddick (casting coordinator). No headshots, tapes, or demos accepted by mail at this time. Don't phone or visit. (See also Nickelodeon.)

Todd Thaler Casting
130 W. 57th Street, #10A
New York, NY 10019
Casting director: Todd Thaler (president) casts union and nonunion talent for films and TV. Interviews by appointment only. Accepts photos and résumés by mail only. Don't phone, fax, or visit.

Toni Roberts Casting, Ltd.
1133 Broadway. Suite 630
New York, NY 10010
Toni Roberts (owner/casting director); Terry Ronca (casting director). Cast through agents only for film, TV, commercials, theater. Photos and résumés accepted by mail only. Don't phone or visit.

Tuffy Questell T.E.C. Casting
P.O. Box 859
Bronx, NY 10462
(718) 792-8447
(917) 356-8399
E-mail: tuffyseyecandee@aol.com
www.TECCast ing.com
Casting directors: Tuffy Questell, Serena Rosario (associate), Rodney "Rara" Taylor (assistant), and Tracie Runcie-Hubbard (associate) cast principals and extras for commercials, films, industrials, music videos, print advertising, TV, and voice-overs. Union and nonunion. Accepts photos and résumés by mail only. Please send only one copy; this office has fileshare. Please indicate union affiliation on envelopes. No unscheduled visits. No drop-ins. No phone calls. Audio and videotapes by request only. Tapes will not be returned. Attends showcases.

VH1
1633 Broadway, 6th Floor
New York, NY 10019
Casting director: Jim Kozloff
(manager talent development). Don't phone, fax, or
visit. Interviews by appointment only. Accepts photos
and résumés and audio/
video demos by mail only.
Attends showcases and accepts invitations. Please send
on-air (video) submissions
and voice-over submissions
to Jim Kozloff.

VideoActive Talent
1780 Broadway, Studio 804
New York, NY 10019
(212) 541-8106
E-mail: wworks@aol.com
www.videoactive prod.com
www.joefranklin.com
www.dinemusicworld.com
Casting directors: Louise
Moore, Emily DeGrass, and
Steve Garrin cast all types
(except children) for film, TV,
commercials, sitcoms, industrials, voice-overs. Casts comedians for comedy work at
Joe Franklin's Restaurant.
Send videotapes of your act.
No children. No unsolicited
tapes. Conducts the Voice-
Works voice-over workshop
independent of casting.
Please send photos by mail
only. Don't phone or visit.

Vince Liebhart Casting
1710 First Avenue, #122
New York, NY 10128
Casting directors: Vince Liebhart and Tom Alberg cast for
film, theater, and TV. Don't
phone, fax, or visit. Interviews by appointment only.
Accepts photos and résumés
by mail only. Accepts tapes
by request only. Accepts
showcase invitations. Union.

**Warner Bros.
Television Casting**
1325 Sixth Avenue,
32nd Floor
New York, NY 10019
(212) 636-5145
Casting directors: Meg Simon, John Power (associate),
and Kathryn Clark (casting
Coordinator) cast TV.

**Winsome Sinclair &
Associates**
2575A Eighth Avenue
New York, NY 10030
(212) 397-1537
E-mail: SINCO65@aol.com
Casts principals and extras
for films, commercials, industrials, infomercials, print advertising, theater, and TV.
Don't phone, fax, or visit. Interviews by appointment
only. Accepts photos and résumés by mail only. Attends
showcases. Please indicate
SAG membership on photos.
No audio/video tapes or visits unless requested.

11.
PRODUCTION
COMPANIES
Off Broadway

**Atlantic Theater
Company**
366 W. 20th Street
New York, NY 10011
(212) 645-8015
Fax: (212) 645-8755
www.atlantictheater.org

**Ensemble Studio
Theatre (EST)**
549 W. 52nd Street
New York, NY 10019
(212) 247-4982
www.ensemblestudio
theatre.org/

Manhattan Theatre Club
Casting Department
311 W. 43rd Street,
8th Floor
New York, NY 10036
(212) 399-3000
Fax: (212) 399-4329
E-mail: questions@
mtc-nyc.org
www.mtc-nyc.org

**New York Shakespeare
Festival**
The Public Theater
425 Lafayette Street
New York, NY 10003
www.publictheater.org

Pantheon Productions
303 W. 42nd Street
New York, NY 10036
(212) 582-5856
(212) 459-9620
E-mail: lorusso333@aol.com
www.pantheon-productions.
com

**The Pearl Theatre
Company**
Non-Equity Casting
80 St. Marks Place
New York, NY 10003
(212) 505-3401
Fax: (212) 505-3404
www.pearltheatre.org
(Uses non-Equity for understudy; will earn equity points
by understudying)

Playwright Horizons
416 W. 42nd Street
New York, NY 10036
(212) 564-1235
Fax: (212) 594-0296
E-mail: marketing@
playwrightshorizons.org
www.playwrightshorizons.
org
(Casting office has a "no
call" policy; however actors
are welcome to drop off
their headshots.)

**Richard Frankel
Productions**
729 Seventh Avenue,
12th Floor
New York, NY 10019
(212) 302-5559
Fax: (212) 302-8094
E-mail: lori@rfpny.com
www.rfpny.com

**Town Square
Productions**
226 W. 47th Street,
Suite 900
New York, NY 10036
(212) 997-7284
Fax: (212) 997-7285
E-mail: back40@earthlink.net
www.townsquare
productions.com

The Wooster Group
Internship Coordinator
P.O. Box 654
Canal Street Station
New York, NY 10013
(212) 966-9796
Fax: (212) 226-6576
E-mail: mail@thewooster
group.org
www.thewoostergroup.org
(Accepts interns.)

Off-Off
Broadway

**Abingdon Theatre
Company**
312 W. 36th Street,
1st Floor
New York, NY 10018-6494
(212) 868-2055
Fax: (212) 868-2056
E-mail: atcnyc@aol.com
www.abingdon-nyc.org

Apricot Sky Productions
16 Paris Circle
West Orange, NJ 07052-
1128
(201) 321-0760
Fax: (973) 509-2515
E-mail: apricotsky@aol.com
www.hometown.aol.com/
apricotsky

**ARTGroup (A Regional
Theatre Group)**
P.O. Box 1751
Murray Hill Station
New York, NY 10156-1751
E-mail: anartgroup@aol.com
www.artgroupnewyork.cjb.
net

Circle East Theatre
Circle East, Inc.
140 W. 42nd Street,
4th Floor
New York, NY 10036
(212) 719-5699
(212) 252-5510 Hotline
Fax: (212) 391-1909
E-mail: CircleEastTheaCo@
aol.com
www.circleeast.com

**Emerging Artists
Theatre Company**
518 Ninth Avenue,
Suite 2
New York, NY 10018

Group Theatre Too
467 W. 164th Street,
Studio 3C
New York, NY 10032
(917) 521-1357
Fax: 509 471-6057
E-mail: info@grouptheatre
too.org
www.grouptheatretoo.org

Inverse Theater
506 7th Street, #2
Brooklyn, NY 11215-3613
(718) 633-3757
E-mail: info@inversetheater.
org
www.inversetheater.org

Metropolitan Playhouse
220 E. 4th Street
New York, NY 10009
(212) 995-8410
E-mail: connect@
metropolitanplayhouse.org
www.metropolitanplayhouse.
org

Other Side Productions
64 W. Seventh Avenue, #3B
New York, NY 10011
(212) 696-8561
E-mail: mail@otherside
productions.org
www.othersideproductions.
org

Urban Stages
259 W. 30th Street (bet. 7th
and 8th Aves.)
New York, NY 10001
(212) 421-1380
Fax: (212) 421-1387
E-mail: urbanstage@aol.org
www.urbanstages.org

Vital Theatre Company
432 W. 42nd Street,
3rd Floor
New York, NY 10036
(212) 268-2040
Fax: (212) 268-0474
E-mail: vital@vitaltheatre.org
www.vitaltheatre.org

12. MODELING
AGENCIES

There are hundreds of
modeling agencies in
New York City. Here
are a few.

Boss Models
1 Gansevoort Street
New York, NY 10014
(212) 242-2444
E-mail: johnwbabin@
bossmodels.com
www.bossmodels.com
Known for men, but also represents women

Elect Management
108 E. 16th Street, 6th Floor
New York, NY 10003
(212) 533-7333
www.electmodels.com

Elite
111 E. 22nd Street
New York, NY 10010
(212) 529-9700
www.elitemodel.com

FFT/Funny Face Today, Inc.
381 Park Avenue South,
Suite 821
New York, NY 10016
(212) 686-4343
Fax: (212) 689-8619
E-mail: fft@fftmodels.com
www.fftmodels.com

Flaunt Model Management, Inc.
114 E. 32nd Street,
Suite 501
New York, NY 10016
(212) 679-9011
Fax: (212) 679-0938
E-mail: flauntmodels@
earthlink.net
www.flauntmodels.com
(Also a talent agency.)

Ford
142 Greene Street,
4th Floor
New York, NY 10012
(212) 219-6500
(212) 966-1531
www.fordmodels.com

Fuel New York
244 Fifth Avenue,
Suite D244
New York, NY 10001
(212) 725-4562
Fax: (212) 725-3456
E-mail: info@fuelmodels.com
www.fuelmodels.com

Gilla Roos
16 W. 22nd Street,
3rd Floor
New York, NY 10010
(212) 727-7820
(212) 727-7833
E-mail: droos@gillaroos.com
www.gillaroos.com
(Also a talent agency.)

GMT (Gonzalez Model & Talent Agency)
112 E. 23rd Street
New York, NY 10010
(212) 982-5626
http://gmt.20m.com

Grace Del Marco: Model and Talent
350 5th Avenue, Suite 3108
New York, NY 10118
(212) 629-6404
Fax: (212) 629-6403
E-mail: gracedelmarco@aol.
com

I D Model Management
137 Varick Street, Suite 401
(at Spring St.)
New York, NY 10013
(212) 206-1818
Fax: (212) 206-3838
E-mail: info@idmodels.com
www.idmodels.com

Ikon Model Management
140 W. 22nd Street
New York, NY 10011
(212) 691-2363
Fax: (212) 691-3622
E-mail: info@ikonmodels.com
www.ikonmodels.com

Ingrid French Management (IFM)
928 Broadway, Suite 302
New York, NY 10010
(646) 602-0653
Fax: (646) 602-0720
E-mail: fren743@aol.com
www.ifmmodels.com
(Also a personal manager.)

Jones Model Management New York
462 W. 142nd Street
New York, NY 10031
(917) 251-2812
E-mail: info@jonesmodels.
com
www.jonesmodels.
ceoclubs.org

Lyons Group
505 Eighth Avenue,
12th Floor, Studio 1
New York, NY 10018
(212) 239-3539
Fax: (212) 239-4221
E-mail: lyonsgrpny@aol.com
www.lyonsgroupny.com

Madison Models
84 Wooster Street
New York, NY 10012
(212) 941-5577
Fax: (212) 941-5559
E-mail: info@madison
models.com
www.madisonmodels.com

McDonald/Richards Model Management
232 Madison Avenue,
Mezzanine
New York, NY 10016
(212) 684-9800
Fax: (212) 684-9723
E-mail: mcdr156@hotmail.
com
www.mcdrnyc.com

New York Model Management
596 Broadway, Suite 701
New York, NY 10012
(212) 539-1700
Fax: (212) 539-1775
E-mail: admin@newyork
models.com
www.newyorkmodels.com

Next
23 Watts Street, 5th Floor
New York, NY 10013
(212) 925-5100
(212) 925-5931
E-mail: newyork@next
models.com
www.nextmodels.com

Pauline's Model Management
379 W. Broadway,
Suite 502
New York, NY 10012
(212) 941-6005

Q Model Management
180 Varick Street,
13th Floor
New York, NY 10014
(212) 807-6777
(212) 807-8999
E-mail: nyc@Qmodels.com
www.Qmodels.com

SVM New York

13 Crosby Street, Suite 30
New York, NY 10013
(212) 966-7727
E-mail: info@svmny.com
Fax: (212) 966-7998
www.svmny.com

Thompson Agency

50 W. 34th Street,
Suite 6C6
New York, NY 10001
(212) 947-6711
Fax: (212) 947-6732
E-mail: kimberlythompson@
email.msn.com
www.blufire.com/ny.
thompson.home.html

Wilhelmina

300 Park Avenue South,
2nd Floor
New York, NY 10010
(212) 473-0700
www.wilhelmina.com

13.
EMPLOYMENT
AGENCIES

Kimshelley's Spotlight On: A.T. Temps

Let's face it, as yucky as they are, most of us need day jobs. Temping is a great option for actors to make rent! That way you can take off the days you have auditions and work the days you don't. I was lucky to get in with a great temp agency off the bat. I sat down with the two lovely women I work for, Galit Rachimi and Dana Turner of A.T. Temps, to get some information and advice:

K: Tell me about A.T. Temps.

G and D: A.T. Temps opened in 1990. It's a part of A.Taylor and Salem Associates, a permanent employment agency that's been around for about twenty-five years.

K: How many temps would you say you have?

G and D: We've got over 500 registered.

K: So are you at your limit?

G and D: We *always* take on new people.

K: Is it important to have computer skills?

G and D: Yes. But if you don't have them, don't be discouraged. We offer training tutorials in Word, Excel, and Power-Point.

K: Do you place within the industry?

G and D: Of course! Whenever we can.

K: What tips can you give actors who want to temp?

G and D: For wardrobe you'll need corporate attire. Be flexible with assignments and hourly rates: The more you give us to work with, the better chance we can get you something. A positive attitude is a *must*. And be honest. Let us know when you have an audition and other conflicts.

K: What is the best way for people to apply to you?

G and D: You can go to www.attemps.com and fill out an application.

A.T. TEMPS

292 Madison Avenue,
Suite 1518
New York, NY 10017
(212) 213-5656
Fax: (212) 213-5660
E-mail: info@attemps.com
www.attemps.com

Other Employment Agencies

Adecco Recruiting Office

500 Fifth Avenue
New York, NY 10165
(212) 391-7000

Atrium Staffing

420 Lexington Avenue,
Suite 1410
New York, NY 10170
(212) 292-0550
Fax: (212) 292-0551
E-mail: resume@atriumstaff.
com
www.atriumstaff.com

Bilanz Bilinguals

60 E. 42nd Street,
Room 1433
New York, NY 10165
(212) 697-8081

Buckley Temporary Services

40 Exchange Place,
Suite 1309
New York, NY 10005
(212) 344-9111
Fax: (212) 344-9268
E-mail: tbuckley@buckley
staffing.com
www.buckleystaffing.com

Core Staffing Services
59 Maiden Lane, 23rd Floor
New York, NY 10038
(212) 766-1222

**Madison Avenue
Temporary Service**
275 Madison Avenue
New York, NY 10016
(212) 922-9040
Fax: (212) 922-9048
E-mail: info@matsfor
communications.com
www.matsfor
communications.com

**Metropolitan
Companies**
110 E. 42nd Street,
Suite 802
New York, NY 10017
(212) 983-6060
Fax: (212) 983-7406
E-mail: info@metstaff.com
www.metstaff.com

**Millennium Personnel
Corporation**
12 W. 37th Street,
Suite 1203
New York, NY 10018
(212) 244-2777
Fax: (212) 244-1551
www.mpc-nyc.com

Office Team
245 Park Avenue,
25th Floor
New York, NY 10167
(212) 687- 4040

Oliver Staffing, Inc.
124 E. 40th Street,
Suite 401
New York, NY 10016
(212) 634-1234
Fax: (212) 634-1235
www.oliverstaffing.com

**Randstad Creative
Talent**
419 Park Avenue South
New York, NY 10016
(646) 742-1757

**Sentech Staffing
Solutions**
1452 E. Gunhill Road,
2nd Floor
Bronx 10469
(718) 547-8811
Fax: 212-752-1771
E-mail: sentina.brown@
sentechstaffing.com
www.sentechstaffing.com

**Staff America
Corporation**
130 Madison Avenue
New York, NY 10016
(212) 696-1492
Fax: (212) 696-1640
E-mail: staffamerica@staffam.
com
www.staffam.com

Taylor Hodson, Inc.
133 W. 19th Street
New York, NY 10011
(212) 924-8300
Fax: (212) 924-1503
www.taylorhodson.com

**Temporary Staffing by
Suzanne, Ltd.**
380 Madison Avenue
New York, NY 10017
(212) 856-4445
Fax: (212)
E-mail: info@suzannenyc.
com
www.suzannenyc.com

Tempositions
420 Lexington Avenue
New York, NY 10170
(212) 490-7400
Fax: (212) 867-1759
E-mail: nyinfo@tempositions.
com
www.tempositions.com

The Tuttle Agency
295 Madison Avenue
New York, NY 10017
(212) 499-0759
Fax: (212) 499-9164
E-mail: ny-info@tuttleagency.
com
www.tuttleagency.com

**Unique Support
Services, Inc.**
160 Broadway, Suite 905
New York, NY 10038
(212) 406-0062
1-800-232-4303
Fax: (212) 406-5882

**Vanguard Temporaries,
Inc.**
633 E. Third Avenue
New York, NY 10017
(212) 682-6400
Fax: (212) 682-7416
E-mail: info@temporary
personnel.com
www.temporarypersonnel.
com

FOUR

getting
the look

14. PHOTO-GRAPHERS

Liz's Spotlight On: Headshot Photographers Mickey Pantano and Robert Kim

There are no two ways about it. Commercials? Theater? Film? On the other side of that résumé, you're going to need a headshot.

There are headshot photographers galore in the city. You will see their ads in the trade magazines, their flyers pasted around town, and a limitless number of Web sites devoted to their photos. You'll read testimonies swearing by studio light, lauding the virtues of natural light, and spe-

cial offers allowing you to keep your negatives. You'll read why black and white is the only way to go—ditto for sepia and color. And what about makeup and hair? You'll find yourself wondering whether you should use a makeup artist, do your own, or go au natural. You'll see evidence both supporting and arguing against patterns, sleeveless, turtleneck, business attire, and casual.

And then just when you think you've finally made up your mind, someone will show you their great new headshots giving you a conflicting argument for every facet you've already considered a half a million times.

"Arghhh!" How to decide? Do not despair, you are not alone. As you read this, there are thousands of actors going through this very situation. That said, there is much to consider and no shortage of opinion. But the only way to get the headshot photographer that is right for you in New York City is to do your homework. It means investing a significant amount of time and/or money. It means talking to other actors and researching the photographers' work. It means making appointments with photographers to meet with them to better understand what they do.

Admittedly, it's a time-consuming chore

but one well worth the effort because your headshot serves as the best possible calling card to get you in a door that thousands of other aspiring actors would love to squeeze through at exactly the same time.

To help with the process *Act NY 2005* features two New York City headshot photographers, Mickey Pantano and Robert Kim. Acting as a headshot guinea pig of sorts, I spent a complete session with each of them and some of the makeup artists they work with — Christine Kolenda for the Mickey Pantano session and Colleen Brock for the Robert Kim session — to delve further into their process, their opinions, and their work.

Mickey Pantano

Every photographer has a specific style, and Mickey Pantano's is fused with a photojournalism and musical theater background. It colors the way she approaches the actors who come to her in search of a headshot.

"The actor needs to work with the camera and the photographer as if he were actually doing a film. He needs to create a certain amount of accessibility and have his own energy come through. So I talk to the actor straight off the bat; just get them relaxed, see where they're coming from, where they want to go in their career, what their goals are. It's a true collaboration. There's a huge difference between the kind of headshot that you would use for commercials as opposed to film. So a commercial headshot is not a film headshot. There's a different energy behind it, a different feel to it."

Pantano helps decide what colors and styles of clothing to wear and spends time comparing previous headshots or pictures to get a better idea of what each person wants. "And then I start looking at the person through the lens of the camera. Now when you look at someone through the lens of a camera, they look very different. There are a lot of subtleties — the shape of the person's face, the way their nose turns. No two sides look exactly alike. Different profiles can look very different. So I'm always looking to make sure that I see the side that they will photograph best on. General-

ly I have people close their eyes in between pictures, and I shoot really slowly. So then, when I do take the shot, you're looking at the lens and I'm looking for a connection and it happens in your eyes."

When asked about what doesn't work, Pantano says all too often she sees headshots that have a vacant look with an image that physically resembles the person but lacks his or her energy and personality.

"If you look at a good picture, no matter where you hold it, it should look like that person is looking right at you so that when a casting director or an agent is looking at your pictures, they're arrested by the accessibility of your eyes."

And while some photographers swear by studio light and others won't use any other light than natural, Pantano uses a combination of both. She says it provides her with a variety of ways to capture an image whether indoors or outside on the roof of her building. Over the years, Pantano says one of the mistakes actors make, time and again, is to select a headshot photographer solely on the basis of price. It is a mistake she equated to putting one's career on hold and essentially wasting both time and money.

In Pantano's eyes, a good rapport is key to choosing a headshot photographer. "I think it's a huge mistake to photograph with someone you don't feel a connection with regardless of whether they're the best photographer you've ever heard of," she said. "If you don't feel comfortable when you're interviewing them, then I don't see how you could feel comfortable with them in a shoot. I mean, you're at your most vulnerable when you're sitting there in front of a camera, so you've got to completely trust the person that you're shooting with."

And just how vital is an actor's headshot to his or her future?

"A good headshot is not going to get you a job, but it's going to get you in the door. That's it. If you have a mediocre headshot, you probably are not going to be seen through a mail-in submission. Now that doesn't mean that if you've got a great headshot, you're going to be seen either; there are other things involved in the process. But a re-ally good headshot will get you noticed."

Pantano added that a true representation of how you look is a necessary ingredient. She cautioned against getting a photo that is so radically different from the way you look that casting directors do a double take when you walk into the room. She says it will not only turn them off, but it could cost you the job.

Robert Kim

Robert Kim is a New York City photographer who also has an acting background. With twenty-four feature films and fifty-six TV shows to his credit, alongside a thirty-year-plus career snapping headshots, Kim says he has an abundance of experience both behind and in front of the camera.

Kim says that the actor's headshot is absolutely critical to getting in the door to audition; the time in which you have to say, "Look at me! I'm the person you want!" is essential. "The typical casting director looks at a headshot for 1.4 seconds — 1.4 seconds ladies and gentlemen to make or break your career," Kim said. "They [casting directors] don't have time to peruse these or study them. You must make that impression, that impact immediately. It has to tell them so many things about you, so quickly."

With that always foremost in his mind, Kim first asks a potential client to bring a current headshot to give him an idea of what the actor likes or doesn't like. He says he talks with the actor to determine career goals, what he or she plans to do. As part of the decision process, one of Kim's points of pride is his "Before and After" portfolios of compiled headshots of more than one thousand photographers from around the world. He keeps them for potential clients to compare his work to that of others.

Once you book a session, Kim will advise you on what necklines and colors to wear. He'll discuss makeup and hair and answer any other questions you may have. His aim is that you leave with an accurate representation of what you look like on your best day. "Preparation is key," Kim says. "I compare it to seeing a play. Just like the saying 'the play is the thing,' the photo is the thing. How important every aspect of the photo is — I can't stress that enough —that everything must be perfect. Once you start screwing up on that regard, the picture will begin to suffer. What constitutes a great headshot? Hundreds of small details all executed perfectly. To the degree that you leave out these details is the degree to which the picture will suffer."

And when it comes to a shoot, Kim does not shy away from giving direction. "Actors thrive on direction, and nowhere is it more important than in the headshot," he says. "When I look at bad headshots, I can tell right away that the actor didn't get proper direction or didn't get any direction at all. I've found this time and time again in headshots that just aren't working for the actor."

Kim says he finds that a lot of actors in search of a headshot photographer make the huge mistake of vesting too much importance in the personality of the person behind the camera. "The only thing the casting directors will see is your photo — not the rapport between you and the photographer. The casting director does not see the photographer's wonderful, winning personality. They see the headshot only, and it better be great."

And when it comes to lighting, Kim is adamant that studio light is superior to natural light. "Take photographers of equal ability using no light and studio light and hands down, day after day, the studio-light photo will blow that natural light picture away. They are not alike; they are not comparable. Have you ever seen a feature film shot with no lighting? Have you ever gone to a play with no lighting? Have you ever seen a cover of a national magazine or a fashion shoot with no lighting? Is it then a logical assumption that your headshot should be done with no lighting?"

Over the years, Kim says the most common mistake he sees is actors taking a frugal approach to headshots — undermining the importance of its value as a necessary part of marketing their careers.

"Price is always a consideration — there's no question about it. I find that the supreme irony is that an actor will spend thousands of dollars — tens of thousands of dollars — on acting classes, scene studies, cold readings, seminars. They go to a gym to get their body in shape; they have their hair colored; they go to vocal classes, stage movement, voice — spending all this money. And when it comes to the most important step in their entire career, they want to find the cheapest guy they can. And I just say no wonder there's so many failing actors — no wonder."

Kim added, "My job is to get actors interviews. Period. And that's what a headshot can do. It can completely revolutionize your career. If you're a pro, it can take you to the next level. If you're unknown, it can make you known; it can open up every single door. That's how important it is. I can't even emphasize it enough. And once again, the people who don't know it, they've never had the benefit, the experience of having a killer headshot. Therefore, they miss this wonderful experience — it can literally transform your career. If you don't have a great headshot, you're going to go to your grave with your talent.

"There are two words

in the term *show business*. First, *show* which is the training and the experience. And second, *business*, which is the representation and marketing. That's my business — to help market the actor.

You're going to be going up against people who have wonderful résumés, tremendous experience, top representation, personal managers, A-list agents, and killer headshots. And you think you're going to break into the same industry with a cheap and unflattering headshot? I don't think so. This is the most competitive industry in the world. Ninety-nine percent of the time unless you have connections up the yazoo, it's the headshot that's going to get you the audition. Not your winning personality, not chanting into the doorknob — it's the headshot."

Mickey Pantano
1-888-546-3686
(212) 645-5788

Robert Kim
(212) 539-8486

Read more about both photographers in the listings beginning on page 112.

Featured Photographer: Richard Blinkoff

The staff of Actorscraft.com was invited recently to the lovely Chelsea loft of headshot photographer, Richard Blinkoff. It was a sunny day, and the movie-set-like space was filled with light. We had a lively discussion in which we experienced a true pro speaking with passion about his art.

Richard Blinkoff in First Person

After getting a Ph.D. in Medical Research from Rockefeller University and teaching for two years at Harvard Medical School, I began a career in photography. What a change that was. After years of concentrating on huge quantities of scientific information, I suddenly was dealing with light, shadow, and expressing feelings through imagery. I never looked back.

Many years of building a successful photographic career and working for top fashion and beauty clients in the New York advertising business followed, and then my work took a slight detour. Although I never stopped doing advertising work, and I still do some to-

day, I found myself introduced to the world of headshots. My son was studying for a graduate degree at Yale Drama, and I did a headshot for him. Luckily, it was good, and it was noticed by his classmates. That was about nine years ago.

I photograph my clients here in my open, sunlit loft in Chelsea. Fifty feet of southern exposure makes daylight photography not only possible, but very easy. Still, I've been dealing with studio strobe lighting for over twenty years, and I'm very confident in my ability to create any mood I want, even if the sky is dark outside.

I can shoot either with film or digitally, although I prefer to use film. It has a greater sensitivity and range of tone, and it delivers a print that is more subtle in its gradations. If requested to do so, I will shoot digitally to accommodate a client.

Otherwise, I shoot with film, deliver contact sheets after one and a half days, and then scan the chosen negatives into my computer for retouching. Digital retouching allows me to remove slight distractions from the picture and to produce a very polished final product. The actor receives a black-and-white or color 8-by-10 print and a CD containing the digital files of all chosen negatives.

Despite the readiness of some clients to sign up for a session over the phone, I mostly insist that actors come to the studio to meet me and see the surroundings before deciding. They need to look at my pictures extensively and see if my personality and style agree with them. I have no strict method to which each subject must adapt himself. I work at whatever pace seems best, and I care much more about achieving some kind of flow rather than micromanaging body posture and expression during a shoot. Capturing a moment of real projection is more important to me than exquisite lighting and graphic composition.

Unlike other kinds of photographs — snapshots, fashion or beauty shots, portraits, or illustrations — a headshot must fulfill its function of introducing the actor to someone who has never seen him, someone who will be getting a very important first impression based on what he sees. And, when the headshot is

left behind or sent after an audition, it must remind the casting person exactly what he saw in the first place.

Because the function is so specific, the headshot must communicate certain things. The first rule is probably the most confusing: The headshot must look like you — and hopefully at your best. But not so glamorized that the presentation becomes unbelievable. In your session with me, I explore the different looks that you can have. That is why I shoot over one hundred pictures with three to four changes of clothing in three completely different lighting and background conditions. Character actors get to express vastly different sides of themselves, and other types of actors are encouraged to express a variety of emotions and looks within their own range. It is impossible as a photographer to always guess beforehand which look will be the most successful and convincing. Hopefully, the actor will find all three looks exciting, and he will have a terribly difficult time deciding which to use. That problem occurs with many of my clients, and it always makes me feel

great that the decision process is very hard.

For me, the most important quality a headshot must express is total professionalism. Long before that casting person looks at the résumé to read about experience, he has gotten a definite impression about the professional abilities of the actor. If the headshot is poorly printed with no contrast, focus, or graphic balance, if it is tattered, scratched, and without basic retouching corrections, if the lighting is horrible and the make-up and hair destructive to the person, then the immediate conclusion is that this actor does not know good from bad and that he is not to be trusted in professional work situations. Basically, the photographer's responsibility is to make his client look totally like a pro.

That said, I am constantly trying for much more in a session. I want to show energy in the picture, intelligence, focus, and concentration, a center of projection that is solid and calm. I want to show the actor's personality, even his sense of humor. All these qualities are the resources that a casting person, a director, a producer, a filmmaker, or a photographer hopes to draw on during a job. Without showing these in a headshot, an actor is disabled in representing what he can do, and I constantly direct my clients both before and during a session to keep each quality sharp and expressive.

From my start as a fashion photographer to my current business doing portraiture and headshots, I love to work with people. Still-life photography has always bored me because it is infinitely per-fectible; there is no end to going back and moving something to the left or right. But no matter how young or old, how inexperienced or how famous, there is always a moment to be captured when you photograph a person — a moment that can't be predicted, controlled, or re-created, a moment totally dependent on a successful collaboration between photographer and subject, and a moment that is there for the taking only if it is pursued with energy and skill.

Richard Blinkoff Photography
147 West 15th Street
(212) z620-7883.
See all the details for Richard in the photographer listings that follow.

Photographers

Aries
61 Clinton Street, #2
New York, NY 10002
(646) 729-3541
E-mail: malachi@
malachiweir.com
www.malachiweir.com
Years of experience: 16
Pricing: $450 for 3 rolls B & W; $350 for 2 rolls B & W; $200 for 1 roll color
Negatives: No
Proofs: Yes
Makeup: Yes, $150
"Theatrical headshots and portraits. Other work has included publicity shots for musicians, authors, and theater companies."

Arthur Cohen Photography
56 W. 22nd Street, 8th Floor
New York, NY 10010
(212) 691-5244
E-mail: arthur@arthurcohen. com
www.arthurcohen.com
Years of experience. 20
Pricing: $625 for digital, 4-hour session
Negatives: No
Proofs: Yes, a low-res CD and contact sheets
Makeup: Yes, $160
"Headshots, book covers, soap stars, CD covers."

Babaldi Studio
10 Bleecker Street, #1D
New York, NY 10012
(212) 253-8795
E-mail: mm@babaldi.com
www.babaldi.com
Years of experience: 15
Pricing: $650 for digital
Negatives: No
Proofs: On CD. Contact sheets can be printed for $10 each.
Makeup: Yes, $150
"All types of headshots and

models portfolios, comp cards and commercial print."

Benjamin Dimmitt Photography
34 W. 88th Street
New York, NY 10024
(212) 595-1816
E-mail: questions@benjamin headshots.com
www.benjaminheadshots. com
Years of experience: 27
Pricing: $525 for 4 rolls and two 8-by-10 prints; $450 for 2 rolls and one 8-by-10 print; extra prints $25 each; extra rolls, $75 each
Negatives: No
Proofs: Yes
Makeup: Yes, $100 to $175
"Theatrical, commercial, and legit shots."

Brian Appel Photography
365 Seventh Avenue #3 South
New York, NY 10001
(212) 563-5929
E-mail: brianappel@earth link.com
www.brianappel photography.com
Years of experience: 13
Pricing: $600 for 6 to 10 rolls; contacts and two 8 by 10s are included
Negatives: No
Proofs: Yes
Makeup: Yes, $125 (women only)
"Headshots that capture different facets of the actors personality."

Bill Morris Studio
42 Greene Street, 5th Floor
New York, NY 10013
(212) 274-1177
E-mail: billm@billmorris.com
www.billmorris.com/ headshots
Years of experience: 25
Pricing: $395 for digital 2-look shoot with a retouched

master print for both looks; additional looks $125 each (student discount price $350)
Negatives: No
Proofs: Yes, CD and contact sheet
Makeup: Yes, $150
"Theatrical headshots."

Chia Messina Photography
15 W. 24th Street, #3E
New York, NY 10010
(212) 929-0917
E-mail: messinastudio@earthlink.net
www.chiamessina.com
Pricing: $625 for 3 rolls; $675 for 4 rolls
Negatives: No
Proofs: Yes
Makeup: Yes, $150
"Theatrical headshots primarily but also corporate, kids and models."

Christian Pollard Studio
Midtown Manhattan, location varies
(212) 768-2202
Years of experience: 16 in New York City
Pricing: $295 adults; $195 children
Negatives: Depends on shoot
Proofs: Yes
Makeup: Yes, $100 and up
"We photograph mostly actors, dancers, singers, and musicians as well as commercial, beauty, and corporate."

David Plakke Photography
55 Bethune Street, Suite H215
New York, NY 10014
(212) 675-6925
E-mail: david@davidplakke.com
www.davidplakke.com
Years of experience: 20
Pricing: $475 for digital

Negatives: No
Proofs: Yes, via JPEGs on CD
Makeup: Yes, an assistant who does touch up.
"Theatrical, musicians, models, and corporate headshots."

Eaglenest Studio
259 W. 30th Street, 13th Floor
New York, NY 10001
(212) 736-6221
E-mail: leduceaglesnest@aol.com
www.grantleduc.com
Years of experience: 20
Pricing: $350 for 2 rolls film and two 8 by 10s; $425 for 3 rolls film and three 8 by 10s; $525 for 5 rolls film and four 8 by 10s
Negatives: Yes
Proofs: Yes
Makeup: Yes, $100
"Theatrical headshots and model portfolios."

Evan Cohen Photography
39 W. 14th Street, Suite 501
New York, NY 10011
(212) 242-0350
E-mail: evan@evancohenstudio.com
www.evancohenstudio.com
Years of experience: 23
Pricing: $350 for 2 rolls, two 8 by 10s with minor retouching; free one-page Web site with headshots showcased.
Negatives: No
Proofs: Yes
Makeup: Yes, $140
"Natural energetic theatrical headshots using the best of studio and natural light. Traditional and digital techniques."

Helen's Studio
114 7th Avenue, 3C
New York, NY 10011
(212) 242-0646
Years of experience: 40
Pricing: $320 for 3 rolls, two 8 by 10s; $390 for 4 rolls, three 8 by 10s
Negatives: No
Proofs: Yes
"I transport an actor beyond beauty-contest pictures in a theatrical portrait with an emotional range to inspire casting directors."

Hoebermann Studio Photography
281 Sixth Avenue
New York, NY 10014
(212) 807-8014
E-mail: hoebermann@earthlink.net
www.hoebermannstudio.com
Years of experience: 16
Pricing: $900 plus tax for 4 rolls and two 8 by 10s; additional prints $25 each
Negatives: No
Proofs: Yes
Makeup: Yes, $150 for women

Hunyady International
111 3rd Avenue, 2E
New York, NY 10003
(212) 505-9177
E-mail: bhunyady@nyc.rr.com
www.brookehunyady.com
Years of experience: 15
Pricing: $1,500 per session for digital
Negatives: No
Proofs: No
Makeup: Yes, $250 per hour
"Theatrical headshots, kids, models."

Ira Fox Photography
20 W. 22nd Street, Suite 1610
New York, NY 10010
(212) 989-2345
E-mail: ira@irafox.com

www.irafox.com
Years of experience: 10
Pricing: $500 for 4 rolls
(medium format) contacts
and one 8 by 10; extra 8
by 10s at $25 each
Negatives: Yes
Proofs: Yes
Makeup: Yes, $150
"I photograph actors in my
studio, outdoors available,
weather permitting."

Jeffrey Hornstein Studios

137 W. 14th Street, #301
New York, NY 10011
(212) 352-1186
E-mail: jeffreyhornstein@
aol.com
www.jeffreyhornstein.com
Years of experience: 15
Negatives: Conditional
Proofs: Yes
Makeup: Yes
"Theatrical headshots,
kids, models, and celebrity
portraiture."

Jeremy Folmer Photography

(646) 765-3027
E-mail: mail@jeremyfolmer.
com
www.jeremyfolmer.com
Pricing: varies, see Web site
Negatives: No
Proofs: Yes
Makeup: Yes, $125
"Actors, models."

Jonnie Miles Photography

309 W. 99th Street, Apt.
3B1
New York, NY 10025
(212) 865-7956
E-mail: jonniemiles@jonnie
miles.com
www.jonniemiles.com
Years of experience: 15
Pricing: $500 (model releas-
es required)
Negatives: No
Proofs: Yes
Makeup: No

"Lifestyle, models, actors,
'real people' advertising."

Joseph Moran Photography

104 W. 14th Street,
5th Floor
New York, NY 10011
(212) 206-9345
E-mail: joseph@josephmoran
inc.com
www.moranhead shots.com
Years of experience: 20
Pricing: $500 for digital,
4 rolls, contact sheets, 2 un-
retouched 8 by 10s. $125
each additional roll.
Negatives: No
Proofs: Yes, digital contact
sheets burned to CD and
posted on private portion of
photographer's Web site.
Makeup: Prices vary but
start at $75 for men and
$125 for women.
"Actors, models, celebrities,
musicians, corporate clients
and children."

Julie Brimberg Photography, Inc.

143 W. 29th Street
New York, NY 10001
(212) 594-2096
E-mail: juliebrimberg@
earthlink.net
www.juliebrimberg.com
Years of experience: 9
Pricing: $550 for 3 rolls,
two 8 by 10s; $475 for
same package as above for
a 9 AM session; additional
8 by 10s for $20 each
Negatives: No
Proofs: Yes
Makeup: Yes, $140 women.
Basic men's makeup is free.
"Headshots, models, musi-
cians. I tailor sessions to
each client's individual
needs and create images
that give a sense of personality."

Jussen Studio

4 W. 37th Street, 6th Floor
New York, NY 10018
(212) 268-1340
E-mail: juspix@aol.com
www.jussenstudio.com
Years of experience: 20
Pricing: $600 for digital, 2
retouched 8 by 10s
Negatives: No
Proofs: Yes, contact sheets
Makeup: Yes, $175
"Professional actors and
actresses."

Kevin Fox Photography

515 Greenwich Street, #502
New York, NY 10012
(646) 431-0214
E-mail: Kevin@Fox
Photography.net
www.FoxPhotography.net
Years of experience: 11
Pricing: $350 for 120 digi-
tal shots plus two 8 by 10s
Negatives or disk: Yes
Proofs: Yes
Makeup: Yes, $150
"Headshots for all perform-
ers, corporate headshots,
and weddings in the tri-state
area."

Kris Carr Photography

(917) 846-4784
Fax: (212) 861-9022
E-mail: kris@kriscarr
photography.com
www.kriscarrphotography.
com
Years of experience: 4
Pricing: $525 for four rolls,
four contact sheets and neg-
atives, student discount
Negatives: Yes, free
Proofs: No
Makeup: Yes, $125

Manning Gurney Studio

25 W. 38th Street
New York, NY 10018
(212) 391-0965
www.manninggurney.com
Years of experience: 25
Pricing: $575 for women;
$525 for men

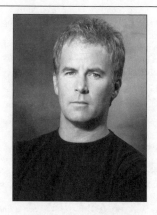

Negatives: No
Proofs: Yes
Makeup: Yes, $200 women only
"Theatrical headshots, children."

Marni Angel Photography
(212) 594-6291
1-888-330-4660
E-mail: myangelshot@yahoo.com
www.angelshots.com
Years of experience: 6
Pricing: $595 for 3 rolls; $395 for children under 15 for 2 rolls
Negatives: No
Proofs: Yes
"Actors, models, celebrities, weddings."

Mickey Pantano Photography
(212) 539-8486
www.mickeypantano.com
Pricing: $495 for adult headshot, includes 4 rolls of film, contact sheet, negatives, and clothing consultation; $275 for child headshots, includes 2 rolls of film, contact sheet, negatives, and clothing consultation.
"Every actor is unique, every actor is an individual. Every headshot should be as individual as the actor whom it represents."

Nancy Pindrus Photography
21 W. 68th Street, #3F
New York, NY 10023
(212) 724-4681
E-mail: pindrus@earthlink.net
Years of experience: 20
Pricing: $275 for B & W, 3 rolls with contact sheets, enlargements $32.50 up to 8 by 10; $325 for color, twenty to thirty 4 by 5 proofs included, enlargements $42.50
Negatives: No
Proofs: Yes

Makeup: Yes, prices conditional
"Faces are my forte. Faces have never ceased to fascinate me with their expressiveness, their beauty, and their uniqueness."

Paper Muse/ Wayne Takenaka/
511 W. 25th Street, Studio #509
New York, NY 10001
(212) 722-3669
E-mail: waynetakenaka@verizon.net
www.waynetakenaka.com
Years of experience: 25
Pricing: Call for pricing
Negatives: No
Proofs: Yes, contact sheets
Makeup: Yes, $150
"Portraits for film and stage."

Peter Sweyer Photography
601 W. 26th Street, 13th Floor
New York, NY 10001
(917) 488-7946
E-mail: petersweyer@yahoo.com
www.petersweyer.com
Years of experience: 14
Pricing: $595 for digital
Negatives: No
Proofs: Yes, contact sheets and entire session in jpeg format on CD.
Makeup: Yes, $140
"We consistently create high impact intimate portraits that focus on your eyes. We make sure all of our clients pop off the page."

Ray Block Studio
231 W. 29th Street, #603
New York, NY 10001
(212) 967-9470
Years of experience: 25
Pricing: $325 for women; $300 for men
Negatives: Yes
Proofs: Yes
Makeup: included in price

"Theatrical headshots, corporate, kids, dancers."

Richard Blinkoff Photography
147 W. 15th Street, 3rd Floor
New York, NY 10011
(212) 620-7883
E-mail: rblinkoff@earthlink.net
www.richardblinkoff.com
Years of experience: 25
Pricing: $650 for 3 rolls and three 8 by 10s (fully retouched). Special rates for persons 16 years of age and younger; call for other special discounts.
Negatives: No
Proofs: Yes
Makeup: Yes, $150
"I work equally well with actors, children and models. My forte is capturing the personality, energy, intelligence and humor in each."

robertkim Studio
New York / Los Angeles
101 W. 18th Street, Suite 5D
New York, NY 10011
(212) 645-5788
1-888-546-3686
E-mail: kimfoto@earthlink.net
www.robertkim.com
Years of experience: 30
Pricing: $699
Negatives: No
Proofs: Yes
Makeup: Yes, $150
"Theatrical headshots."

Sasha Nialla Photos
(917) 776-5349
E-mail: info@sashanialla.com
www.sashanialla.com
Years of experience: 5
Pricing: Call for prices
Negatives: No
Proofs: Yes
Makeup: Yes, call for prices
"Portraits, music, photojournalism, documentary."

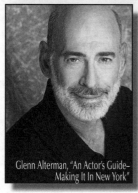

Scott Wynn Photography
Upper West Side
(212) 874-1449
E-mail: scottwynnphoto@aol.com
www.scottwynn.com
Years of experience: 18
Pricing: $400 for 3 rolls
Negatives: Yes
Proofs: Yes
Makeup: Yes, $175
"Actor headshots, theatrical productions, music, events."

Sean Kahlil Studio
57 W. 16th Street
New York, NY 10011
(212) 665-3828
E-mail: sean@seankahlilphotography.com
www.seankahlilphotography. com
Years of experience: 17
Pricing: $350 for headshots, 2 rolls, 3 looks; $550 for comp cards, 4 rolls, 6 looks; $1,000 for portfolio day shoots for 8 rolls, 12 looks
Negatives: Yes
Proofs: Yes
Makeup: Yes, $125 headshots, $175 comps
"Beauty, body, healthy lifestyle. Soap and legit headshots."

Speliotis Photography
309 E. 4th Street, #1D
New York, NY 10009
(917) 282-5086
E-mail: speliotis2000@yahoo.com
www.yourtype.com/speliotis
Years of experience: 20
Pricing: From $395 and up: $525 for 4 rolls, polaroids, wardrobe consultation, contact sheets, two 8 by 10s; additional 8 by 10s at $25 each
Negatives: Yes
Proofs: Yes
Makeup: Yes, $125 for men, $175 for women
"Actor's headshots that are

more like a portrait of the actor."

Stephanie Badini Photography
34 Watts Street, #14
New York, NY 10013
(212) 966-9524
Years of experience: 8
Pricing: $375 for 3 rolls; $425 for 4 rolls
Negatives: No
Proofs: Yes
Makeup: Yes, $150
"Theatrical headshots."

Tom Bloom Photography
277 W. 10th Street, #6M
New York, NY 10014
(212) 924-8276
E-mail: tombloom@juno.com
www.tombloom.com
Years of experience: 27
Pricing: $375 for 3 rolls, two 8 by 10s; $20 each for extra prints; reshoots: $40 per roll (unlimited)
Negatives: No
Proofs: Yes
Makeup: Yes, $85; $150 for makeup and hair
"I am a working actor myself. I shoot transitions, between active thoughts, so the photos convey more complexity and subtext than posed shots." Portfolio is on view at Ken Taranto Lab, 38 E. 30th Street, 2nd Floor.

Trevor Oswalt Photography
(212) 696-6453
E-mail: trevor@trevoroswalt.com
www.trevoroswalt.com
Years of experience: 8
Pricing: $575 for 4 rolls, contacts, and 2 prints
Negatives: No
Proofs: Yes
Makeup: Yes, $150
"Actors, musicians, writers and some kids, PR, couples, and corporate."

15. MAKEUP ARTISTS

Kimshelley's Spotlight On: Jaime Perez

Who better to know what looks good for headshots than an actor who is also a gifted makeup artist! Charming Jaime Perez received his degree in communications from the University of Massachusetts, where he was a member of the U. Mass Theatre Guild. Then he came to New York to pursue his career in acting. Luckily for us, he's continued to do makeup. I asked Jaime a few questions while he was doing my makeover.

K: What's your makeup advice for people starting out?
JP: Though you don't need a lot of it, it's beneficial to know how to apply makeup. You should have at least one professional lesson, so you'll know what to use.
K: What's your biggest beauty tip?
JP: *Exfoliate!* I can't tell people enough. It gets rid of all the gunk and dry skin.
K: Anything else?
JP: Moisturize. Even if you have oily skin,

get an oil-free moisturizer. It's very important. Use your SPF. And you don't need too much makeup for daily wear. Just mascara and lip gloss can have a great effect.

K: What makeup do you use?

JP: I use a range (like most artists), but I use a lot of English Ideas cosmetics. They're great for actresses, because it stays put, through just about everything, for eight to twelve hours.

K: What are your fees?

JP: At the moment I charge around the standard $75 for headshot and makeup.

K: One last question. But it's a weird one . . .

JP: Yes?

K: I've been yelled at before for attacking my skin too close to a shoot. Is it easier to cover a blemish or a scab?

JP: Easier to cover a blemish by far! A blemish tends to be light in color and smooth. A scab tends to be dark and the texture is very hard to conceal.

Jaime Perez
(718) 219-0756
Jaime is available for headshots, student and independent film, weddings, and fashion photography.

Other Makeup Artists

Colleen Brock
(212) 592-4728
Professional makeup artistry in print, film, and video

Candace Corey
(917) 881-0044
Contact: Richard Francis (rep)
E-mail: candacecorey@ yahoo.com
www.candacecorey.com
Professional hair and makeup artist for print, TV, video, and fashion shows.

Sandra Curran
(201) 656-9379
E-mail: sandracurran2003@ yahoo.com
Specializes in makeup for headshots, fashion, TV, film, weddings.

Robert Dolphin
(212) 222-1481
Specializes in makeup for headshots, makeup lessons, and eyebrows.

Facciabella
(917) 406-9159
Makeup for professional still and live photography.

Faces by Jeff
Jeff Meyer
(718) 457-5254
E-mail: contactjeff@facesby jeff.com
Makeup for commercial print, film, headshots, retail, industrials, TV. Makeup lessons, private consultations.

Elena Giannini
(917) 447-9888
Makeup for film, video, print, weddings, special occasions, and private instruction.

Kerry
(718) 230-9831
(646) 369-2173
E-mail: umaagemakeup@ aol.com
Specializes in makeup for headshots, fashion, TV, film (some special effects), weddings.

Christine Kolenda
(646) 345-2826
All-natural mineral makeup, skin care, and facials, bridal makeup, camouflage makeup, headshots, individual and group lessons

Lori
(646) 369-0116
E-mail: juicelbd@aol.com
Specializes in makeup for headshots, weddings, fashion.

The Make-Up Artist Shop/ Alicia Vanore
267 Kinderkamack Road
Oradell, NJ 07649
(201) 967-7117
E-mail: Alicia@makeupartist shop.com
www.makeupartistshop.com
Retail, specializes in makeup for headshots, print, album covers, makeovers, film (light special effects), and weddings and makeup artist training.

The Make-Up Center
150 W. 55th Street
New York, NY 10019
(212) 977-9494
Specializes in makeup for makeup lessons for headshots, daily wear, evening wear, eyebrows, and skin care.

Marcelle
(201) 493-7590

E-mail: makeupbymarcelle@softhome.net
Specializes in makeup for headshots, fashion, weddings, TV, film.

Jeff Silverman
(646) 554-9955
E-mail: biglesworth12@yahoo.com
Makeup for all events: film, TV, video, print, and private instruction.

16.
PHOTO LABS

Here are just a handful of the many photo labs in New York City. For a much more comprehensive list, go to rasource. com, a great site for all things photographic.

A-1 Color Lab
130 W. 26th Street
New York, NY 10001
(212) 627-9494
Fax: (212) 627-9533

Advance Color Labs
350 W. 31st Street, 7th Floor
New York, NY 10001
(212) 564-3977

Alkit Pro Camera
222 Park Avenue South
New York, NY 10003
(212) 674-1515
1-800-285-1698
E-mail: customerservice@alkit.com
www.alkit.com

Baboo Color Labs
37 W. 20th Street (5th and 6th Aves.)
New York, NY 10011
(212) 807-1574
(212) 727-2727

Chelsea Professional Color Lab
159 W. 27th Street
New York, NY 10001
(212) 229-2929

Clone-A-Chrome
133 W. 25th Street
New York, NY 10001
(212) 206-1644
E-mail: info@colneachrome.com
www.cloneachrome.com

Color Edge
38 W. 21st Street (5th and 6th Aves.)
New York, NY 10010
(212) 633-6000

Color Wheel
227 E. 45th Street, 7th Floor
New York, NY 10017
(212) 697-2434
(212) 953-6999
(212) 661-0457

Colorite
117E. 31st Street
New York, NY 10016
(212) 532-2116
www.aols.com/colorite

CYMK
641 Washington Street
New York, NY 10014
(212) 633-0001

Diapositive
22 Bond Street
New York, NY 10012
(212) 253-2200

Duggal Digital Imaging
3 W. 20th Street
New York, NY 10011
(212) 941-7000
www.duggal.com

Emulsion Photo Lab
46 W. 17th Street
New York, NY 10011
(212) 229-1669

Flatiron Color Lab
110 W. 17th Street (6th and 7th Aves.)
New York, NY 10011

(212) 633-9191
E-mail: flatironcolorlab@qwest.net
www.flatironcolorlab.com

Fine Art Color Labs
150 Fifth Avenue
New York, NY 10011
(212) 645-7224

Foto Motal Inc.
43 W. 32nd Street, 5th Floor
New York, NY 10036
(212) 868-8500
www.fotomotal.com

Graphics Systems Group
20 W. 22nd Street, 9th Floor
New York, NY 10010

Image Photographic Labs
308 Madison Avenue
New York, NY 10017
(212) 867-4747

Ken Lieberman Labs
118 W. 22nd Street
New York, NY 10011
F-mail: Lieberman@lieberman-labs.com
www.lieberman-labs.com

Liberty Color Lab
171 Christopher Street
New York, NY 10014
(212) 627-1212

Modernage Custom Imaging Labs
1150 Sixth Avenue (at 44th St.)
New York, NY 10036
(212) 997-1800
(212) 869-4796
1-800-997-2510
E-mail: info@modernage.com
www.modernage. com

MV Photo NYC
33 Little W. 12th Street, No. 204
New York, NY 10014

(212) 929-3036
Fax: (212) 929-3149
www.mvlabs.com

Reproductions
6 W. 37th Street, 4th Floor
New York, NY 10018
(212) 967-2568
1-800-647-3776
Fax: (212) 629-8304
E-mail: info@reproductions.
com
www.reproductions. com

**Spectra Photo
(2 locations)**
www.spectraphoto.com

404 Park Avenue South (at
28th St.)
New York, NY 10016
(212) 871-1800
Fax: (212) 871-1801
E-mail: photodigital@
earthlink.net

140 E. 44th Street
New York, NY 10017
(212) 986-6030
Fax: (212) 986-8770
E-mail: spectra44@aol.com

Taranto Labs
(a division of
Color by Pergament)
38 E. 30th Street, 2nd Floor
New York, NY 10016
(212) 691-6070
E-mail: lab@tarantolabs.com
www.tarantolabs.com

**Time-Life Photo
Laboratories**
1271 6th Avenue,
28th Floor
New York, NY 10020
(212) 522-2020

U.S. Color Labs
65 Bleecker Street (at
Lafayette St.)
New York, NY 10012
(212) 254-7200

Westside Color
148 W. 24th Street
New York, NY 10011
(212) 675-6800

17.
HAIR SALONS

Kimshelley's Spotlight On: Capelli D'oro Salon

Perched on the second floor overlooking Lexington Avenue sits Capelli D'oro Salon. Always bustling, this is a choice salon of soap stars and celebrities, as well as other New Yorkers who want a great cut, color, facial, wax, manicure, or one of the many other services offered. Leslie Correa (owner and master stylist) opened the salon in 1988. He additionally has a location in Cancun. Leslie also travels often giving seminars across America. The salon offers a training day on Tuesdays from 10 AM to 1 PM. A cut is $10, and a single process color is $20 (call on Monday to make an appointment). Leslie himself supervises all students. When asked for a tip for actors, Leslie said, "The last thing you want in an audition is to be worried about your hair. Choose a style that's not-so-neat; that will look good messy." Check out their great Web site for fees and more information: www.capellidoro.com.

Capelli D'oro
847 Lexington Avenue,
2nd Floor (bet. 64th
and 65th Sts.)
New York, NY 10021
(212) 288-7100
E-mail: cuts100@aol.com

Other Hair Salons

There are hundreds of salons in New York City — hundreds! Even so, it can be hard to find a stylist that works perfectly for you. You will probably have to try several places. Call ahead to see what their prices are as some can be outrageously expensive. Your average haircut will run you at least $60, but some can go as high as $400. For those on a very tight budget, Dramatics and Jean Louis David are wonderful salons on the lower priced end of the scale.

Chelsea Barber
465 W. 23rd Street
New York, NY 10011
(212) 741-2254

**Dramatics (several
locations)**
www.dramaticsnyc.com

77 Fifth Avenue
New York, NY 1003
(212) 243-0068

1488 Third Avenue
New York, NY 10028
(212) 535-0073

2468 Broadway
New York, NY 10025
(212) 595-2830

305 Columbus Avenue
New York, NY 10023
(212) 721-9313

1185 Second Avenue
New York, NY 10021
(212) 826-4146

340 W. 57th Street
New York, NY 10019
(212) 586-1035

4 E. 28th Street
New York, NY 10016
(212) 683-5467

127 E. 34th Street
New York, NY 10016
(212) 686-8430

158 E. 23rd Street
New York, NY 10010
(212) 460-5709

**Jean Louis David
(several locations)**
30 Vesey Street
New York, NY 10007
(212) 732-4938

303 Park Avenue
New York, NY 10010
(212) 260-3920

485 Sixth Avenue
New York, NY 10011
(212) 741-7911

12 E. 41st Street
New York, NY 10017
(212) 779-3555

367 Madison Avenue
New York, NY 10019
(212) 808-9117

1385 Broadway
New York, NY 10018
(212) 869-6921

783 Lexington Avenue
New York, NY 10021
(212) 838-7372

591 Lexington Avenue
New York, NY 10022
(212) 317-8820

2113 Broadway
New York, NY 10023
(212) 873-1850

7 W. 42nd Street
New York, NY 10036
(212) 354-8067

1180 Avenue of the
Americas
New York, NY 10036
(212) 944-7389

485 Sixth Avenue
New York, NY 10011
(212) 741-7911

2146 Broadway
New York, NY 10023
(212) 873-1850

Prive
310 West Broadway
New York, NY 10013
(212) 274-8888

Salon Above
2641 Broadway
New York, NY 10025
(212) 665-7149

Simon Salon
22 E. 66th Street
New York, NY 10021
(212) 517-4566

Training Days

There are some high-
end salons that have a
training day. On this
day, newly trained styl-
ists, supervised by a
master stylist, will give
you a new do for a con-
siderably lower price
(usually around $25,
but some can be as high
as $40). Some also offer
color at a lesser price
also. This is open to
anyone who knows
about it (most salons
don't advertise their
training days), but the
days and times can

change a lot. Following
is a list of salons that
offer training days; call
to find out what their
days and times are and
what you need to do.

**Angelo David Interna-
tional Hair Salon**
48 E. 43rd Street
New York, NY 10017
(212) 883-6620
www.angelodavid.com

Anthony's Hair Salon
445 Park Avenue
New York, NY 10022
(212) 688-4932
(212) 759-2340

Antonio Prieto Salon
25 W. 19th Street
New York, NY 10011
(212) 255-3741

Bumble and Bumble
146 E. 56th Street
New York, NY 10022
(212) 521-6500

Crisca
21 E. 51st Street
New York, NY 10022
(212) 759-4743
www.saloncrisca.baweb.
com

**David's Haircutting
Studio**
301 E. 82nd Street
New York, NY 10028
(212) 288-5127

Jeff Merritt Hair Salon
210 W. 79th Street
New York, NY 10024
(212) 496-9595

John Barrett Salon
Bergdoff Goodman
754 5th Avenue, 9th Floor
New York, NY 10019
(212) 872-2700 ext. 2712

John Frieda Salon
797 Madison Avenue,
2nd Floor

New York, NY 10021
(212) 879-1000

John Sahag Salon
425 Madison Avenue,
2nd Floor
New York, NY 10017
(212) 750-7772

Julien Farel Salon
605 Madison Avenue,
2nd Floor
New York, NY 10021
1-888-8988

Luis Licari Salon
693 Fifth Avenue, 15th Floor
New York, NY 10022
(212) 758-2090

Marc Avram
925 Fifth Avenue
New York, NY 10021
(212) 734-4007

Miwa Alex Hair Salon
24 E. 22nd Street
New York, NY 10010
(212) 228-4422

Oribe
Elizabeth Arden Salon
691 Fifth Avenue
New York, NY 10022
(212) 319-3910

Oscar Blandi Salon
The Plaza Hotel
768 Fifth Avenue
New York, NY 10019
(212) 593-7930

Sacha & Olivier, Inc.
6 W. 18th Street
New York, NY 10011
(212) 255-1100

Salon 123
123 Fifth Avenue
New York, NY 10003
(212) 777-12335

Seventh Heaven Hair
90 Seventh Avenue
New York, NY 10011
(212) 627-9222

Soon Salon
318 E. 11th Street
New York, NY 10003
(212) 260-4423

Sumiko Salon
152 W. 57th Street
New York, NY 10019
(212) 247-1282

Turning Heads
218 Lenox Avenue
New York, NY 10027
(212) 828-4600

Vidal Sassoon
(2 locations)
90 Fifth Avenue
New York, NY 10011
(212) 229-2200

730 Fifth Avenue
New York, NY 10019
(212) 535-9200

Warren Tricomi
16 W. 57th Street, 4th Floor
New York, NY 10019
(212) 262-8899

World Salon Systems
1585 St. Nicholas Avenue
New York, NY 10040
(917) 521-7948
www.worldsalonsystems.com

18. COSTUME RENTAL

Abracadabra
19 W 21st Street (bet. 5th
and 6th Aves.)
New York, NY 10014
(212) 627-5745
Rentals, magic tricks, gags
and novelties, masks, wigs,
theatrical makeup, and
more.

Allan Uniform Company
121 E. 24th Street
New York, NY 10010
(212) 529-4655

California Costume
200 Fifth Avenue
New York, NY 10010
(212) 620-7644

Charades
200 Fifth Avenue
New York, NY 10010
(646) 336-0835

Coe Sidney Co.
306 W. 38th Street
New York, NY 100018
(212) 631-0220

Creative Costumes
Company
242 W. 36th Street
New York, NY 10018
(212) 564-5552
E-mail: costume@creative
costume.com
www.creativecostume.com
Rentals, no extra charge for
alterations, will make a costume to your specification
and then charge for rental
price only. No children's
costumes.

Disguise, Inc.
200 Fifth Avenue
New York, NY 10010
(212) 727-3267

Euroco Costumes
247 W. 30th Street
New York, NY 10001
(212) 629-9665

Gothic Renaissance
108 Fourth Avenue
New York, NY 10003
(212) 780-9554

Halloween Adventure
104 Fourth Avenue (bet.
11th and 12th Sts.)
New York, NY 10003
(212) 673-4546
Costumes, swords, masks,
hats, magic tricks, and
more.

Jennifer Love Costumes
216 W. 18th Street
New York, NY 10011
(212) 367-9114

Lara Corsets
325 W. 38th Street #1406
New York, NY 10018
(212) 244-2060
Fax: (212) 244-2030
E-mail: lara@laracorsets.com
www.laracorsets.com
By appointment only. Specializes in the construction of period accurate and inspired corsets and gowns. Custom work and some ready-made garments available for purchase.

M. Gordon Novelty Co., Inc.
52 W. 29th Street
New York, NY 10001
(212) 696-9664
Costumes, wholesale and retail. Doesn't take personal checks.

Manhattan Costumes
250 W. 57th Street, #1609,
New York, NY 10017
(212) 245-6770
Rentals, ready made and custom made.

Menkes Theatrical Shoes
250 W. 54th Street,
4th Floor (bet. 8th Ave. and Broadway)
New York, NY 10019
(212) 541-8401

Psyche's Tears
240 W. 15th Street
New York, NY 10011
(212) 924-3190
Cell: (917) 697-4520
E-mail: suzanne@psyches-tears.com
www.psyches-tears.com
Vintage women's and men's clothing and accessories from veteran costumer and wardrobe supervisor. Rental policy available upon request.

Screaming Queens Entertainment
(212) 714-8097
E-mail: alex@screamingqueens.com
www.screamingqueens.com
Custom costuming available.

Space Kiddets
46 E. 21st Street
New York, NY 10010
(212) 420-9878
Rentals, clothing and accessories. Has some period children's costumes.

Theatreworks USA Costumes Shop
151 W. 26th Street
New York, NY 10001
(212) 627-9644

FIVE

getting some space

19. REHEARSAL SPACE

Liz's Spotlight On: The New York Solo Play Lab

Breakout box: With a stage for a Bunsen burner and the chemistry of lighting, marketing, sound, and production, the New York Solo Play Lab at the Where Eagles Dare Theatre, is a place where experiments are taking place. But you won't find any mad scientists here. Instead, you have Artistic Director Cheryl King who's come up with one way to address the vexing problem that solo per-

formers face in trying to polish their acts without losing their shirt.

For any actor, the oh-so-vital necessity of rehearsal is one thing — getting up in front of an audience is quite another. For a solo performance, the distinction is perhaps even more glaring.

"It's impossible to polish a solo piece without an audience. There's a whole different energy. The audience is part of the equation. They are the ones who let you know if a piece works or not," Cheryl King said.

King should know. With more than twenty-five years of experience as an actor, writer, solo performer, stand-

up comedian, and mime, she has first-hand knowledge of the invaluable tool of getting a performance up and running in front of an audience. "It's a trial and error thing," King said. "Art doesn't exist in a vacuum. That's the only way you can polish an act. There's always room for growth and refinement."

To that end, starting in October 2003, King began producing a weekly showcase she calls The New York Solo Play Lab at the Where Eagles Dare Theatre. Each week the lab offers four to six performers the opportunity to work on their solo pieces at no cost to them.

"I definitely believe I

fill a profound need. When a solo performer is on their own, they have to find a theater and somehow manage to pay for it. Then they've got to worry about sound, finding a lighting person, and promoting the show. After a while, you're spending all your time being the producer, and your creative functions have been shut out of the equation."

Taking a break from her busy schedule, King met me at a Union Square coffee shop where she explained how the concept of the lab came to be. "I got the idea while working on my own show, *Not a Nice Girl*. The process of getting a show on its feet means you have to do it a lot of times," she said. "You've got to do it in increments, and finally, you've got to do the whole thing, and finding a place to do the show is hard."

Having done the legwork of production herself, King knows the value of letting someone else take the reins.

"In the lab, the stage is set up and broken down, the program has been printed with the names and bios of the performers, and there's a lighting person who works with the actors and/or directors. . . . The performers can just show up and perform."

Paul Ricciardi is one of the many solo performers who have brought their acts to the lab to hone their skills. A recent transplant to New York City, he began looking for a place to perform Moving Vehicles, a solo show he's been working on for two years. In those two years, his show has been done at festivals and other venues, and it continues to evolve. After coming across her postcard at Drama Book Shop, Ricciardi got in touch with King via e-mail. He told her about his show and sent her a press packet, which got him a performance spot at the lab.

"She's [King] very efficient. She has her act together. I am so impressed. She's got a million things going on; it's amazing. She does the Solo Play Lab, she has her own solo show, she teaches, she's doing the Vagina Monologues right now, and the other day I picked up this newspaper called *The Soul of the American Actor* and she had a big article in it. What does this woman not do? And what is really key

is that Cheryl coproduces it. I mean, I do a lot of my own press, but the fact that Cheryl prints the postcards, Cheryl gets the space, Cheryl gets the tech person. That is so valuable because that stuff is a pain in the butt — a huge pain in the butt. So to have someone who does all that really makes life a lot easier. Self-producing stinks."

King said her hunch for the value of a place like the lab has been answered in the form of a nearly full house each week. "The solo show is an up-and-coming form. Actors and writers are getting tired of begging for an opportunity to show that they know what they are doing. So people are getting very entrepreneurial about art, and I think it's a very good sign of growth in an industry that's been cheapened by crappy blockbuster movies that cater to the lowest common denominator, or the fact that theater has gotten so expensive that you can't do it anymore. Well, artists are finding that there's a way you can do it yourself. Kind of like a vegetable stand on the side of the road. I'm going to do it myself — by God!

"The reason we can afford to do this is because we make the money at the door. We ask our performers to guarantee three audience members, and that goes to cover the cost of the theater and all of our various expenses." Each act is requested to bring three audience members whose admission will cost $15 each.

And while the lab isn't making her a rich woman, King says she is deeply satisfied with its success. Citing a woman who took advantage of the Lab earlier in the year, Cheryl beams with pride. "She developed it to the point with us that she could take it out there on tour, and she's doing very well. Because of what she did in New York, she got it solid enough that she said, 'I'm going to take this on tour.'"

As word gets out and more people approach her with their acts, King says she is thinking about expanding the Lab to include a second night. In the meantime, performers like Riccciardi said he has made minor nips and tucks to his script and that his show has improved. "Just in the one time that I've been to the Solo Lab, I feel like I am tapping into a new community — a creative, artistic community."

Where Eagles Dare Theatre
347 W. 36th Street
For more information on the New York Solo Play Lab, go to www.CherylKing Productions.com.

Other Rehearsal Spaces

Abazaid Arts
107 Grand Street, 2nd Floor
New York, NY 10013
(212) 941-8480

Alvin Ailey Studios
211 W. 61st Street,
3rd Floor
New York, NY 10023
(212) 767-0590
Fax: (212) 767-0625
www.alvinailey. org

American Theatre of Actors
314 W. 54th Street
New York, NY 10019
(212) 581-3044

Atlantic Acting School
453 W. 16th Street
New York, NY 10011
(212) 691-5919

Ballet Hispanico
167 W. 89th Street
New York, NY 10024
(212) 362-6710
Fax: (212) 362-7809
E-mail: info@ballethispani-co.org
www.ballethispanico.org

The Basement Space
102 W. 75th Street
New York, NY 10023
(212) 501-7776
E-mail: carolfoxprescott@aol.com
www.carolfoxprescott.com

The Bridge for Dance Space
2726 Broadway
New York, NY 10024
(212) 749-1165

CAP 21 Studios
18 W. 18th Street, 6th Floor
New York, NY 10011
(212) 807-0202
Fax: (212) 807-0166
www.cap21.org

Champions Studios
257 W. 39th Street,
14th Floor
New York, NY 10018
(212) 307-7707

Chelsea Studios
151 W. 26th Street,
6th Floor
New York, NY 10001
(212) 924-5877
www.TheatreWorksUSA.org/chelsea_rates.cfm

City Center Studios
130 W. 56th Street
New York, NY 10019
(212) 247-0430
E-mail: thtr@citycenter.org
www.citycenter.org

Dance Center 21
21 E. 26th Street
New York, NY 10010
(212) 481-8342
E-mail: dancenter21@hotmail.com

Dance New York
237 W. 54th Street,
3rd Floor
New York, NY 10019
(212) 246-5797
E-mail: info@dancenewyork.com
www.dancenew york.com

Dick Shea Spaces
69 W. 14th Street, 4th Floor
New York, NY 10011
(212) 229-1631

Empire Dance Studios
127 W. 25th Street
New York, NY 10001
(212) 645-2441
E-mail: info@empirdance.com
www.empiredance.com

Harlerquin Studios
203 W. 46th Street,
2nd Floor
New York, NY 10036
(212) 819-0120

**Inerterboro
Repertory Theatre (IRT)**
154 Christopher Street
New York, NY 10012
(212) 206-6875
Fax: (212) 206-7037
E-mail: irtonline@yahoo.com
www.irt.dream host.com

Kingsley Studios
250 W. 54th Street,
4th Floor
New York, NY 10019
(212) 307-6909

Lotus Arts Dance Studio
109 W. 27th Street,
8th Floor
New York, NY 10001
(212) 627-1076
E-mail: info@lotusarts.com
www.lotusarts.com/
studiorental.htm

Manhattan Motion
215 W. 76th Street,
4th Floor
New York, NY 10023
(212) 724-1673
E-mail: info@manhattan
motion.com
www.manhattanmotion.com

Morocco
6 W. 20th Street, 2nd Floor
New York, NY 10011
(212) 727-8326
E-mail: morocco@casbah
dance.org
www.casbahdance.org

Musical Theatre Works
440 Lafayette Street
New York, NY 10003
(212) 677-0040
Fax: (212) 598–0105
E-mail: reception@
mtwnyc.org
www.mtwnyc.org

**New Dance
Group Studios**
254 W. 47th Street
New York, NY 10036
(212) 719-2733
Fax: (212) 719-0457
E-mail: mburns@ndg.org
www.ndg.org

**New York Spaces
(3 locations)**
(212) 799-5433
Fax: (917) 464-8920
E-mail: nyspaces@
monmouth.com
www.newyorkspaces.com

Eighth Avenue Studios
939 8th Ave.
New York, NY 10019
(212) 799-5433

Ripley/Grier Studios
520 8th Ave.
New York, NY 10018
(212) 799-5433

West 72nd Street Studios
131 W. 72nd St.
New York, NY 10023
(212) 799-5433

Nola Sound Studio
250 W. 54th Street
New York, NY 10019
(212) 582-1417

Philip Stark Studio
231 W. 29th Street,
10th Floor
New York, NY 10001
(212) 868-5555
E-mail: info@2stopsbrighter.com
www.2stopsbrighter.com

Producers Club Theatres
358 W. 44th Street
New York, NY 10036
(212) 315-4743

Sandra Cameron
20 Cooper Square,
6th Floor
(212) 674-0505
E-mail: info@sandra
cameron.com
www.sandracameron.com

Shetler Studios
939 Eighth Avenue
New York, NY 10019
(212) 246-6655
Fax: (212) 262-3668

**Source of Life
Conference Center**
22 W. 34th Street, 5th Floor
New York, NY 10001
(212) 244-5888
1-888-844-5888
Fax: (212) 594-0152
E-mail: solctr@aol.com
www.sourceoflifecenter.com

Stepping Out Studios
37 W. 26th Street, 9th Floor
New York, NY 10010
(646) 742-9400
Fax: (646) 742-0681
E-mail: info@steppingout
studios.com
www.steppingoutstudios.com

Steps Studio, Inc.
2121 Broadway, 3rd Floor
New York, NY 10023
(212) 874-2410
Fax: (212) 787-2449
E-mail: info@stepsnyc.com
www.stepsnyc. com

Three of Us Studios
39 W. 19th Street,
12th Floor
New York, NY 10011
(212) 645-0030
Fax: (212) 645- 0039

The Tribeca Playhouse
111 Reade Street
New York, NY 10007
(212) 571-1576
Fax: (212) 571-1585

West Side Dance Project
357 W. 36th Street,
3rd Floor
New York, NY 10018
(212) 563-6781
Fax: same as above
E-mail: info@joria
productions.com
www.joriaproductions.com

York Theatre Company
(Theater at St. Peter's Church)
619 Lexington Avenue
New York, NY 10022
(212) 935-5824
Fax: (212) 832-0037
E-mail: sdelacruz@york
theatre.org
www.yorktheatre.org

20.
PERFORMANCE
RENTAL SPACE

Note: When you call for
prices, make sure to ask
if insurance is required
and whether it is includ-
ed in the rental fee.

**Abingdon Theatre
(2 spaces)**
312 W. 36th Street,
1st Floor
New York, NY 10018
(212) 868-2055
Fax: (212) 868-2056
E-mail: atcnyc@aol.com
www.abingdon-nyc.org

June Havoc Theatre
Stage: proscenium
Seating Capacity: 98

Stage II Theatre
Seating Capacity: 56, flexible seating

Access Theatre
380 Broadway, 4th Floor
New York, NY 10013
(212) 966-1047
E-mail: accesstd@verizon.net
www.accesstheater.com

Stage: Black box
Seating Capacity: 50 fixed
seats, optional row of 10
loose seats. 60 with loose
seating

**Actors Theatre
Workshop**
145 W. 28th Street
New York, NY 10011
(212) 947-1386
Fax: (212) 947-0642
Stage: 3 studios
Seating Capacity: 30 to 40
each studio

Altered Stages
212 W. 29th Street,
2nd Floor
New York, NY 10001
(212) 712-8712
Fax: (212) 465-0575
www.29thstreetrep.com
Stage: Black box; 22 by
20 ft.
Seating Capacity: 75

**American Place Theatre
(4 spaces)**
314 W. 54th Street
New York, NY 10019
(212) 581-3044

Beckmann Theatre
Stage: 17 by 18 ft. with
13-ft. ceilings
Seating Capacity: 40

Chernuchin Theatre
Stage: 45 by 22 ft. with
24-ft. ceilings
Seating Capacity: 140

Outdoor Theatre
Stage: 20 by 20 ft.
Seating Capacity: 60

Sargeant Theatre
Stage: 22 by 22 ft. with
22-ft. ceilings
Seating Capacity: 65

**The Arthur Seelan
Studio Theatre**
(Drama Book Shop)
259 W. 40th Street
New York, NY 10018
(212) 944-0595, ext. 416

Stage: Modified black box;
35 by 17 ft.

**Atlantic Theater
Company**
336 W. 20th Street
New York, NY 10011
(212) 645-8015
Fax: (212) 645-8755
Stage: Modular, removable
stage, 29 by 30 ft.
Seating Capacity: 165

Bat Theatre Company
41 White Street
New York, NY 10013
(212) 226-2407
Stage: Open architecture
box with painted walls
Seating Capacity: Flexible

Bouwerie Lane Theatre
330 Bowery
New York, NY 10012
(212) 677-0060
Stage: Proscenium, with a
raked stage
Seating Capacity: 140

Café Carlye
35 E. 76th Street
New York, NY 10021

Center Stage Theatre
48 W. 21st Street, 4th Floor
New York, NY 10010
(212) 929-2228
Stage: Black box
Seating Capacity: 74

**Chelsea Studios
(Theatreworks USA)**
151 W. 26th Street,
6th Floor
New York, NY 10001
(212) 647-1100
www.chelseastudios.org
Stage: Studios; 40 by 28 ft.
to 19 by 14 ft.

Cherry Lane Theatre
38 Commerce Street
New York, NY 10014
(212) 989-2020
Stage: Proscenium
Seating Capacity: 178

Chicago City Limits
1105 First Avenue
New York, NY 10021
1-888-5233
Stage: Proscenium
Seating Capacity: 190

Clemente Soto Velez Cultural Center (3 spaces)
107 Suffolk Street
New York, NY 10002
(212) 260-4080, ext. 11

Flamboyan
Chairs on risers.

Milagro
Chairs on risers

La Tea
Chairs on risers

Common Basis Theatre
750 Eighth Avenue,
Room 500
New York, NY 10036
(212) 563-0152
Stage: Black box
Seating Capacity: 50

The Connelly Theatre (2 spaces)
220 E. 4th Street
New York, NY 10009
(212) 982-3995

Connelly
Stage: Raised

Metropolitan
Seating Capacity: 51

Creative Acting Company
122 W. 26th Street
New York, NY 10001
(212) 352-2103
Fax: (212) 352-2076
www.creativeacting
company.com
Stage: Black box
Seating Capacity: 40

Creative Place Theatre
750 Eighth Avenue, #602
New York, NY 10036
(212) 388-2772

Stage: Black box
Seating Capacity: 55 to 60

Dance Theatre Workshop
219 W. 19th Street
New York, NY 10011
(212) 691-6500, ext. 204
Studios: 2
Stage: Black box
Seating Capacity: 192

Danny's Skylight Room
346 W. 46th Street
New York, NY 10014

Dick Shea's Spaces
69 W. 14th Street
New York, NY 10011
(212) 229-1631
Studios: 6; 20 by 40 ft. to
25 by 60 ft.

Dillon's Theater
245 W. 54th Street
New York, NY 10019

Don't Tell Mama
343 W. 46th Street
New York, NY 10036

Douglas Fairbanks Theatre
(see also John Houseman Theatre)
432 W. 42nd Street
New York, NY 10036
(212) 967-9077
Stage: Proscenium
Seating Capacity: 287
Studios: 2 black box studios available with seating capacities of 50 and 74

The Duke on 42nd Street
229 W. 42nd Street,
2nd Floor
New York, NY 10036
(646) 223-3042
E-mail: dukeinfo@new42.org
www.duke.new42.org
Stage: Black box
Seating Capacity: 199

Duplex Cabaret Theatre
61 Christopher Street
New York, NY 10014
(212) 989-3015
Stage: Cabaret
Seating Capacity: 70

Emerging Artists Theatre
432 W. 42nd Street,
4th Floor
(212) 594-1404
E-mail: eattheatre@aol.com
www.eatheatre.org
Stage: Black box; 17 by
20 ft.
Seating Capacity: 40

Ensemble Studio Theatre (EST)
549 W. 52nd Street
New York, NY 10019
(212) 247-4982
www.ensemblestudiotheatre.
org
Stage: Black box
Seating Capacity: 99

Evolving Arts Theatre at Dance Space Center
451 Broadway, 2nd Floor
New York, NY 10013
(212) 625-8369
Stage: Black box
Seating Capacity: 90

Fez (Time Café)
61 Christopher Street
New York, NY 10014

45th Street Theatre
354 W. 45th Street
New York, NY 10036
(212) 333-4052
www.NYTheatre. com/
primary.htm
Stage: Raked proscenium
Seating Capacity: 99

Gene Frankel Studio
24 Bond Street
New York, NY 10012
(212) 777-1767
Stage: Black box
Seating Capacity: 74

Gramercy Theatre
127 E. 23rd Street
New York, NY 10010
(212) 459-3000
Stage: Proscenium
Seating Capacity: 499

Greenwich House Theatre
27 Barrow Street
New York, NY 10014
(212) 243-6262
Stage: Proscenium
Seating Capacity: 99

Greenwich Street Theatre
547 Greenwich Street
New York, NY 10013
(212) 255-3940
www.greenwichstreet.com
Stage: Black box
(proscenium possible)
Seating Capacity: 74

Grove Street Playhouse
39 Grove Street
New York, NY 10014
(212) 741-6434
Stage: Black box
Seating Capacity: 74

Henry Street Settlement
466 Grand Street
New York, NY 10002
(212) 598-0440
www.HenryStreetArts.com
Stages: Black box (has three spaces, including proscenium stage and recital hall)
Seating Capacity: 150

HERE Arts Center (3 spaces)
145 Sixth Avenue
New York, NY 10013
(212) 647-0202, ext. 310
www.here.org

MAINSTAGE Theatre
Stage: 45 by 40 ft.
Seating Capacity: 99

Dorothy B. Williams
Stage: Raised; 18 by 32 ft.
Seating Capacity: 74

Performance Club
Stage: Raised; 16 by 16 ft.
Seating Capacity: 99

Horsetrade Theater Group (3 spaces)
85 E. 4th Street (office)
New York, NY 10003
(212) 777-6088
www.horsetrade.info

St. Marks Theatre
94 St. Mark's Place
New York, NY 10009
Seating Capacity: 50,
L-shaped seating around stage

Kraine Theatre
85 E. 4th Street
New York, NY 10003
Stage: Black Box
Seating Capacity: 50 to 60

Red Room Theatre
85 E. 4th Street
New York, NY 10003

Hudson Guild Theatre Company
Fulton Center
119 Ninth Avenue
New York, NY 10011
(212) 924-6710
Fax: (212) 924-6872
E-mail: info@hudsonguild.org
www.hudsonguild.org
Stage: Proscenium
Seating Capacity: 107

Irish Arts Center
553 W. 51st Street
New York, NY 10019
(212) 757-3318, ext. 202
Stage: Proscenium
Seating Capacity: 99

Jane Street Theatre
(see also Westside Theatre)
Hotel Riverview
113 Jane Street
New York, NY 10014
(212) 315-2302
Stage: Proscenium
Seating Capacity: 280

John Houseman Theatre
(see also Douglas Fairbanks Theatre)
450 W. 42nd Street
New York, NY 10036
(212) 967-9077
Stage: Proscenium
Seating Capacity: 287
Studios: 2 black box studios with seating capacities of 50 and 74

Joyce Soho
(see Joyce Theatre below)
155 Mercer Street
New York, NY 10012
(212) 431-9233
E-mail: staff@joyce.org
www.joyce.org
Stage: Open space
Seating Capacity: 94

The Joyce Theatre
175 Eighth Avenue
New York, NY 10011
(212) 691-9740
E-mail: staff@joyce.org
www.joyce.org
Stage: Proscenium
Seating Capacity: 472
Note: Booking by application in the fall prior to season. This theater is strictly for dance.

Kaufman Cultural Center (2 spaces)
(see also Lucy Moses School)
129 W. 67th Street
New York, NY 10023
(212) 501-3308
E-mail: info@kaufman-center.org
www.ekcc.org

Merkin Concert Hall
Seating Capacity: 450

Ann Goodman Hall (recital)
Seating Capacity: 100

Kingsley Studios
244-250 W. 54th Street
New York, NY 10019
(212) 307-6909
Studios: 2; 24 by 12 ft. and 53 by 26 ft.

Lamb's Theatre
130 W. 44th Street
New York, NY 10036
(212) 575-0300, ext. 25
Stage: 2 spaces, 1 with
proscenium, 1 without
Seating Capacity: 349, 125

LaTEA Theatre
107 Suffolk Street, Suite 200
New York, NY 10002
(212) 529-1948
Fax: (212) 529-7362
E-mail: info@teatrolatea.com
www.teatrolatea.com
Stage: Flexible
Seating Capacity: 74

Looking Glass Theatre
422 W. 57th Street
New York, NY 10019
(212) 307-9467
E-mail: LGTheatre@aol.com
www.thelooking glass
theatre.homestead.com
Stage: Black box
Seating Capacity: 60

Lucy Moses School
129 W. 67th Street
New York, NY 10023
(212) 501-3360

MAP Penthouse Theatre
127 Fulton Street, Penthouse
New York, NY 10038
(212) 571-6644
E-mail: mappenthouse@
yahoo.com
www.mappenthouse.com
Stage: 2 studios, 1 theater,
lots of outdoor space—
approx. 4,000 sq. ft. total

**Marymount
Manhattan Theatre**
221 E. 71st Street
New York, NY 10021
(212) 774-0765
Stage: Proscenium
Seating Capacity: 249

**Merce Cunningham
Studio Theatre**
55 Bethune Street
New York, NY 10014
(212) 691-9751, ext. 37
www.merce.org

Stage: Open space
Seating Capacity: 100

Michael Carson Studios
250 W. 54th Street,
10th Floor
New York, NY 10019
(212) 765-2300
www.nycastings.com
Stage: black box; 20 by
20 ft.
Seating Capacity: 37
Studios: 2; 20 by 30 ft.

The Mint Theatre
311 W. 43rd Street,
5th Floor
New York, NY 10036
(212) 315-9434
Fax: (212) 977-5211
E-mail: rental@minttheater.
org
www.minttheater.org
Stage: Black box
Seating Capacity: 82

Mulberry Street Theatre
70 Mulberry Street
New York, NY 10013
(212) 349-0126
Fax: (212) 349-0494
E-mail: info@htchendance.
org
www.htchendance.org
Stage: Black box
Seating Capacity: 70

Musical Theatre Works
440 Lafayette Street
New York, NY 10003
(212) 677-0040
Stage: Black box
Seating Capacity: 30 to 60
Studios: 14

New Actors Workshop
259 W. 30th Street,
2nd Floor
New York, NY 10001
(212) 947-1310
1-800-947-1318
Fax: (212) 947-9729
E-mail: newactorsw@aol.com
www.newactorsworkshop.
com
Stage: Open space
Seating Capacity: 60

**New York Spaces (3 lo-
cations, 39 studios)**
(main office)
131 W. 72nd Street
New York, NY 10023
(212) 799-5433
www.newyorkspaces.com
Stages: 10 by 10 ft. to 23
by 54 ft.

W. 72nd Street Studios
131 W. 72nd Street
New York, NY 10023
(212) 799-5433

Ripley-Grier Studios
520 Eighth Avenue
New York, NY 10018
(212) 799-5433

8th Avenue Studios
939 Eighth Avenue
New York, NY 10019
(212) 397-1313

**New York Theatre
Workshop**
79 E. 4th Street
New York, NY 10003
Stage: Proscenium
Seating Capacity: 150

Nola Rehearsal Studios
250 W. 54th Street,
11th Floor
New York, NY 10019
(212) 582-1417
Studios: 6; 9 by 19 ft. to
21 by 43 ft.

Orpheum Theatre
126 Second Avenue
New York, NY 10003
(212) 477-2477
Stage: Proscenium
Seating Capacity: 350

Pantheon Theatre
303 W. 42nd Street,
Suite 201
New York, NY 10036
(212) 957-6348
www.pantheonproductions.
com
Stages: 2; 13 by 15 ft.,
20 by 22 ft.
Seating Capacity: 75, 99

Pelican Studio Theatre
750 Eighth Avenue
New York, NY 10027
(212) 730-2030
Stage: Black box
Seating Capacity: 60

**Phil Bosakowski
Theatre (2 spaces)**
354 W. 45th Street,
2nd Floor
New York, NY 10036
(212) 352-3101
www.primarystages.com
Stage: 21 by 18.8 ft.
Seating Capacity: 47

45th Street Theater
Stage: black box, raked
proscenium, 21.5 by 20 ft.
Seating Capacity: 99

Players Theatre
115 MacDougal Street
New York, NY 10012
(212) 254-8138
Seating: 248

Producers Club Theatre
358 W. 44th Street
New York, NY 10036
(212) 315-4743
Stages: 5; 4 prosceniums,
one three-quarter thrust
Seating Capacity: (theaters)
30,50, 77, 99, 120
Studios: 4

Pulse Ensemble Theatre
432 W. 42nd Street
New York, NY 10036
(212) 695-1596
www.pulseensembletheatre.
org
Stages: Black box and
cabaret space
Seating Capacity: 55

Raw Space Theatre
529 W. 42nd Street
New York, NY 10036
(212) 643-6399
Stages: 5 black box theaters
Seating Capacity: 19 to 80

**The Riant Theatre
(2 spaces)**
P.O. Box 1902
New York, NY 10013
(646) 623-3488
E-mail: TheRiantTheatre@
aol.com
www.therianttheatre.com
Stage: Flexible
Seating Capacity: 67

Saint Michael's Hall
225 W. 99th Street
New York, NY 10025
(212) 222-2700
Seating Capacity: 110

**Sanford Meisner
Theatre**
164 Eleventh Avenue (bet.
22nd and 23rd Sts.)
New York, NY 10011
(212) 206-1764
Stage: Black box but with
formal raked seating
Seating Capacity: 74

**The School for Film &
Television/Three of
Us Studios (2 locations)**
39 W. 19th Street,
12th Floor
New York, NY 10011

30 W. 24th Street,
2nd Floor
New York, NY
(212) 645-0030
Studios: 12; 10 by 14 ft. to
42 by 18 ft.

**78th Street Theatre Lab
(2 spaces)**
236 W. 78th Street
New York, NY 10024
(212) 873-9050
Fax: (212) 873-1156
www.78thstreettheatrelab.
org

2nd floor theater
Studio Workshop Theater
Stage: Black box, 20 by
30 ft.
Seating Capacity: 30

3rd floor theater
Stage: Fully equipped
theater, 23 by 30 ft.
Seating Capacity: 60

**Shakespearewright's
Players Theatre**
115 MacDougal Street
New York, NY 10012
(212) 254-8138
Stage: Proscenium
Seating Capacity: 248

**Signature Theatre
Company**
Peter Norton Space (bet.
10th and 11th Aves.)
555 W. 42nd Street
New York, NY 10036
(212) 967-1913
Fax: (212) 714-9083
www.signaturetheatre.org
Stage: Proscenium
Seating Capacity: 166

SoHo Playhouse
15 Vandam Street
New York, NY 10013
(212) 315-0800, ext. 217
1-800-251-2185
www.sohoplayhouse.com
Stage: Proscenium
Seating Capacity: 199

The Tenement Theatre
97 Orchard Street
New York, NY 10002
(212) 431-0233
www.tenement.org
Stage: Tenement space
Seating Capacity: 60
(American historical and
immigrant theme productions
sought.)

Theatre at St. Clements
423 W. 46th Street
New York, NY 10036
(212) 246-7277
Stage: Black box
Seating Capacity: 60

Theatre at West Park Church
165 W. 86th Street
New York, NY 10024
(212) 946-5321
Stage: Open space
Seating Capacity: 350

Theatre 80
80 St. Marks Place
New York, NY 10003
(212) 505-3401
www.pearltheatre.org
Stage: Proscenium
Seating Capacity: 160

Theatre for the New City (4 spaces)
155 First Avenue
New York, NY 10003
(212) 254-1109
Fax: (212) 979-6570
E-mail: info@theaterforthe
newcity.net
www.theaterforthenewcity.
net
Stages: All black box

Joyce and Seard Johnson
Theater
Seating Capacity: 270

Cino Theater
Seating Capacity: 99

Community Space Theater
Seating Capacity: 99

Cabaret Theater
Seating Capacity: 65

Theatre Row Studios
410 W. 42nd Street
New York, NY 10036
(212) 645-0030

Theatre 3
311 W. 43rd Street
New York, NY 10036
(212) 246-5877
Fax: (212) 246-5882
www.thedirectorscompany.
org
Stage: Black box
Seating Capacity: 96

Triad Theatre
158 W. 72nd Street
New York, NY 10023
(212) 877-7176
www.triadnyc.com
Stage: Black box with
elevated stage
Seating Capacity: 130

Trilogy Theatre
341 W. 44th Street
New York, NY 10036
Stage: Black box
Seating Capacity: 70

Union Square Theatre
100 E. 17th Street
New York, NY 10003
(212) 505-0700
Stage: Proscenium
Seating Capacity: 499

Vineyard Theatre
108 E. 15th Street
New York, NY 10003
(212) 353-3366
Fax: (212) 353-3803
www.vineyardtheatre.org
Stage: proscenium
Seating Capacity: 129

Washington Square Methodist Church Sanctuary
135 W. 4th Street
New York, NY 10012
(212) 777-2528
Stage: Church sanctuary
Seating Capacity: 200

Westside Dance Project
357 W. 36th St.
New York, NY 10018
(212) 563-6781
Studios: 3; 400 sq. ft. to
900 sq. ft.

Westside Theatre (2 spaces)
(see also Jane Street Theatre)
407 W. 43rd Street
New York, NY 10036
Stages: 2, both proscenium
Seating Capacity: 299, 250

Wings Theatre
154 Christopher Street
New York, NY 10014
(212) 627-2960
Fax: (212) 462-0024
E-mail: jcorrick@wings
theatre.com
www.wingstheatre.com
Stage: Proscenium
Seating Capacity: 74

Women's Project Theatre
424 W. 55th Street
New York, NY 10019
(212) 765-1706
www.womensproject.org
Stage: Proscenium
Seating Capacity: 199 to
250

York Theatre Company
(Theater at St. Peter's Church)
619 Lexington Avenue
New York, NY 10022
(212) 935-5824
Stage: Adaptable
proscenium/thrust
Seating Capacity: 147

getting it together

21. RÉSUMÉ SERVICES

Most actors prepare their own résumés, or their agency does it for them. But if you need some help, here are a few places to try:

Bruce Johnson Photography/ Graphic Design
(212) 568-7949 studio
(917) 806-0122 mobile
E-mail: bjohnsonphotos@ mac.com
www.brucealanjohnson.com
Résumés , commercial photography, graphic design, headshots, CD design.

Career Pro New York
3380 Sheridan Drive, #252
Amherst, NY 14226
(905) 828-0599
(866) 433-6033
Fax: (212) 202-4882
E-mail: info@rezcoach.com
www.rezcoach.com
Résumés, job and career transition coach.

Compu-Craft Business Services
124 E. Lexington Avenue, Suite 403
New York, NY 10016
(212) 451-0471
www.resumejumpstart.com

Gilbert Career Resumes
(212) 661-6878
1-888-Resume-2
Fax: (212) 661-7595
E-mail: gilcareer@aol.com
www.resumepro.com
Professional résumé writing and job search support.

Millennium Personnel Corporation
12 W. 37th Street, Suite 1203
New York, NY 10018
(212) 244-2777
Fax: (212) 244-1551
www.mpc-nyc.com
Full-service staffing company: résumés, cover letters and placement.

The Resume Shop
116 University Place, 2nd Floor
New York, NY 10003
(212) 206-8569
Fax: (212) 206-1368
E-mail: service@theresume shop.com
www.theresumeshop.com
Résumés, cover letters, and other business communication.

Resumes for Actors (division of Professional Resumes, Inc.)
60 E. 42nd Street, Suite 839
New York, NY 10165
(212) 697-1282
1-800-221-4425
Fax: (212) 867-8971
E-mail: info@resumesfor actors.com
www.resumesforactors.com
Résumés, cover letters, bios and more.

Talent Search at Shakespeare Mailing
311 W. 43rd Street, 4th Floor
New York, NY 10036
(212) 560-8958
1-888-4-EASY-MAIL
Fax: (212) 560-8959
E-mail: support@shakespeare mailing.com

www.shakespearemailing.
com
Résumés, cover letters, mail-
ings, postcard messages,
headshot reproductions,
headshot postcards. Stores
headshots and résumés on-
line so you can download
and print from any computer.
Allows casting agents to peruse headshots online for
casting needs.

Winning Resumes/
Matt Greene
(718) 435-8036
Fax: (718) 435-7491
E-mail: mattgreene@aol.com
www.winning-resumes.com
Résumés.

22.
ANSWERING
SERVICES AND
PAGERS

Liz's Spotlight
On: Message
Bureau Inc.

Is your phone ringing
off the hook? Need that
script faxed over right
away so you can ready
yourself for your up-
coming appearance on
Law and Order? Do
you want to run to the
gym to get some exer-
cise, but you're afraid
to leave your phone be-
cause your answering
machine is on the
blink?

By the time you get
to this section, hopeful-
ly you are so busy audi-
tioning that you need
some assistance in the
business end of your

acting career. To help
with that, Message Bu-
reau Inc. is one place
you can turn. Business
correspondence such as
call handling, voice
mail, and faxing are es-
sential to any business,
and the business of
your acting career
should be no exception.
Since 1991, Message
Bureau Inc. has been
providing service to the
New York City area
businesses to provide a
professional image us-
ing live operators who
work as office assis-
tants to help you get a
handle on your busi-
ness, depending on
your individual needs.

Message Bureau Inc.
(212) 255-3155
www.messagebureau.com

Other
Answering
Services

Aardvark Answering
Service
1501 Broadway
New York, NY 10036
(212) 626-9000

ABCO Mail and Typing
Service
60 E. 42nd Street, Suite
1166
New York, NY 10165
(212) 697-1360
Fax: (212) 986-8731
www.abcoservice.
webatonce.com
Live Operator answering
service, mailboxes, and
more.

Actorfone
545 Eighth Avenue,
Room 401
New York, NY 10018
(212) 502-0666
E-mail: info@efls.net
www.efls.com

Aerobeep and
Voicemail Services
244 Fifth Avenue (bet. 27th
and 28th Sts.)
New York, NY 10001
(212) 679-0000
E-mail: service@nymail.com
www.nymail.com
Voice mail with paging or
e-mail delivery, mail, fax,
and more.

Bells Are Ringing
545 Eighth Avenue, Suite
401
New York, NY 10018
(212) 714-3888
Answering service, voice
mail, pager, fax, and more.

Blask Answering
Service
70-34A Austin Street
Forest Hills, NY 11375
1-800-369-1529
www.blaskanswering
service.com
Answering service

City Never Sleeps
545 Eighth Avenue,
Suite 401
New York, NY 10018
(212) 714-5500
Answering service, voice
mail, mail, and more.

EFLS
545 Eighth Avenue, Suite
401
New York, NY 10018
(212) 330-0300
E-mail: info@efls.net
www.efls.com
Answering service, pagers,
mail, fax, and more

EGIX
853 Broadway, Suite 1516,
New York, NY 10003
(212) 420-8200
Answering service, pagers,
mail, and more.

Empire Paging Group
230 Grand Street
New York, NY 10013
(212) 625-1199

**Encore Answering
Service**
250 W. 54th Street,
Suite 800
New York, NY 10019
(212) 489-1300

Message Bureau
80 Fifth Avenue
New York, NY 10011
(212) 255-3155
Fax: (212) 255-4015
E-mail: sales@message
bureau.com
www.messagebureau.com

**Messages Plus
Corporation**
1317 Third Avenue
New York, NY 10021
(212) 879-4144
1-800-776-4448
E-mail: dean@mpcallcenters.
com
www.mpcallcenters.com

**Procommunications/
Signius**
445 W. 45th Street
New York, NY 10036
(212) 245-4900
1-800-744-6487
www.signius.com
Live answering service, mail
service, voice mail, 1-800-
services.

23. FAX
SERVICES AND
MAIL BOXES

Fax and Mail
Services

**ABCO Mail and
Typing Service**
60 E. 42nd Street,
Suite 1166
New York, NY 10165
(212) 697-1360
Fax: (212) 986-8731C
www.abcoservice.
webatonce.com
Live operator answering
service, mailboxes and
more.

**Aerobeep and
Voicemail Services**
244 Fifth Avenue
New York, NY 10001
(212) 679-0000
E-mail: service@nymail.com
www.nymail.com
Voice mail with paging or
email delivery, mail, fax,
and more.

Bells Are Ringing
545 Eighth Avenue,
Suite 401
New York, NY 10018
(212) 714-3888
Answering service, voice
mail, pager, fax, and more.

City Never Sleeps
545 Eighth Avenue,
Suite 401
New York, NY 10018
(212) 714-5500
Answering service, voice
mail, mail, and more.

EFLS
545 Eighth Avenue, #401
New York, NY 10018
(212) 330-0300
E-mail: info@efls.net
www.efls.com
Answering service, pagers,
mail, fax, and more.

**Kinkos (several
locations)**
Faxing, photocopies,
computer services, and
more.
www.kinkos. com

1211 6th Avenue
New York, NY 10036
(212) 391-2679
Fax: (212) 391-0263
E-mail: usa0264@kinkos.com

641 Lexington Avenue
(at 54th St.)
New York, NY 10022
(212) 572-9995
Fax: (212) 572-9994
E-mail: usa0876@kinkos.com

747 Third Avenue
(at 47th St.)
New York, NY 10017
(212) 753-7778
Fax: (212) 753-7779
E-mail: usa0896@kinkos.com

650 Sixth Avenue (at
20th St.)
New York, NY 10011
(646) 638-9238
Fax: (646) 638-9239
E-mail: usa0904@kinkos.com

100 Wall Street
(bet. Pine and Wall Sts.)
New York, NY 10005
(212) 269-0024
Fax: (212) 269-1225
E-mail: usa0346@kinkos.com

153 E. 53rd Street
(at Lexington Ave.)
New York, NY 10022
(212) 753-7580
Fax: (212) 753-7703
E-mail: usa0537@kinkos.com

240 Central Park South
(bet. 59th St. and Broadway)
New York, NY 10019
(212) 258-3750
Fax: (212) 258-3381
E-mail: usa0763@kinkos.com

221 W. 72nd Street
(at Broadway)
New York, NY 10023

(212) 362-5288
Fax: (212) 362-3546
E-mail: usa0812@kinkos.com

110 William Street
(bet. John and Fulton Sts.)
New York, NY 10038
(212) 766-4646
Fax: (212) 766-0938
E-mail: usa0883@kinkos.com

245 Seventh Avenue (at
24th St.)
New York, NY 10001
(212) 929-2679
Fax: (212) 929-1560
E-mail: usa0203@kinkos.com

250 E. Hudson Street (bet.
Aves.A and B.)
New York, NY 10002
(212) 253-9020
Fax: (212) 253-9029
E-mail: usa0267@kinkos.com

21 Astor Place (bet. Broad-
way and Lafayette St.)
New York, NY 10003
(212) 228-9511
Fax: (212) 228-9281
E-mail: usa0230@kinkos.com

105 Duane Street (bet.
Broadway and Church St.)
New York, NY 10007
(212) 406-1220
Fax: (212) 406-1216
E-mail: usa0231@kinkos.com

600 Third Avenue (at 39th
St.)
New York, NY 10016
(212) 599-2679
Fax: (21) 599-1733
E-mail: usa0268@kinkos.com

191 Madison Avenue (at
34th St.)
New York, NY 10016
(212) 685-3449
Fax: (212) 685-3831
E-mail: usa0202@kinkos.com

305 E. 46th Street (bet. 1st
and 2nd Aves.)
New York, NY 10017
(212) 319-6600
Fax: (212) 319-6991
E-mail: usa0266@kinkos.com

233 W. 54th Street (bet. 8th
and Broadway)
New York, NY 10019
(212) 977-2679
Fax: (212) 977-3089
E-mail: usa0265@kinkos.com

1122 Lexington Avenue (at
78th St.)
New York, NY 10021
(212) 628-5500
Fax: (212) 628-6703
E-mail: usa0219@kinkos.com

16 E. 52nd Street (bet. 5th
and Madison Aves.)
New York, NY 10022
(212) 308-2679
Fax: (212) 838-8065
E-mail: usa0212@kinkos.com

**Mail Boxes Etc. (several
locations)**
Mail services and copies.
Most Mail Boxes Etc.
have Fed Ex services,
some also have UPS.
They also offer notary
services. Hours vary, but
most are between 9 AM
and 7 PM.
www.mbe.com

350 Third Avenue (bet. 25th
and 26h Sts.)
New York, NY 10010
(212) 696-9250
Fax: (212) 696-9541
E-mail: mbe3467@mbemail.
com

4049 Broadway (bet. 170th
and 171st Sts.)
New York, NY 10032
(212) 795-1217
Fax: (212) 795-4286
E-mail: store4131@
theupsstore.com

2840 Broadway (bet. 110th
and 111th Sts.)
New York, NY 10025
(212) 865-9601
Fax: (212) 865-9611
E-mail: mbe1786@mbemail.
com

2565 Broadway (bet. 96th
and 97th Sts.)
New York, NY 10032
(212) 866-5511
Fax: (212) 866-5533
E-mail: mbe2992@mbemail.
com

676 Ninth Avenue (bet. 46th
and 47th Sts.)
New York, NY 10036
(212) 957-9090
Fax: (212) 957-9191
E-mail: mbe4086@mbemail.
com

163 Amsterdam Avenue (at
67th St.)
New York, NY 10023
(212) 595-5353
Fax: (212) 595-5353
E-mail: mbe0594@mbemail.
com

1710 First Avenue (bet. 88th
and 89th Sts.)
New York, NY 10128
(212) 423-5555
Fax: (212) 423-5706
E-mail: mbe3566@mbemail.
com

302A W. 12th Street (at 8th
Ave.)
New York, NY 10014
(212) 206-6996
Fax: (212) 206-7640
E-mail: mbe3854@mbemail.
com

666 Fifth Avenue (bet. 52nd
and 53rd Sts.)
New York, NY 10103
(212) 315-0228

954 Lexington Avenue (bet.
69th and 70th Sts.)
New York, NY 10021
(212) 288-4425
Fax: (212) 288-4826
E-mail: mbe@1223@mbe-
mail.com

244 Madison Avenue (bet.
37th and 38th Sts.)
New York, NY 10016
(212) 532-5590
Fax: (212) 532-5375

E-mail: mbe1492@mbe-mail.com

163 Third Avenue (at 16th St.)
New York, NY 10003
(212) 533-9100
Fax: (212) 533-9124
E-mail: mbe0490@mbemail.c om
(Only has UPS, no FedEx.)

168 Second Avenue (bet. 10th and 11th Sts.)
New York, NY 10003
(212) 673-6313
Fax: (212) 673-7141
E-mail: store3433@theupsstore.com

527 Third Avenue (at 35th St.)
New York, NY 10016
(212) 683-9634
Fax: (212) 683-9784
E-mail: mbe1227@mbemail.com

2124 Broadway (bet. 74th and 75th Sts.)
New York, NY 10023
(212) 877-1050

1202 Lexington Avenue (81st and 82nd Sts.)
New York, NY 10028
(212) 439-6104
Fax: (212) 439-6107
E-mail: mbe0523@mabemail.com

331 W. 57th Street (bet. 8th and 9th Aves.)
New York, NY 10019
(212) 489-8004
Fax: (212) 489-8011
E-mail: mbe1141@mbemail.com

459 Columbus Avenue (at 82nd St.)
New York, NY 10024
(212) 724-1600
Fax: (212) 724-1436
E-mail: mbe1343@mbemail.com

1173A Second Avenue (at 60th St.)
New York, NY 10021
(212) 832-1390
Fax: (212) 832-1586
E-mail: mbe0647@mbemail.com

1562 First Avenue (at 81st St.)
New York, NY 10028
(212) 861-0581
Fax: (212) 861-0588
E-mail: store1382@theupsstore.com

511 Sixth Avenue (at 14th St.)
New York, NY 10011
(212) 924-4002
Fax: (212) 924-4121
E-mail: mbe1844@mbemail.com

295 Greenwich Street (bet. Chambers and Warren Sts.)
New York, NY 10007
(212) 964-5528
Fax: (212) 964-5530
E-mail: mbe2038@mbemail.com

111 E. 14th Street (bet. 3rd and 4th Aves.)
New York, NY 10003
(212) 979-8785

217 E. 86th Street (bet. 2nd and 3rd Aves.)
New York, NY 10028
(212) 996-7900
Fax: (212) 996-9003
E-mail: store0515@the upsstore.com

24. PRINTING

Photos

ABC Pictures
1867 E. Florida Street
Springfield, MO
65803-4583
1-888-526-5336
www.abcpictures.com
These people are great! You have to wait a week or two because they are out of state, but the prices are fantastic. Call for a catalogue.

Alluring Images
208 W. 29th Street, Suite 408
New York, NY 10001
(212) 967-1610
Fax: (212) 967-6654
www.alluringimages.com

Chromazone Inc.
69 Leonard Street
New York, NY 10013
(212) 625-9666

Clone-A-Chrome
15 W. 20th Street
New York, NY 10011
(212) 206-1644
(866) 820-0722
Fax: (212) 206-1757
E-mail: info@cloneachrome.com
www.cloneachrome.com

Eye Max Photo Corporation
231 E. 53rd Street
New York, NY 10022
(212) 421-9472

First Street Photo
21 1st Street
New York, NY 10003
(212) 777-1186

Green Rhino Inc.
37 W. 28th Street
New York, NY 10001
(212) 686-0066

Ideal Photos of NYC
155 W. 46th Street
New York, NY 10036
(212) 575-0303
www.idealphotosofnyc.com

Image King Visual Solutions
222 E. 44th Street
New York, NY 10017
(212) 867-4747
Fax: (212) 867-0624

E-mail: info@imagekingvs.com
www.imagekingvs.com

JB Photos Services
307 W. 36th Street
New York, NY 10018
(212) 244-6959

Jellybean Photographics, Inc.
99 Madison Avenue
New York, NY 10016
(212) 679-4888
Fax: (212) 545-0986

Laumont Color Lab Co., Inc.
333 W. 52nd Street
New York, NY 10019
(212) 245-2113

Modernage Photo Labs
1150 Sixth Avenue
New York, NY 10030
(212) 997-1800
Fax: (212) 869-4796
www.modernage.com/headshots.htm

Northeastern Photo & Design
224 W. 30th Street,
11th Floor
New York, NY 10001
(212) 563-1646
www.nephotoanddesign.com

Precision Photos
750 Eighth Avenue (at 46th)
New York, NY 10036
(212) 302-2724
1-800-583-4077
Fax: (212) 302-2820
www.precisionphotos.com

Postcards

4over4
24-64 45th Street
Astoria, NY 11103
1-888-546-8374
E-mail: support@4over4.com
www.4over4.com

212-PostCard
121 Varick Street, 3rd Floor
New York, NY 10013
(212) 767-8227
www.212postcard.net

1-800-Postcards
121 Varick Street, 3rd Floor
New York, NY 10013
(212) 741-1070
Fax: (212) 741-1332
E-mail: info@1800postcards.com
www.1800postcards.com

Precision Photos
750 Eighth Avenue (at 46th)
New York, NY 10036
(212) 302-2724
1-800-583-4077
Fax: (212) 302-2820
www.precisionphotos.com

25. VIDEO DEMO AND DUPLICATION SERVICES

So you've done some TV or film, and you need to create a reel. Here are some people who can help you with that.

Akhnaton Films
1 Sickles Street, D14
New York, NY 10040
(646) 259-1880
E-mail: akhnaton@hotmail.com
http://akhnatonfilms.tripod.com
Directorial, videography, editorial, DVD authoring.

Bruce Johnson Photography/ Graphic Design
(212) 568-7949 (studio)
(917) 806-0122 (mobile)

E-mail: bjohnsonphotos@mac.com
www.brucealanjohnson.com
Demo reels, editing, titles, music.

C & L Video Services
22 Woodoak Lane
Huntington, NY 11743
1-800-570-3999
(631) 421-2847
Fax: (631) 421-2832
E-mail: clvideo@optonline.net
www.takeonenetwork.com
DVD and digital video services, video editing, video production services, photo and slide keepsakes.

Chromavision
49 W. 27th Street (6th Ave and Broadway)
New York, NY 10001
(212) 686-7366
Fax: (212) 686-7310
E-mail: info@chromavision.net
www.chromavision.net
Video editorial, sound design, graphics, duplication, DVD authoring, Web compressions, demos.

Classic Video Duplication (CVD)
463 Union Avenue
Westbury, NY 11590
1-800-227-1382
www.classicvideodubs.com
Videotape duplication, packaging, fulfillment and CD replication.

Editors Hideaway Inc.
219 E. 44th Street
New York, NY 10017
(212) 661-3607
DVD, AVID, duplication, graphics, multimedia services, audio recording.

ESPY Duplication
611 Broadway, Suite 708
New York, NY 10012
(212) 353-0362
1-800-735-6521
E-mail: info@espytv.com

www.espytv.com
Video duplication, standard conversions, digital editing, DVD mastering and duplications.

Globe Video Services, Inc.
286 Fifth Avenue (bet. 30th and 31st Sts.)
New York, NY 10001
(212) 695-6868
Editing, duplication, conversions, digital (CD and DVD), video production, animation, graphics, package design.

Image Video NY
356 7th Avenue, 2nd Floor (at 30th St.)
New York, NY 10001
(212) 594-8599
E-mail: ImageVideo@aol.com
www.ivny.tv
Video production, postproduction, duplication, digital encoding, Web design, motion graphics, A/V presentations.

Impact Showreels VMX Media Int'l.
285 W. Broadway
New York, NY 10013
(212) 334-2441
E-mail: info@impactshow reels.com
www.impactshowreels.com
Video demo, DVD, voiceover, Web site

Professional Tape Corporation
100 Pratt Oval
Glen Cove, NY 11542
(516) 656-5519
1-800-824-1851
Fax: (516) 656-5523
E-mail: questions@protapeco. com
www.protapeco.com
Small or large quantity dubs, conversion, duplication and packaging facility, film to tape/DVD transfer, tape to DVD transfer, custom length videotapes.

Tobin Productions, Inc.
1333 W. 19th Street
New York, NY 10011
(212) 727-1500
1-800-877-8273
Fax: (212) 727-1766
E-mail: TobinVideo@aol.com
www.tobinproductions.com
Video production, duplication, CD and DVD compression, authoring, replication.

Worldview Productions
(718) 549-7894
E-mail: worldviewproductions @msn.com
Feature films/video, performances, lectures, demo reels, music videos

26.
POST OFFICES

A & P Food Emporium
228 W. End Avenue
New York, NY 10023
(212) 799-3544

Ansonia
178 Columbus Avenue
New York, NY 10023
(212) 362-1697

Audobon
511 W.165th Street
New York, NY 10032
(212) 568-2387

Bowling Green
25 Broadway
New York, NY 10004
(212) 363-9152

Bryant Station
23 W. 43rd Street
New York, NY 10036
(212) 279-5961

Canal Street Retail
6 Doyers Street
New York, NY 10013
(212) 349-8264

Canal Street Station
350 Canal Street
New York, NY 10013

(212) 966-9573

Cathedral Station
215 W. 104th Street
New York, NY 10025
(212) 662-0355

Cherokee Station
1483 York Avenue
New York, NY 10021
(212) 517-8361

College Station
217 W. 140th Street
New York, NY 10030
(212) 283-7096

Colonial Park
99 Macombs Place
New York, NY 10039
(212) 368-4956

Columbia University Station
534 W. 112th Street
New York, NY 10025
(212) 864-7813

Columbus Circle Station
27 W. 60th Street
New York, NY 10023
(212) 265-8748

Cooper Station
93 Fourth Avenue
New York, NY 10003
(212) 254-1390

Empire State Station
19 W. 33rd Street (front)
New York, NY 10118
(212) 279-5473

Fort George Station
4558 Broadway
New York, NY 10040
(212) 942-5266

Fort Washington
556 W. 158th Street (front)
New York, NY 10032
(212) 923-1763

Franklin D. Roosevelt
909 Third Avenue
New York, NY 10022
(212) 330-5508

Gracie Station
229 E. 85th Street
New York, NY 10028
(212) 988-8504

Grand Central Station
450 Lexington Avenue
New York, NY 10017
(212) 330-5829

Greeley Square Station
39 W. 31st Street
New York, NY 10001
(212) 279-5474

**Hamilton Grange
Station**
521 W. 146th Street
New York, NY 10031
(212) 281-1538

Hell Gate Station
153 E. 110th Street
New York, NY 10029
(212) 860-1896

Inwood Station
90 Vermilyea Avenue
New York, NY 10034
(212) 567-7821

James A. Farley Station
421 Eighth Avenue
New York, NY 10001
(212) 330-3002

Knickerbocker
128 W. Broadway
New York, NY 10002
(212) 608-3598

Lenox Hill Station
217 E. 70th Street
New York, NY 10021
(212) 879-4403

Lincolnton
2266 Fifth Avenue
New York, NY 10037
(212) 281-3281

Madison Square Station
149 E. 23rd Street
New York, NY 10010
(212) 673-3770

Manhattanville Station
365 W. 125th Street
New York, NY 10027
(212) 662-1540

Midtown Station
221 W. 38th Street
New York, NY 10018
(212) 819-9604

Morningside Annex
365 W. 125th Street
New York, NY 10026
(212) 864-3158

Murray Hill Finance
115 E. 34th Street
New York, NY 10016
(212) 679-0730

Office Depot
521 Fifth Avenue
New York, NY 10175
(212) 557-3757

Old Chelsea Station
217 W. 18th Street
New York, NY 10011
(212) 675-0548

Peck Slip Station
1 Peck Slip
New York, NY 10038
(212) 964-1056

Peter Stuyvesant
432 E. 14th Street
New York, NY 10009
(212) 677-2165

Pitt Station
185 Clinton Street
New York, NY 10002
(212) 254-6159

Planetarium Station
127 W. 83rd Street
New York, NY 10024
(212) 873-3991

Prince Station
124 Greene Street
New York, NY 10012
(212) 226-7869

Radio City Station
322 W.52nd Street
New York, NY 10019
(212) 265-6676

Rockefeller Center
610 Fifth Avenue
New York, NY 10020
(212) 265-8024

Roosevelt Island
694 Main Street
New York, NY 10044
(212) 751-4348

Staples Corporation
535 Fifth Avenue
New York, NY 10017
(646) 227-0585

Times Square Station
340 W. 42nd Street
New York, NY 10036
(212) 502-0421

Triborough Station
167 E. 124th Street
New York, NY 10035
(212) 534-0381

Village Station
201 Varick Street (front)
New York, NY 10014
(212) 645-0327

Wall Street Station
73 Pine Street
New York, NY 10005
(212) 809-6108

**Washington Bridge
Station**
555 W. 180th Street
New York, NY 10033
(212) 568-2690

West Village
527 Hudson Street
New York, NY 10014
(212) 645-0327

Yorkville Station
1617 Third Avenue
New York, NY 10128
(212) 369-2747

Buildings with Their Own Zipcodes

American International Group Bldg.
70 Pine Street
New York, NY 10270

Architect & Design Bldg.
964 Third Avenue
New York, NY 10155

150 E. 58th Street
New York, NY 10155

Bear Sterns Bldg.
245 Park Avenue
New York, NY 10167

Bristol Myers Bldg.
345 Park Avenue
New York, NY 10154

Burlington Bldg.
1345 Sixth Avenue
New York, NY 10105

Chanin Bldg.
122 E. 42nd Street
New York, NY 10168

Chemical Bank Bldg.
277 Park Avenue
New York, NY 10172

Chrysler Bldg.
405 Lexington Avenue
New York, NY 10174

Empire State Bldg.
350 Fifth Avenue
New York, NY 10118

Fisk Bldg.
250 W. 57th Street
New York, NY 10107

French Bldg.
551 Fifth Avenue
New York, NY 10176

General Electric Bldg.
30 Rockefeller Plaza
New York, NY 10112

General Motors Bldg.
767 Fifth Avenue
New York, NY 10153

Graybar Bldg.
420 Lexington Avenue
New York, NY 10170

Helmsley Bldg.
230 Park Avenue
New York, NY 10169

International Bldg.
630 Fifth Avenue
New York, NY 10111

Lincoln Bldg.
60 E. 42nd Street
New York, NY 10165

Marine Midland Bldg.
250 Park Avenue
New York, NY 10177

Met Life
200 Park Avenue
New York, NY 10166

Park Ave. Plaza Bldg.
55 E. 52nd Street
New York, NY 10055

Pavilion
500 E. 77th Street
New York, NY 10162

Pennsylvania Bldg.
225 W. 34th Street
New York, NY 10122

Seagram Bldg.
375 Park Avenue
New York, NY 10152

Tishman Bldg.
666 Fifth Avenue
New York, NY 10103

West Vaco Bldg.
299 Park Avenue
New York, NY 10171

Woolworth Bldg.
233 Broadway
New York, NY 10279

605 Third Avenue
New York, NY 10158

500 Fifth Avenue
New York, NY 10110

521 Fifth Avenue
New York, NY 10175

745 Fifth Avenue
New York, NY 10151

1290 6th Ave.
New York, NY 10104

120 Broadway
New York, NY 10271

450 Fashion Avenue
New York, NY 10123

888 Fashion Avenue
New York, NY 10106

26 Federal Plaza
New York, NY 10278

342 Madison Avenue
New York, NY 10173

101 Park Avenue
New York, NY 10178

1 Penn Plaza
New York, NY 10119

2 Penn Plaza
New York, NY 10121

475 Riverside Drive
New York, NY 10115

55 Water Street
New York, NY 10041

112 W. 34th Street
New York, NY 10120

SEVEN

getting the facts

27. UNIONS

American Federation of Television and Radio Artists (AFTRA)
260 Madison Avenue, 7th Floor (bet. 38th and 39th Sts.)
New York, NY 10001
(212) 532-0800
www.aftra.com

American Guild of Variety Artists (AGVA)
184 Fifth Avenue (at 23rd St.)
New York, NY 10010
(212) 675-1003

Artists Equity Association (AEA)
165 W. 46th Street (east of 7th Ave.)
New York, NY 10036
(212) 869-8530
www.actorsequity.org

Directors Guild of America (DGA)
110 W. 57th Street (bet. 6th and 7th Aves.)
New York, NY 10019
(212) 581-0370

1-800-356-3754
www.dga.org

Screen Actors Guild (SAG)
360 Madison Avenue, 12th Floor
New York, NY 10017
(212) 944-1030
www.sag.org

Writers Guild of America, East (WGAE)
555 W. 57th Street (at 11th Ave.)
New York, NY 10019
(212) 767-7800
Fax: (212) 582-1909
E-mail: info@wgaeast.org
www.wgaeast.org

Writers Guild of America, West (WGA)
7000 West 3rd Street
Los Angeles, CA 90048
(323) 951-4000
1-800-548-4532
Fax: (323) 782-4800
www.wga.org

28. ORGANIZATIONS

Academy of American Poets
588 Broadway, Suite 604
New York, NY 10012
(212) 274-0343
www.poets.org
Founded in 1934 to support American poets at all stages of their careers and to foster the appreciation of contemporary poetry. The largest organization in the country dedicated to the art of poetry.

The Alliance
245 Love Lane, P.O. Box 96
Mattituck, NY 11952-0096
(631) 298-1234
Fax: (631) 298-1101
E-mail: awippert@the alliance.org
www.thealliance.org

Artists from Abroad
www.artistsfromabroad.com
E-mail: askus@artistsfrom abroad.com

Arts International
251 Park Avenue South,
5th Floor
New York, NY 10010
(212) 674-9744
Fax: (212) 674-9092
E-mail: info@artsinternational.
org
www.artsinternational.org

**Artslynx International
Arts Resources**
E-mail: rfinkels@msn.com
www.artslynx.org

**City of New York,
Department of
Cultural Affairs**
330 W. 42nd Street,
14th Floor
New York, NY 10036
(212) 643-7770
www.ci.nyc.ny.us/ html/dcla
The DCLA's goal is to sustain
and promote the cultural life
of the City of New York.

**Dance Theater
Workshop (DTW)**
219 W. 19th Street
New York, NY 10011
(212) 691-6500
Fax: (212) 633-1974
www.dtw.org

The Field
161 6th Avenue, 14th Floor
New York, NY 10013
(212) 691-6969
Fax: (212) 255-2053
E-mail: info@thefield.org
http://thefield.org

**Hispanic Organization
of Latin Actors (HOLA)**
Clemente Soto Velez
Cultural Center
107 Suffolk Street, Suite 302
New York, NY 10002
(212) 253-1015
Fax: 212-253-9651
E-mail: holagram@hello
hola.org
www.hellohola.org

Movement Research
P.O. Box 49
Old Chelsea Station
New York, NY 10113
(212) 598-0551
Fax: (212) 598-5948
E-mail: info@movement
research.org
www.movementresearch.org

**The National Asian
American Theatre Co.,
Inc. (NAATCO)**
674 President Street
Brooklyn, NY 11215
E-mail: info@naatco.org
www.naatco.org

**New York City
Arts Coalition**
351-A W. 54th Street
New York, NY 10019
(212) 246-3788
(212) 246-3366
E-mail: info@nycityarts
coalition.org
www.nycityartscoaliton.org

**New York Foundation
for the Arts (NYFA)**
155 Sixth Avenue,
14th Floor
New York, NY 10013
(212) 366-6900
Fax: (212) 366-1778
E-mail: NYFAweb@nyfa.org
www.nyfa.org

**New York International
Fringe Festival
(FringeNYC)
The Present Company**
520 8th Avenue, Suite 311
New York, NY 10018
(212) 279-4488
Fax: (212) 279-4466
E-mail: info@FringeNYC.org
www.fringenyc.org
Every summer there's a multi-
cultural, multiarts theater
festival.

**New York State
Council on the Arts**
175 Varick Street
New York, NY 10014
(212) 627-4455
E-mail: helpdesk@nysca.org
www.nysca.org
New York State funding and
support agency. Offers funding and support to arts agencies and nonprofit art groups
throughout New York State.

Nuyorican Poets Café
236 E. 3rd Street (bet.
Aves. B and C)
New York, NY 10009
(212) 505-8182
www.nuyorican.org

NY Play Development
E-mail: jude@pipeline.com
www.pipeline.com
Offers a supportive environment to foster and support
the playwright's process.
Our lab program is de-
signed from the ground up
to provide the playwright
with all the tools needed to
develop and perfect the classic long-form stage work —
the two-act play. Also accepts actors' résumés for performances of new works.
E-mail your résumé and a
brief letter of interest.

Pentacle
246 W. 38th Street,
8th Floor
New York, NY 10018
(212) 278-8111
Fax: (212) 278-8555
www.pentacle.org

**Sanctuary Playwrights
Theatre**
616 E. 19th Street
Brooklyn, NY 11230
(718) 859-6625
Fax: (718) 421-4178
E-mail: jude@pipeline.com
http://sanctuarytheatre.
home.pipeline.com

Sanctuary Playwrights Theatre empowers playwrights to experiment, while never losing sight of the fundamentals of the playwriting craft. Playwrights make the production and artistic choices; they read and select plays (not literary managers) and select directors, designers, and actors. Sanctuary sees the playwright as the crucial curator of new plays for the stage and asserts that having a writer select work for production according to the writer's vision is the best route both for the dramatist's artistic growth and for the development of world-changing new stage plays.

651 Arts

651 Fulton Street
Brooklyn, NY 11217
(718) 636-4181
Fax: (718) 636-4166
E-mail: info@651arts.org
www.651arts.org

Theatreworks/USA

151 W. 26th Street,
7th Floor
New York, NY 10001
(212) 647-1100
Fax: (212) 924-5377
www.theatreworksusa.org
Always accepts photos and résumés. Non-equity actors can audition; actors can earn their Equity cards (works under Equity TYA contract). Actors are signed on as second assistant stage managers; must be willing to do load in and load out, handle props, costumes, and set. Musicals and nonmusicals. Tours are between two and six months: September–December and January–June. Fall auditions: early to mid-August to mid-September. Spring auditions: late November to early December (check *Back Stage*).

Also looking for playwrights, lyricists, and composers.

29. PERIODICALS AND TRADE PUBLICATIONS

Alternative Theater

A multilingual resource for theater with an international focus. Information on jobs, funding and gatherings. Also highlights information about little-known theater artists as well as the more well-known, established artists. Web site: www.alternativetheater.com

American Theatre Magazine

Articles on directors, actors, and goings-on in the regional theater world. Also offers a new play script in every other issue. Comes out ten times a year. Can be purchased at Drama Book Shop and some Barnes and Nobles bookstores. Web site: www.tcg.org

Back Stage

A must for actors. Weekly list of auditions for theater, film, cabaret, dance, and so on. Plus articles and advertisements for services. Comes out once a week. Can be purchased at Drama Book Shop, most bookstores, and most newsstands. Or get an Internet subscription to *Back Stage* online. Web site: www.backstage.com.

Performink

A Chicago-based biweekly trade paper filled with reviews, auditions, listings, and articles for the film and theater industries in Chicago. Web site: www. performink.com/

The Regional Theatre Directory

A guide to employment in regional and dinner theater (for both Equity and non-Equity). Comes out once a year. Can be purchased at Drama Book Shop or online at Amazon.com.

Ross Reports

A listing of all agencies and casting directors (individual offices and for films, shows, and networks) for both New York City and Los Angeles. Updated monthly, it lists who's at which office and what they cover. Comes out monthly. Can be purchased at Drama Book Shop and at most Barnes and Nobles and Borders bookstores. Web site: www.backstage.com/back stage/rossreports/index.jsp.

Show Business Weekly

Similar to *Back Stage*. May have some different auditions listed. Has some great articles. Comes out once a week. Can be purchased at Drama Book Shop, at most Barnes and Nobles bookstores, and newsstands.

The Stage

News, reviews, and features covering all aspects of the arts and entertainment industry. Also includes job listings, legal advice, and a behind-the-scenes look at everyone from the agent to the master carpenter. Web site: www.thestage.co.uk

Summer Theatre Guide

A guide to summer employment for professionals and students (both Equity and non-Equity). Comes out once a year. Can be purchased at Drama Book Shop or online at Amazon.com.

The Soul of the American Actor: America's Artists' Newspaper
Quarterly newspaper that includes articles, interviews, artist resources, and events. Can be found at Drama Book Shop. Web site: www. SoulAmericanActor.com

Theatrical Index
Includes contact information for all productions. Comes out once a year. Can be purchased by e-mailing Theatrical Index@nyc.rr.com or phoning (212) 586-6343.

Theatre Magazine
A Yale publication that includes articles, essays, commentaries, previously unpublished script submissions, and advertising primarily focusing on experimental theater—American and international. Web site: www.yale.edu/drama/publications/theater/

Variety Magazine
Entertainment news, columns, analysis, features, and photos. Web site: www.variety.com

30. HANDY WEB SITES AND PHONE NUMBERS

Web Sites

The Academy of Motion Picture Arts and Sciences
www.ampas.org
The official site of the Oscars.

The Academy Players Dictionary Online
www.acadpd.org
Shows you how to become a member of the APDO. (There is a fee to be listed.) (*Act New York* does not endorse this or any site fee.)

Acting Biz
www.actingbiz.com
Offers resources such as articles about getting started, audition skills, and so on, plus book reviews.

Actorscraft
www.actorscraft.com
Hey, we brought you the book, check us out!

Actorpoint
www.actorpoint.com
Casting notices, free monologues, questions answered by an industry pro, features, and forums.

The Actor's Checklist,
www.actorschecklist.com
Articles on everything from what to think about when getting your headshot to tax and legal considerations for actors. Also has articles and listings of events.

The Actor's Fund of America
www.actorsfund.org
An organization that works to help people in the entertainment industry when some personal or family crisis threatens their well-being.

American Theatre Web
www.americantheatreweb.com
Theater and show information by U.S. region. Theater news. Lists all theaters: what they're playing, their addresses, and other information. A great site.

The American Theatre Wing, Tony Awards
www.tonys.org
The official site of the Tonys.

Backstage
www.Backstage.com
Theater news and reviews. You can get into just about everything without being a paid member, except, of course, the casting notices.

BigBreakNY
www.bigbreakny.com
Casting notices, calendar of events, articles, a resident clairvoyant success coach whom you can e-mail with questions, and more.

Breakdown Services
www.breakdownservices.com
Allows actors to access Showfax, and agents and managers to access Sides Express. There are a small number of breakdowns that actors can view for free.

The Casting Network
www.thecastingnetwork.com
A fee-membership site where you pay to have your headshot and résumé on the Internet. (AGTNY does not endorse this or any other fee site.)

City Search
www.newyork.citysearch.com
The absolutely most essential site for knowing what's going on in town. You can find everything: movie listings, store information, and addresses, restaurant reviews, tips for living in New York City, theater locations, show reviews, and on and on. Get to know this site and use it often!

ELAC Writers Workshop
www.perspicacity.com/elactheatre/workshop/workshop.htm
Guide to playwriting resources. You can publish

your play online or read other people's plays. Great for actors because you can read and use works that are available for production and monologues that are available for audition purposes.

The EPGuides
www.epguides.com
The data base for Episodic Television. Clicking on an actor's name will take you to his or her page on IMDB.

Internet Broadway Data Base
www.IBDB.com
Choose from show, people/organization, theater, or season to get the information you need on Broadway shows.

Internet Movie Data Base
www.IMDB.com
Great site that lists facts on actors, directors, producers, films, and much, much more. A must-visit site!

Internet Theatre Bookshop
www.stageplays.com
Shop and order plays by searching for the title, genre, author, or keyword. Also has a selection of books on other performance-related topics, such as makeup, auditioning, lighting, and design. Check out the Bargain Basement link.

The Internet Theatre Magazine of Reviews
www.curtainup.com
Features and annotated listings, reviews (past and current) and more.

Madscreenwriter
www.madscreenwriter.com
Resources for the arts, acting, filmmaking, screenwriting, and more, plus a large list of acting websites.

Musical Cast Album Data Base
www.eur.com/musicals
Search titles, composers, lyricists, book authors, artists, conductors, and songs for your musical theater needs.

Musical Heaven
www.musicalheaven.com
Lists many musicals; features information such as author, lyricist, opening dates, as well as synopses and song list (for some, not all).

New York City Insider:
www.theinsider.com
Great tips for living in New York City. Only problem seems to be it isn't updated constantly. Use information, but call ahead.

The New York Public Library
www.nypl.org
Allows you to find the book you're looking for on the Internet.

New York Theatre wire:
www.nytheatre-wire.com
News, reviews, and coupons plus more.

NYCastings
www.nycastings.com
Job listings, news, and resources for models, actors, musicians and production.

NYC Tourist
www.NYCTourist.com
The official site of New York City Tourism. Lists upcoming events, maps of the airports, and helpful information on theater, dining, hotels, museums, shopping. and more.

NYTheatre.com
www.nytheatre.com
Theater news, reviews, list of theaters and what they're playing (with specific information and in order of

neighborhood), plus much more. This great site is worth visiting!

The Off-Broadway Internet Data Base
www.lortel.org
Choose from Show Title, Theatre, People, Awards, or Company name to find information for Off Broadway.

On Stage: The Performers Resource
www.onstage.org
Actors' homepages, list of theaters across the United States, auditions, classified section listing apartments, items for sale, employment (check the date; some postings are displayed for years), book reviews, and theater reviews.

Playbill Online
www1.playbill.com/playbill
Theater news, *Playbill* online club, theater listings, message board, chat rooms, and more.

Show Business Weekly
www.showbusinessweekly.com
Theater news, reviews, classifieds, message board. Gives you a casting teaser, lists a couple of castings, but the others can only be viewed by paying members.

Snopes
www.snopes.com
Completely unrelated, but a must-have for those with e-mail. Tired of getting e-mails full of phony stories and bogus deals? Go to Snopes and find the real truth behind those Internet legends. You can check out all those fishy stories, then e-mail the correct information from Snopes to the people who

forwarded you the annoying nonsense in the first place.

Stu Hamstra's Cabaret Hotline
www.svhamstra.com
All about cabaret acts going on across the world.

The Theatre Data Base
www.theatredb.com
Search for show, person, theater, song title, character/role, or production role for the information you need on a show or person in regional theater.

Urban Insider
www.urbaninsider.com
A community for black, Latino, and Asian Hollywood. Includes casting notices, forums, job listings, events, industry links, profiles, and more.

YourType.com
www.yourtype.com
Audition listings, computer assistance, tips for apartment hunting in New York City, vocal coaches, and teacher listings and more.

Phone Numbers

Mailing/Shipping Services

DHL Worldwide Express
1-800-225-5345
www.dhl.com

Emery Worldwide
1-800-443-6379
www.emeryworld.com

FedEx
1-800-463-3339
www.fedex.com

United States Post Office
1-800-222-1811
www.usps.com

UPS
1-800-742-5877
www.ups.com

Credit Card Companies

American Express
1-800-528-4800
www.americanexpress.com

Mastercard
1-800-307-7309
www.mastercard.com

Visa
1-800-847-2911
www.visa.com

Car Rental Companies

Avis Rent-A-Car
1-800-230-4898
www.avis.com

Budget Rent-A-Car
1-800-527-0700
www.drivebudget.com

Dollar Rent-A-Car
1-800-800-3665
www.dollarcar.com

National Car Rental
1-888-227-7368
www.nationalcar.com

Thrifty
1-800-847-4389
www.thrifty.com

Other General Information

American Red Cross
150 Amsterdam
New York, NY 10023
(212) 580-2821
www.redcross.org

Better Business Bureau of Metropolitan NY, Inc.
257 Park Avenue, 4th Floor
New York, NY 10001
(212) 533-7500
www.betterbusinessbureau.com

Chamber of Commerce of Greater NY
350 5th Ave.
New York, NY 10018
(212) 244-6461

Directory Assistance
1-555-1212 or 411

DMV Offices (3 locations)
11 Greenwich Street
(bet. Battery Park Place and Morris St.)
New York, NY 10004
(212) 645-5550
(718) 966-6155
www.nydmv.state.ny.us

2110 Adam Clayton Powell, Jr. Boulevard (at 126th St.)
New York, NY 10027
(212) 645-5550
(718) 966-6155

1293-1311 Broadway, 8th Floor (bet. W. 33rd and W. 34th Sts.)
New York, NY 10001
(212) 645-5550
(718) 966-6155

The Lesbian, Gay, Bisexual, and Transgender Community Center
208 W. 13th Street
New York, NY 10011
(212) 620-7310

INS: New York District Office
26 Federal Plaza
New York, NY 10278
www.ins.usdoj.gov

Passport Service
376 Hudson Street
New York, NY 10014
(212) 206-3500

Social Security
237 W. 48th Street
New York, NY 10036
1-800-772-1213
www.ssa.gov

EIGHT

getting inspired

31. THE COMPLETE LIST OF LIVE THEATERS

Kimshelley's Spotlight On: The Cherry Lane Theatre

Almost hidden, on a little two-block street in the West Village, is the historic Cherry Lane Theatre. Founded by Edna St. Vincent Millay in 1924, this seventy-eight-year-old theater has showcased the works of such theater luminaries as Edward Albee, Samuel Beckett, David Mamet, Harold Pinter, Sam Shepard, and Lanford Wilson. Actors such as Tyne Daly, Bea Artur, Gary Senise, and John

Malkovich have graced its stage.

The Cherry Lane Main Stage features four incredible Art Deco sconces, which were a gift from the Radio City Music Hall when they renovated in the 1950s. There is a fleur-de-lis motif that runs throughout. This is due to owner, Angelina Fiordelisi (Fiordelisi being Italian for fleur-de-lis). An actress since age four, Angelina purchased the Cherry Lane in 1996. Her intention was to have a theater where established artists and new up-and-coming artists could work together.

When Angelina transformed the large unkempt storage area into what is now the Cherry Lane Alternative, she consulted her

teacher, mentor, and good friend and noted artist and director Jose Quintero. They developed the space into a black box theater, which opened in 1999 and is used specifically for developing new works.

When Jose died of cancer in late 1999, Angelina changed the name of her other theater, the Kaufman on 42nd Street, to the Jose Quintero Theatre in his honor. Angelina's primary goal for the Cherry Lane is to have a full season on the main stage while continuing to showcase new works in the Alternative Theatre.

The Cherry Lane is building a casting file and accepts pictures and résumés. They hold open calls every year

(listed in Back Stage).
They do not accept un-
solicited scripts. See
Web site for more info-
www.cherrylane
theatre.com.

P.S. They also accept
ushers for shows. Call
to sign up, arrive an
hour early, help seat the
show, and see the show
for free.

Cherry Lane Theatre
38 Commerce Street
New York, NY 10014
(212) 989-2020

Jose Quintero Theatre
534 W. 42nd Street
New York, NY 10036
(212) 563-1864

Visit www.nytheatre.
com before you go to
find out more informa-
tion on the theater (you
can check things like
what's currently playing
and seating charts for
Broadway houses). Try
Citysearch.com also.
It's best to let the the-
ater know in advance if
you will need wheel-
chair assistance. It al-
most goes without say-
ing that you should
always aim to get to the
theater an hour ahead.
Do not aim for the ac-
tual showtime—so
much can happen to de-
lay you. The theaters
have the right to seat
late arrivals later in the
show, or not to seat
them at all.

Broadway

Al Hirschfeld Theatre
302 W. 45th Street
New York, NY 10036
WC, S = 1,302

Ambassador Theatre
219 W. 49th Street (bet.
Broadway and 8th Ave.)
New York, NY 10019
Theater District
WC, S = 1,125

**American
Airlines Theatre**
227 W. 42nd Street (bet.
7th and 8th Aves.)
New York, NY 10036
Theater District
WC, S = 750
Home of Roundabout
Theatre Company.

American Place Theatre
266 W. 37th Street
New York, NY 10018
(212) 594-4482
Fax: (212) 594-4208
E-mail: contact@american
placetheatre.org
www.americanplacetheatre.
org

Belasco Theatre
111 W. 44th Street (bet. 6th
and 7th Aves.)
New York, NY 10036
Theater District
WC, S = 1,018

Biltmore Theatre
261 W. 47th Street
New York, NY 10036
Theater District
WC, S = 600 to 650

Booth Theatre
222 W. 45th Street (bet.
Broadway and 8th Ave.)
New York, NY 10036
Theater District
WC, S = 781

Broadhurst Theatre
235 W. 44th Street (bet.
Broadway and 8th Ave.)
New York, NY 10036
Theater District
WC, S = 1,186

Broadway Theatre
1681 Broadway (at 8th
Ave.)
New York, NY 10019
Theater District
WC, S = 1,752

**Brooks Atkinson
Theatre**
256 W. 47th Street (bet.
Broadway and 8th Ave.).
New York, NY 10036
Theater District
WC, S = 1,086

**Circle in the
Square Theatre**
1633 Broadway (bet. Broad-
way and 8th Ave.).
New York, NY 10019
Theater District
WC, S = 681

Cort Theatre
138 W. 48th Street (bet. 6th
and 7th Aves.)
New York, NY 10036
Theater District.
WC, S = 1,084

**Ethel Barrymore
Theatre**
243 W. 47th Street (bet.
Broadway and 8th Ave.).
New York, NY 10036
Theater District
WC, S = 1,096

Eugene O'Neill Theatre
230 W. 49th Street (bet.
Broadway and 8th Ave.).
New York, NY 10036
Theater District
WC, S = 1,108

Ford Center Theatre
213 W. 42nd Street (bet.
7th and 8th Aves.)
New York, NY 10036
Theater District.
WC, S = 1,839

Gershwin Theatre
222 W. 51st Street (bet. 7th
Ave. and Broadway).
New York, NY 10019
Theater District
WC, S = 1,933

Helen Hayes Theatre
240 W. 44th Street (bet. 7th
and 8th Aves.)
New York, NY 10036
Theater District
WC, S = 597

Henry Miller's Theatre
124 W. 43rd Street (bet.
Broadway and 6th Ave.)
New York, NY 10036
Theater District

Imperial Theatre
249 W. 45th Street (bet.
Broadway and 8th Ave.)
New York, NY 10036
Theater District.
WC, S = 1,421

John Golden Theatre
252 W. 45th Street (bet.
Broadway and 8th Ave.)
New York, NY 10036
Theater District
WC, S = 805

Longacre Theatre
220 W. 48th Street (bet.
Broadway and 8th Ave.)
New York, NY 10036
Theater District
WC, S = 1,095

Lunt-Fontanne Theatre
205 W. 46th Street (bet.
Broadway and 8th Ave.)
New York, NY 10036
Theater District
WC, S = 1,475

Lyceum Theatre
149 W. 45th Street (bet.
6th and 7th Aves.)
New York, NY 10036
Theater District
WC, S = 924
Home of Tony Randall's
Actors Theatre.

Majestic Theatre
247 W. 44th Street (bet.
Broadway and 8th Ave.)
New York, NY 10036
Theater District.
WC, S = 1,607

Marquis Theatre
1535 Broadway (bet. 45th
and 46th Sts.)
New York, NY 10036
Theater District
WC, S = 1,595

Minskoff Theatre
200 W. 45th Street (bet. 7th
Ave. and Broadway)
New York, NY 10036
Theater District
WC, S = 1,685

Music Box Theatre
239 W. 45th Street (bet.
Broadway and 8th Ave.)
New York, NY 10036
Theater District
WC, S = 1,010

Nederlander Theatre
208 W. 41st Street (bet. 7th
and 8th Aves.)
New York, NY 10036
Theater District
WC, S = 1,189

Neil Simon Theatre
250 W. 52nd Street (bet.
Broadway and 8th Ave.)
New York, NY 10019
Theater District
WC, S = 1,334

**New Amsterdam
Theatre**
214 W. 42nd Street (bet.
7th and 8th Aves.)
New York, NY 10036
Theater District
WC, S = 1,771

Palace Theatre
1564 Broadway (bet. 7th
Ave. and Broadway)
New York, NY 10036
Theater District
WC, S = 1,740

Plymouth Theatre
236 W. 45th Street (bet.
Broadway and 8th Ave.)
New York, NY 10036
Theater District
WC, S = 1,078

Richard Rogers Theatre
226 W. 46th Street (bet.
Broadway and 8th Ave.)
New York, NY 10036
Theater District
WC, S = 1,400

Royale Theatre
242 W. 45th Street (bet.
Broadway and 8th Ave.)
New York, NY 10036
Theater District
WC, S = 1,068

Shubert Theatre
225 W. 44th Street (bet. 7th
and 8th Aves.)
New York, NY 10036
Theater District
WC, S = 1,513

St. James Theatre
246 W. 44th Street (bet. 7th
and 8th Aves.)
New York, NY 10036
Theater District
WC

Studio 54
254 W. 54th Street (bet.
Broadway and 8th Ave.)
New York, NY 10019
Theater District
WC (for orchestra only)

Virginia Theatre
245 W. 52nd Street (bet.
Broadway and 8th Ave.)
New York, NY 10019
Theater District
WC, S = 1,275

**Vivian Beaumont
Theatre**
150 W. 65th Street (Lincoln
Center)
New York, NY 10023
Upper West Side
WC, S = 1,080

Walter Kerr Theatre
219 W. 48th Street (bet.
Broadway and 8th Ave.)
New York, NY 10019
Theater District
WC, S = 1,482

The Winter Garden
1634 Broadway (bet. 50th
and 51st Sts.)
New York, NY 10019
Theater District

Off Broadway

A lot of Off Broadway
theaters require you to
go up or down stairs to
get to the auditorium.
Only a few are wheel-
chair accessible. (Off-
Off Broadway theaters
are indicated by OOB.)

Theater District

Abingdon Theatre
432 W. 42nd Street,
4th Floor (bet. 9th and
10th
Aves.)
New York, NY 10036
Theater Row

American Place Theatre
111 W. 46th Street (bet. 6th
and 7th Aves.)
New York, NY 10036
Theater District
S = main stage 299,
smaller theater 74

**American Theatre of
Actors**
314 W. 54th Street (bet. 8th
and 9th Aves.)
New York, NY 10019
Theater District
WC, S = several theaters,
seats vary

City Center Theatre
131 W. 55th Street (bet. 6th
and 7th Aves.)
New York, NY 10019
Theater District

Creative Place Theatre
750 Eighth Avenue,
Suite 602 (bet. 46th and
47th Sts.)
New York, NY 10036
Theater District

**Douglas Fairbanks
Theatre**
432 W. 42nd Street (bet.
9th and 10th Aves.)
New York, NY 10036
Theater Row
WC, S = 286

Duffy Theatre
1553 Broadway (bet. 6th
and 47th Sts.)
New York, NY 10036
Theater District
S = 165

The Duke on 42nd Street
229 W. 42nd Street,
2nd Floor (bet. 7th and 8th
Aves.)
New York, NY 10036
Theater District
WC, S = 199

**Ensemble Studio
Theatre (EST)**
549 W. 52nd Street (bet.
10th and 11th Aves.)
New York, NY 10019
Theater District
WC, S = Main stage 99,
6th floor 60
(See also Medicine Show
Theatre.)

47th Street Theatre
304 W. 47th Street (bet. 8th
and 9th Aves.)
New York, NY 10036
Theater District
WC, S = 196

Harold Clurman Theatre
410 W. 42nd Street (bet.
9th and 10th Aves.)
New York, NY 10036
Theater Row

**Intar (Hispanic
American Arts Center)**
508 W. 53rd Street (bet.
10th and 11th Aves.)
New York, NY 10019
Theater District
WC

Irish Arts Center
553 W. 51st Street (bet.
10th and 11th Aves.)
New York, NY 10019
WC, S = 99

John Houseman Theatre
450 W. 42nd Street (bet.
9th and 10th Aves.)
New York, NY 10036
Has 2 additional theaters:
Studio and Studio, down
one flight of stairs
Theater Row
WC, S = 286

John Jay Theatre
899 10th Avenue (bet. 58th
and 59th Sts.)
New York, NY 10019
Theater District
WC, S = 611

Jose Quintero Theatre
534 W. 42nd Street
New York, NY 10036
Theater Row
S = 93

Lamb's Theatre
130 W. 44th Street (bet. 6th
Ave. and Broadway)
New York, NY 10036
Theater District

Lion Theatre
410 W. 42nd Street (bet.
9th and 10th Aves.)
New York, NY 10036
Theater Row

Little Shubert Theatre
422 W. 42nd Street
New York, NY 10036
WC, S = 499

Manhattan Theatre Club
131 W. 55th Street (bet. 6th
and 7th Aves.)
New York, NY 10019
Theater District

Has 2 spaces
WC, S = main 299,
2nd 150

Medicine Show Theatre

549 W. 52nd Street,
3rd Floor (bet. 10th and
11th Aves.)
New York, NY 10019
Theater District
WC, S = 24
(Part of Ensemble Studio
Theatre)

The Mint Theatre

311 W. 43rd Street,
5th Floor (bet. 8th and
9th Aves.)
New York, NY 10036
Theater District
WC, S = 82

Mitzi Newhouse Theatre

150 W. 65th Street
(Lincoln Center)
New York, NY 10023
Upper East Side
WC, S = 299

New Victory Theatre

209 W. 42nd Street (bet.
6th and 7th Aves.)
New York, NY 10036
Theater District
WC
Theater for children;
families only.

Pantheon Theatre

303 W. 42nd Street (bet.
8th and 9th Aves.)
New York, NY 10036
Theater for children;
families only.

Pelican Studio/
New Perspectives

750 Eighth Avenue,
Suite 601 (bet. 46th and
47th Sts.)
New York, NY 10036
Theater for children;
families only.
S = 60 (black box)

Peter Jay Sharp Theater

416 W. 42nd Street
New York, NY 10036
WC, S = 96 to 128

Phil Bosakowski
Theatre

354 W. 45th Street (bet. 8th
and 9th Aves.)
New York, NY 10036
Theater District
S = 75, OOB
(See also Primary Stages
Theatre)

Playwrights Horizons
(2 theaters)

416 W. 42nd Street
New York, NY 10036
Theater District
WC, S = 198

Primary Stages Theatre

354 W. 45th Street (bet. 8th
and 9th Aves.)
New York, NY 10036
Theater District
S = 99
(See also Phil Bosakowski
Theatre)

Producers Club Theatre

358 W. 44th Street (bet. 8th
and 9th Aves.)
New York, NY 10036
Theater District
S = Several theaters of vary-
ing sizes; often used for
showcases.
OOB

Producers Club II

616 Ninth Avenue
New York, NY 10036
Theater District
S = 99

Raw Space Theatre

529 W. 42nd Street (bet.
10th and 11th Aves.)
New York, NY 10036
Theater District
Several theaters of varying
sizes.

Samuel Beckett Theatre
(5 spaces)

410 W. 42nd Street (bet.
9th and 10th Aves.)
New York, NY 10036
Theatre Row
The Acorn, S = 199
The Beckett, S = 99
The Clurman
The Kirk, S = 99
The Lion, S = 88
2 studio theaters, S = 40 to 50

Second Stage Theatre

307 W. 43rd Street (bet. 8th
and 9th Aves.)
New York, NY 10036
Theater District
WC, S = 299

Signature at Peter
Norton Space

555 W. 42nd Street (bet.
10th and 11th Aves.)
New York, NY 10036
Theater District
WC, S = 160

Studio Theatre

145 W. 46th Street
New York, NY 10036
Theater District
OOB

Theatre at St. Clement's

423 W. 46th Street (bet. 9th
and 10th Aves.)
New York, NY 10036
Theater District
S = 151

Theater Four (WPP)

424 W. 55th Street (bet. 9th
and 10th Aves.)
New York, NY 10019
Theater District
S = 254

Theatre 3

311 W. 43rd Street (bet. 8th
and 9th Aves.)
New York, NY 10036
Theater District
WC, S = 96
(in the same office building
as The Mint Theatre)

The Town Hall
123 W. 43rd Street (bet. 6th
Ave. and Broadway)
New York, NY 10036
Theater District
S = 70

Trilogy Theatre
341 W. 44th Street (bet. 8th
and 9th Aves.)
New York, NY 10036
Theater District
Has 2 spaces.
WC, S = 70

**Vital Theatre
(Theatre on Three)**
432 W. 42nd Street (bet.
9th and 10th Aves.)
New York, NY 10036
Theatre Row
S = 39, OOB
Home of Vital Theatre
Company.

Westside Theatre
407 W. 43rd Street (bet. 9th
and 10th Aves.)
New York, NY 10036
Theater District
Has 2 spaces: Downstairs
S = 250; Upstairs S = 299

**Where Eagles Dare
Theatre**
347 W. 36th Street
New York, NY 10018
WC, S = 35

Lower East
Side/East Village

Astor Place Theatre
434 Lafayette Street (bet.
E.4th St. and Astor Place)
New York, NY 10003
East Village
S = 298

Bleecker 45
45 Bleecker Street (bet.
Broadway and Lafayette)
New York, NY 10012
East Village

Bouwerie Lane Theatre
330 Bowery (bet. Bond and
Great Jones Sts.)
New York, NY 10012
East Village
S = 140

Connelly Theatre
220 E. 4th Street (bet. Aves.
A and B)
New York, NY 10009
East Village
WC
(See also Metropolitan
Theatre.)

**CSV (Clemente Soto
Velez Cultural Center)**
107 Suffolk Street (bet.
Delancy and Rivington Sts.)
New York, NY 10002
Lower East Village
Has three spaces: Flamboy-
an, Milagro, and La Tea.
Seating varies.

**Elysium Theatre
Company**
204 E. 6th Street (bet.
3rd Ave. and Taras
Shevchenko Pl.)
New York, NY 10003
East Village

**Henry Street
Settlement Theatre**
465 Grand Street (bet. Pitt
and Willett Sts.)
New York, NY 10002
Lower East Side
Has 3 spaces: Harry De Jur,
The Recital Hall, and the Ex-
perimental. Experimental the-
ater seats don't have backs.
Seating varies.

**Jean Cocteau Repertory
Theatre (at The
Bouwerie Lane Theatre)**
330 Bowery (at Bond St.)
New York, NY 10012
East Village

**Kraine Theatre
(Horse Trade Theatres)**
85 E. 4th Street (bet. 2nd
and 3rd Aves.)
New York, NY 10003
East Village
(See also Red Room
and St. Marks Theatres.)

La MaMa Theatre
74a E. 4th Street (bet. 2nd
and 3rd Aves.)
New York, NY 10003
East Village
OOB
Has 3 spaces: Special Event,
First Floor Theatre, and The
Club. Seats vary.

Metropolitan Playhouse
220 E. 7th Street (bet. Aves.
A and B)
New York, NY 10009
East Village
S = 52
(See also Connelly Theatre.)

**New York Theatre
Workshop**
79 E. 4th Street (bet. Bow-
ery St. and 2nd Ave.)
New York, NY 10003
East Village
WC, S = 150

Orpheum Theatre
126 Second Avenue (bet.
7th St. and St. Marks Pl.)
New York, NY 10003
East Village
WC, S = 347

Pearl Theatre
80 St. Marks Place (bet. 1st
and 2nd Aves.)
New York, NY 10003
East Village
WC, S = 160

P.S. 122
150 First Avenue (bet. 9th
St. and St. Marks Pl.)
New York, NY 10009
East Village
Has 2 spaces.
S = usually general admis-
sion, OOB

Public Theater

425 Lafayette Street (bet. W. 4th St. and Astor Pl.)
New York, NY 10003
East Village
Has 6 spaces: Florence Anspacher Theatre S = 277; Martison Hall S = 193; Estelle R. Newman Theatre S = 299; Susan Stein Shiva Theatre S = 99; Lu Esther Hall S = 199; Joe's Pub S = 150.
WC

Red Room Theatre (Horse Trade Theatres)

85 E. 4th Street (bet. 2nd and 3rd Aves.)
New York, NY 10003
East Village
(See also Kraine and St. Marks Theatres.)

St. Marks Theatre (Horse Trade Theatres)

94 St. Marks Place (bet. 1st Ave. and Ave. A)
New York, NY 10009
East Village
S = 40
(See also Kraine and Red Room Theatres.)

SoHo/Tribeca/ West Village

Access Theatre

380 Broadway, 4th Floor (at White St.)
New York, NY 10013
Tribeca
S = 64

Actors Playhouse

100 Seventh Avenue South (bet. Grove and Barrow Sts.)
New York, NY 10014
West Village

Bank Street Theatre

155 Bank Street (bet. West and Washington Sts.)
New York, NY 10014
West Village
WC

Castillo Theatre

500 Greenwich Street, 2nd Floor (bet. Spring and Canal Sts.)
New York, NY 10013
Tribeca
WC, S = 71

Circle in the Square (Downtown)

159 Bleecker Street (bet. Sullivan and Thompson Sts.)
New York, NY 10012
West Village

Duplex

61 Chistopher Street (bet. 7th Ave. and Waverly Pl.)
New York, NY 10014
West Village
S = 74

Flea Theatre

41 White Street (bet. Church St. and Broadway)
New York, NY 10013
Tribeca
S = can vary
Home of Bat Theatre Company.

Greenwich Street Theatre

547 Greenwich Street (bet. Charlton and Vandam Sts.)
New York, NY 10013
SoHo
S = 74

HERE Arts Center

145 Sixth Avenue (bet. Spring and Dominick Sts.)
New York, NY 10013
SoHo
Has 2 theaters and a performance club
S = Mainstage 99, Dorothy B. Williams 74, Performance Club 99, OOB

Jane Street Theatre

113 Jane Street (bet. Washington and West Sts.)
New York, NY 10014
West Village
S = 280

Lucille Lortel Theatre

121 Christopher Street (bet. Bleecker and Bedford Sts.)
New York, NY 10014
West Village
WC, S = 299

Manhattan Ensemble Theatre

55 Mercer Street (bet. Broome and Grand Sts.)
New York, NY 10012
SoHo
WC, S = 140

Manhattan Theatre Source

177 MacDougal Street (bet. Waverly Place and 8th St.)
New York, NY 10011
West Village
S = 50
Also has PlaySource Performing Arts Bookstore and Window Box Café, which has a cabaret/live mike space.

Minetta Lane Theatre

18 Minetta Lane (bet. 6th Ave. and MacDougal St.)
New York, NY 10014
West Village
WC, S = 407

Ohio Theatre

66 Wooster Street (bet. Spring and Broome Sts.)
New York, NY 10012
SoHo
S = 75
Home of SoHo Think Tank.

Players Theatre

115 MacDougal Street (bet. Minetta Lane and Bleecker St.)
New York, NY 10012
West Village
S = 248

Rattlestick Theatre

224 Waverly Place (bet. Perry and W. 11th Sts.)
New York, NY 10014
West Village

SoHo Playhouse
15 Vandam Street (bet.
Varick and MacDougal Sts.)
New York, NY 10013
SoHo
S = 198

**SoHo Repertory
(Walkerspace) Theatre**
46 Walker Street (bet.
Broadway and Church St.)
New York, NY 10013
SoHo
WC, S = general admission

13th Street Repertory
50 W. 13th Street (bet. 5th
and 6th Aves.)
New York, NY 10011
West Village
OOB

Tribeca Playhouse
111 Reade Street (bet.
Church St. and West Broad-
way)
New York, NY 10007
Tribeca

Wings Theatre
154 Christopher Street (bet.
Washington and West Sts.)
New York, NY 10014
West Village
S = 74

Chelsea/Union Square/Midtown/ Gramercy/Garment District/Hell's Kitchen

**Actors Theatre
Workshop**
145 West 28th Street (bet.
6th and 7th Aves.)
New York, NY 10011
Chelsea
S = 30 to 40

Atlantic Theater
336 W. 20th Street (bet. 8th
and 9th Aves.)
New York, NY 10011
Chelsea
S = 165

Blue Heron Arts Center
123 E. 24th Street (bet.
Lexington and Park Aves.)
New York, NY 10010
Gramercy.
Has 2 spaces
WC, S = mainstage 98,
Black box 45, OOB

CAP 21
15 W. 28th Street (bet. 5th
and 6th Aves.)
New York, NY 10011
Chelsea
S = usually general
admission, OOB

Center Stage Theatre
48 W. 21st Street, 4th Floor
(bet. 5th and 6th Aves.)
New York, NY 10011
Chelsea
S = 74 (usually general
admission)

Century Center Theatre
111 E. 15th Street (bet.
Union Square East and Irv-
ing Pl.)
New York, NY 10003
Union Square
S = 299

Chelsea Playhouse
125 W. 22nd Street (bet.
6th and 7th Aves.)
New York, NY 10011
Chelsea
S = 72

DR2
103 E. 15th Street (bet. Union
Square East and Irving Pl.)
New York, NY 10003
Union Square
WC, S = 99

East 13th Street Theatre
136 E. 13th Street (bet. 3rd
and 4th Aves.)
New York, NY 10003
Union Square
WC, S = 175

14th Street Y
344 E. 14th Street (bet. 2nd
and 3rd Aves.).
New York, NY 10003
Union Square
Home of Hypothetical
Theatre Company.

Gloria Maddox Theatre
262 W. 26th Street, 7th Floor
(bet. 6th and 7th Aves.)
New York, NY 10011
Chelsea
WC
Home of T. Schreiber Studio.

Gramercy Arts Theatre
138 E. 27th Street (bet.
Lexington and 3rd Aves.)
New York, NY 10016
Gramercy
S = 140
Home of Repertorio Espanol.

Hudson Guild Theatre
Fulton Center
119 Ninth Avenue
New York, NY 10011
Chelsea
S = 105

Irish Repertory Theatre
132 W. 22nd Street (bet.
6th and 7th Aves.)
New York, NY 10011
Chelsea
WC

Maverick Theatre
307 W. 26th Street (bet. 8th
and 9th Aves.)
New York, NY 10011
Chelsea

**Native Aliens'
Flatiron Playhouse**
119 W. 23rd Street,
3rd Floor (bet. 6th and 7th
Aves.)
New York, NY 10011
Chelsea
WC, S = 49

**Sanford Meisner
Theatre**
164 Eleventh Avenue (bet.
22nd and 23rd Sts.)

New York, NY 10011
Chelsea
S = 74, OOB

Union Square Theatre
100 E. 17th Street (bet. Park
Ave. S. and Irving Pl.)
New York, NY 10003
Union Square
S = 499

Upright Citizens Brigade
307 W. 26th Street (bet.
8th and 9th Aves.)
New York, NY 10001
Chelsea
S = 150

Urban Stages Theatre
259 W. 30th Street
New York, NY 10001
(bet. 7th and 8th Aves.)
Midtown
WC

Variety Arts Theatre
110 Third Avenue (bet. 12th
and 13th Sts.)
New York, NY 10003
Union Square
WC, S = 498

Vineyard Theatre
108 E. 15th Street (bet. Union
Square East and Irving Pl.)
New York, NY 10003
Union Square
S = 120

Zipper Theatre
336 W. 37th Street (bet. 8th
and 9th Aves.)
New York, NY 10018
Garment district
S = 199; Belt seats = 80

Upper East Side/ Upper West Side

ArcLight Theatre
152 W. 71st Street (bet. Co-
lumbus and Amsterdam Aves.)
New York, NY 10023
Upper West Side
S = 99

Delacorte
W. 89th Street and
Central Park West
New York, NY 10024
Central Park
Amphitheater

McGinn/Cazale Theatre
2162 Broadway, 4th Floor
(bet. 76th and 77th Sts.)
New York, NY 10024
Upper West Side
WC, S = 108

Playhouse 91
316 E. 91st Street (bet. 1st
and 2nd Aves.)
New York, NY 10028
Upper East Side
S = 299
Home of the Jewish
Repertory Theatre.

Promenade Theatre
2162 Broadway (bet. 76th
and 77th Sts.)
New York, NY 10024
Upper West Side
WC, S = 399

78th Street Theatre Lab
236 W. 78th Street (bet.
Broadway and Amsterdam
Ave.)
New York, NY 10024
Upper West Side
Has 2 spaces
S = 2nd floor theater 35;
3rd floor theater 60
(both are usually general
admission).

Theatre Ten Ten
1010 Park Avenue (bet.
84th and 85th Sts.)
New York, NY 10028
Upper East Side
WC

Triad Theatre
158 W. 72nd Street,
2nd Floor (bet. Broadway
and Columbus Aves.)
New York, NY 10023
Upper West Side
S = 130

York Theatre Company
(Theater at St. Peter's Church)
619 Lexington Avenue (bet.
53rd and 54th Sts.)
New York, NY 10022
Upper East Side
WC (but you must inquire at
the desk), S = 147

Harlem

Apollo Theatre
253 W. 125th Street (bet.
7th and 8th Aves.).
New York, NY 10027

**Classical Theater of
Harlem**
645 St. Nicholas Avenue
New York, NY 10030

National Black Theatre
2031 Fifth Avenue (bet.
125th and 126th Sts.)
New York, NY 10035

32. MOVIE THEATERS

For movie times, we
recommend going to
Citysearch. They list
both by show and by
theater.

AMC Empire 25
234 W. 42nd Street
New York, NY 10036
(212) 398-3939
This theater is huge. Make
sure you leave enough time
to get to your theater section; it can be quite a trek!
It's a very popular theater on
the weekends and week
nights. If you are easily both-
ered by other people's incon-
siderate behavior, you may
want to try a smaller theater.

Angelika Film Center
18 West Houston Street
New York, NY 10012
(212) 995-2570

Astor Place Theatre
434 Lafayette Street
New York, NY 10003
(212) 254-4370

**CC Cinemas 1, 2,
Third Avenue**
1001 Third Avenue
New York, NY 10022
(212) 753-6022

Cinema Village
22 E. 12th Street
New York, NY 10003
(212) 924-3363

**City Cinemas 86th St.
East**
210 E. 86th Street
New York, NY 10028
(212) 650-9773

**City Cinemas Village
East**
181–189 Second Avenue
New York, NY 10003
(212) 529-6799

Civita Colonia Artistica
1633 Broadway
New York, NY 10019
(212) 489-4943

**Clearview's Beekman
Theatre**
1254 2nd Ave.
New York, NY 10021
(212) 737-2622

**Clearview Cinema
Group, Inc.**
400 E. 62nd Street
New York, NY 10021
(212) 752-0709

**Clearview Cinema
Group, Inc**
1254 2nd Ave.
New York, NY 10021
(212) 737-2622

**Clearview Cinema
Group, Inc**
2626 Broadway
New York, NY 10025
(212) 222-1200

**Clearview 62nd and
Broadway**
1871 Broadway
New York, NY 10023
(212) 979-CLVW

**Clearview Cinema
Group, Inc.**
125 E. 86th Street
New York, NY 10028
(212) 534-1880

Clearview's Chelsea
260 W. 23rd Street
New York, NY 10003
(212) 513-5402

Clearview Chelsea West
333 W. 23rd Street
New York, NY 10011
(212) 989-0060

**Clearview Metro
Theatre**
2626 Broadway
New York, NY 10025
(212) 222-1200

**Clearview's Ziegfeld
Theater**
141 West 54th Street
New York, NY 10019
(212) 765-7600

East 86 St Cinemas
210 E. 86th Street
New York, NY 10028
(212) 860-8686

Film Forum
209 W. Houston Street
New York, NY 10014
(212) 627-2035

**IMAX Theatre at the
American Museum of
Natural History**
79th Street and Central
Park West
New York, NY 10024
(212) 769-5000

The Kitchen
512 W. 19th Street
New York, NY 10011
(212) 255-5793

**Landmark
Sunshine Cinema**
143 East Houston Street
New York, NY 10002
(212) 358-7709

**Lincoln Plaza
Cinemas**
1886 Broadway
New York, NY 10023
(212) 757-2280

Loews Cineplex E-Walk
247 W. 42nd Street
(at 8th Ave.)
New York, NY 10036
(212) 840-7761
The same rules apply to this
theater as to the AMC Em-
pire; it's very busy on weekends. The great thing about
these two is that they are opposite each other, and if one
doesn't have the title you're
looking for, chances are the
other one will.

**Loews Cineplex 84th
Street**
2310 Broadway
New York, NY 10024
(212) 877-3600

**Loews Cineplex Lincoln
Square and IMAX**
1998 Broadway
New York, NY 10023
(212) 336-5000

**Loews Cineplex
New York Twin**
1271 2nd Ave.
New York, NY 10021
(212) 744-7339

**Loews Cineplex 72nd
St. East**
1230 Third Ave.
New York, NY 10021
(212) 879-1313

**Loews Cineplex
Village VII**
66 3rd Ave.
New York, NY 10003
(212) 982-0400

Loews Kips Bay
2nd Ave. and 32nd Street
New York, NY 10016
(212) 447-8425

Loews 19th St. East
890 Broadway
New York, NY 10003
(212) 505-6397

Loews Orpheum
1538 3rd Ave.
New York, NY 10028
(212) 505-6397

Loews State Theatre
1540 Broadway
(at 46th St.)
New York, NY 10036
(212) 391-2900

Loews 34th Street
312 W. 34th Street
New York, NY 10001
(212) 244-8686

**MoMA Film at the
Gramercy Theatre**
127 E. 23rd Street
New York, NY 10010
(212) 777-4900

Olympia Theatre
2770 Broadway
New York, NY 10025
(212) 865-8128

Paris Theatre
4 W. 58th Street
New York, NY 10019
(212) 688-3800
This is a lovely little theater.
It shows only one movie at a
time, and the movies tend to
be foreign or high-quality art
films (*Amelie, Iris, The Gold-
en Bowl*), but the auditorium
is wonderful.

Quad Cinema
34 W. 13th Street
New York, NY 10011
(212) 255-8800

Rififi/Cinema Classics
332 E. 11th Street
New York, NY 10001
(212) 677-1027

Two Boots Den of Cin
44 Avenue A
New York, NY 10009
(212) 254-0800

United Artists
1 Union Square South
New York, NY 10003
(212) 253-2225

1210 Second Avenue
(at 64th St.)
New York, NY 10021
(212) 832-1670

1629 First Avenue
(at 85th St.)
New York, NY 10028
(212) 249-5100

Waverly Theatre
323 Sixth Avenue
New York, NY 10014
(212) 929-8037

33. MUSEUMS

**American Folk Art
Museum (2 locations)**
E-mail: info@folkartmuse.org
www.folkartmuseum.org

2 Lincoln Square
New York, NY 10107
(212) 977-7298

45 W. 53rd Street
New York, NY 10019
(212) 595-9533

**American Museum of
Natural History**
Central Park West at
79th Street
New York, NY 10019
(212) 769-5100
www.amnh.org

**American Museum of
the Moving Image**
35 Avenue (at 36th St.)
Astoria NY 11106
(718) 784-4520
www.ammi.org

**Archives of
American Art**
1285 Sixth Avenue
New York, NY 10019
(212) 399-5030
Fax: (212) 307-4501
E-mail: yeckleyk@si.edu
http://artarchives.si.edu

Artists Space
38 Greene Street
New York, NY 10013
(212) 226-3970
Fax: (212) 966-1434
E-mail: artspace@
artistspace.org
www.artistspace.org

**Asia Society and
Museum**
725 Park Avenue
New York, NY 10021
(212) 288-6400
Fax: (212) 517-8315
E-mail: info@asiasoc.org
www.asiasoc.org

**The Chelsea Art
Museum**
160 Eleventh Avenue
New York, NY 10011
(212) 255-0719
E-mail: info@chelseaart
museum.org
www.chelseaartmuseum.org

**Children's Museum of
Manhattan**
The Tisch Building
212 W. 83rd Street
New York, NY 10024
(212) 721-1234
E-mail: info@cmom.org
www.cmom.org

The Cloisters
Fort Tyron Park
New York, NY, 10040
(212) 923-3700
E-mail: cloisters@metmuseum.
org
www.metmuseum.org

Cooper-Hewitt National Design Museum
2 E. 91st Street
New York, NY 10128
(212) 849-8300
TTY: (212) 849-8386
E-mail: edu@si.edu
www.si.edu/ndm/

Frick Collection
1 E. 70th Street
New York, NY 10021
(212) 288-0700
Fax: (212) 628-4417
E-mail: info@frick.org
www.frick.org

Guggenheim Museum
1071 Fifth Avenue
New York, NY 10028
(212) 423-3500
E-mail: visitorinfo@
guggenheim.org
www.guggenheim.org

International Center of Photography
1114 Sixth Avenue
New York, NY 10036
(212) 857-0045
E-mail: info@icp.org
www.icp.org

Intrepid Sea Air Space Museum
Pier 86, (bet. 12th Ave. and 46th St.)
New York, NY 10036
(212) 245-0072
E-mail: info@intrepidmuseum.org
www.intrepidmuseum.org

Jewish Museum
1109 Fifth Avenue
New York, NY 10128
(212) 423-3200
E-mail: info@thejm.org
www.jewishmuseum.org

Madame Tussaud's Wax Museum
234 42nd Street
New York, NY 10036
(212) 512-9600
1-800-246-8872

E-mail: Lee.Jackson@
madametussaudsny.com
www.madame-tussauds.com

Metropolitan Museum of Art
1000 Fifth Avenue
New York, NY 10001
(212) 535-7710
www.metmuseum.org

Museum for African Art
36-01 43rd Avenue
Long Island City, NY 11101
(718) 784-7700
Fax: (718) 784-7718
E-mail: museum@africanart.org
www.africanart.org

Museum of Comic and Cartoon Art
594 Broadway, Suite 401
New York, NY 10012
(212) 254-3511
Fax: (212) 254-3590
www.moccany.org

Museum of Chinese in the Americas
70 Mulberry Street
New York, NY 10013
(212) 619-4785
Fax: (212) 619-4720
E-mail: info@moca-nyc.org
www.moca-nyc.org

Museum of Jewish Heritage: A living Memorial to the Holocaust
36 Battery Place
New York, NY 10280
(646) 437-4200
E-mail: aburgess@mjhnyc.org
www.mjhnyc.org

Museum of Modern Art, Queens
(temporary location)
33rd St. at Queens Blvd.
Long Island City, NY 11101
(212) 708-9400
www.moma.rg
Manhattan location on

W. 53rd Street is being renovated and will reopen in early 2005.

Museum of Natural History
79th Street and Central Park West
New York, NY 10024
(212) 769-5100
Fax: (212) 769-5427
www.amnh.org

Museum of Television and Radio
25 W. 52nd Street
New York, NY 10019
(212) 621-6600
www.mtr.org

Museum of the City of New York
1220 Fifth Avenue (at 103rd St.)
New York, NY 10029
(212) 534-1672
Fax: (212) 423-0758
E-mail: mcny@mcny.org
www.mcny.org

National Academy of Design Museum
1083 5th Ave.
New York, NY 10128
(212) 369-4880
Fax: (212) 360 -6795
E-mail: ppineda@nation
alacademy.org
www.nationalacademy.org

National Museum of Catholic Art and History
447 E. 115th Street
New York, NY 10029
(212) 369-7864

New York City Fire Museum
278 Spring Street
New York, NY 10013
(212) 691-1303
www.nycfiremuseum.org

New York City
Police Museum
25 Broadway
New York, NY 10004
(212) 301-4440
Fax: (212) 480-9757
www.nycpolicemuseum.org

Nicholas Roerich
Museum
319 W. 107th Street
New York, NY 10025
(212) 864-7752
Fax: (212) 864-7704
E-mail: director@roerich.org
www.roerich.org

Songwriters
Hall of Fame
330 W. 58th Street
New York, NY 10019
(212) 957-9230
E-mail: info@songwriters
halloffame.org
www.songwriters hall
offame.org

South Street Seaport
Museum
207 Front Street
New York, NY 10038
(212) 748-8600
Fax: (212) 748-2610
www.southstseaport.org

Spanish Museum and
Library
(Hispanic Society of
America)
613 W. 155th Street
New York, NY 10032
(212) 926-2234
E-mail: info@hispanic
society.org
www.hispanicsociety.org

Tibet House
22 W. 15th Street
New York, NY 10011
(212) 807-0563
Fax: (212) 807-0565
E-mail: info@tibethouse.org
www.tibethouse.org

Ukranian Museum
203 Second Avenue
New York, NY 10003

(212) 228-0110
E-mail: info@ukrainian
musuem.org
www.ukrainianmuseum.org

Whitney Museum of
American Art
945 Madison Avenue
New York, NY 10021
(212) 570-7721
E-mail: feedback@whitney.org
www.whitney.org

34. LIBRARIES

New York
Public Library
455 Fifth Avenue
New York, NY 10016
(212) 340-0833

NY Theosophical
Society
240 E. 53rd Street
New York, NY 10022
(212) 753-3835
Fax: (212) 758-4679

New York Public Library Branches

Aguilar Branch
174 E. 110th Street
New York, NY 10029
(212) 534-1613

Andrew Heiskell
Library for the Blind
40 W. 20th Street
New York, NY 10011
(212) 206-5400

Bloomingdale Regional
150 W. 100th Street
New York, NY 10025
(212) 222-8030

Chatham Square
Regional
33 East Broadway
New York, NY 10002
(212) 673-6344

Columbus
742 10th Avenue
New York, NY 10019
(212) 586-5098

Countee Cullen Regional
104 W. 136th Street
New York, NY 10030
(212) 491-2070

Donnell Library Center
20 W. 53rd Street
New York, NY 10019
(212) 621-0618

Epiphany
228 E. 23rd Street
New York, NY 10010
(212) 679-2645

58th Street
127 E. 58th Street
New York, NY 10022
(212) 759-7358

Fort Washington
535 W. 179th Street
New York, NY 10033
(212) 927-3533

George Bruce
518 W. 125th Street
New York, NY 10027
(212) 662-9727

Hamilton Fish Park
415 East Houston Street
New York, NY 10002
(212) 673-2290

Hamilton Grange
503 W. 145th Street
New York, NY 10031
(212) 926-2147

Harlem Center for
Reading and Writing
9 W. 124th Street
New York, NY 10027
(212) 348-5620

Hudson Park
66 Leroy Street
New York, NY 10014
(212) 929-0815

Inwood Regional
4790 Broadway
New York, NY 10034
(212) 942-2445

Jefferson Market Regional
425 Sixth Avenue
New York, NY 10011
(212) 243-4334

KIPS Bay
446 Third Avenue
New York, NY 10016
(212) 683-2520

Library for the Performing Arts
40 Lincoln Center Plaza
New York, NY 10023
(212) 870-1630

Macombs Bridge
2650 Adam Clayton Powell
New York, NY 10039
(212) 281-4900

Morningside Heights
2900 Broadway
New York, NY 10025
(212) 864-2530

Muhlenberg
209 W. 23rd Street
New York, NY 10011
(212) 924-1585

New Amsterdam
9 Murray Street
New York, NY 10007
(212) 732-8186

96th Street Regional
112 E. 96 Street
New York, NY 10128
(212) 289-0908

115th Street
203 W. 115th Street
New York, NY 10026
(212) 666-9393

125th Street
224 E. 125th Street
New York, NY 10035
(212) 534-5050

Ottendorfer
135 Second Avenue
New York, NY 10003
(212) 674-0947

Riverside
127 Amsterdam Avenue
New York, NY 10023
(212) 870-1810

Roosevelt Island
524 Main Street
New York, NY 10044
(212) 308-6243

Schomburg Center for Research in Black Culture
515 Malcom X Boulevard
New York, NY 10037
(212) 491-2200

Science Industry and Business Library
188 Madison Avenue
New York, NY 10016
(212) 592-7000

Seward Park
192 East Broadway
New York, NY 10002
(212) 477-6770

67th Street
328 E. 67th Street
New York, NY 10021
(212) 734-1717

St. Agnes
444 Amsterdam Avenue
New York, NY 10024

Terrence Cardinal Cooke Cathedral
560 Lexington Avenue
New York, NY 10022
(212) 752-3824

Tompkins Square
331 E. 10th Street
New York, NY 10009
(212) 228-4747

Washington Heights
1000 Saint Nicholas Avenue
New York, NY 10032
(212) 923-6054

Webster
1465 York Avenue
New York, NY 10021
(212) 288-5049

Yorkville
222 E. 67th Street
New York, NY 10021
(212) 744-5824

New York Public Library Department Phone Numbers

Adult Services
(212) 576-0031

Aguilar Language Learning Center
(212) 534-1613

Art (Mid-Manhattan Branch)
(212) 340-0871

Arts and Artifacts Division (Schomburg Center)
(212) 491-2241

Books by Mail (Donnell Branch)
(212) 621-0564

Book Purchasing (Manhattan Borough Office)
(212) 340-0815

Center for Reading and Writing Administration
(212) 576-0071

Children's Services
(212) 340-0906

Choices in Health Information
(212) 576-0078

Community and Outreach Services
(212) 340-0918

Connecting Libraries and Schools Project
(212) 726-9757

Dance Research Collections
(212) 870-1657

Digital Reproductions, Photography Reproduction
(212) 930-9270

Education (Mid-Manhattan Branch)
(212) 340-0864

Exhibits and Events
(212) 869-8089

Film and Video Reservations (Donnell Branch)
(212) 621-0610

Filming and Location Services (Corporate and Special Services)
(212) 642-0147

Friends of the Library
(212) 679-2645

Genealogy, U.S. History, and Local History
(Humanities and Social Sciences Branch)
(212) 930-0828

General Reference Service
(212) 340-0863

General Research and Reference
(212) 491-2218

General Research Division (Humanities and Social Sciences Branch)
(212) 930-0830

Health Information Center (Mid-Manhattan Branch)
(212) 340-0883

History and Social Sciences (Mid-Manhattan Branch)
(212) 340-0888

Hours
(212) 870-1600

Information Circulating Collections
(212) 870-1630

Jewish Division
(212) 930-0601

Job Information Center
(Mid-Manhattan Branch)
(212) 340-0837

Library Gift Shop
(212) 340-0839 (40th St. and 5th Ave.)
(212) 930-0641 (42nd St. and 5th Ave.)
(212) 491-2206 (135th and Malcolm X. Blvd.)

Literature and Language (Mid-Manhattan Branch)
(212) 340-0873

Manuscripts Archives Rare Books (Schomburg Center)
(212) 491-2236

Manuscripts Division
(Humanities and Social Sciences Branch)
(212) 930-0804

Media Center
(212) 621-0609

Microfilm Reproductions, Digital Reproductions, Photography Reproduction
(212) 930-0810

Music Circulating Collections
(212) 870-1625

Music Research Collections
(212) 879-1650

Newspaper
(212) 930-0830

NYPL Express, Article Photocopies, Research, and Document Delivery
(212) 592-7201

Orchestra Collections (Humanities and Social Sciences Branch)
(212) 870-1624

Oriental Division (Humanities and Social Sciences Branch)
(212) 930-0716

Payroll Department
(212) 592-7410

Periodicals Division
(Humanities and Social Sciences Branch)
(212) 930-0579

Photographs and Prints
(Schomburg Center)
(212) 491-2057

Photography Collecttion
(Humanities and Social Sciences Branch)
(212) 930-0837

Picture Collection (Mid-Manhattan Branch)
(212) 340-0877

Popular Library (Mid-Manhattan Branch)
(212) 340-0837

Print Collection
(Humanities and Social Sciences Branch)
(212) 930-0817

Programs and Events
(212) 340-0912

Project Access (Mid-Manhattan Branch)
(212) 340-0843

Prop Product Rentals
(Corporate and Special Services)
(212) 930-0687

Public Education Programs (Humanities and Social Sciences Branch)
(212) 930-0855

Public Relations Office
(Central Services)
(212) 221-7676

Publishing Office
(Central Services)
(212) 512-0202

Purchasing Office
(Central Services)
(212) 592-7600

Rare Books Division
(Humanities and Social
Sciences Branch)
(212) 930-0801

**Recorded Sound
Circulating Collections**
(Humanities and Social
Sciences Branch)
(212) 870-1629

**Recorded Sound
Research Collections**
(Humanities and Social Sciences Branch)
(212) 870-1663

**Renew Items, Cancel
Holds, Review
Borrower Record**
(212) 262-7444

**Scholars and Writers
Center** (Humanities and
Social Sciences Branch)
(212) 930-0056

**Slavic and Baltic
Collection** (Humanities and
Social Sciences Branch)
(212) 930-0714

**Special Events,
Space Rental** (Corporate
and Special Services)
(212) 930-0730

**Telecommunications
Devices**
(212) 206-5458

**Theater Research
Collections**
(212) 870-1639

**Ticket Information
Recording**
(212) 930-0571

Tours (Humanities and
Social Sciences Branch)
(212) 491-2207

Young Adult Sevices
(212) 340-0909

35.
BOOKSTORES

Kimshelley's Spotlight On: The Drama Book Shop

Ask any actor where to
go to get plays, and
they will tell you The
Drama Book Shop.

From its humble be-
ginnings in 1917 as a
cart table in the lobby
of the ANTA Theatre,
the Drama Book Shop
has grown to a very im-
pressive two-floor store
that stocks over 40,000
titles dealing with all
aspects of the perform-
ing arts. It is the place
to go for plays, biogra-
phies, dialect tapes,
mailing labels, and
much more. The store
recently moved to its
40th Street location (as
of December 3, 2001).
The layout, designed by
coowner Allen Hubby,
is very accessible and
has a mezzanine that
features the red couch
from the movie *Moulin
Rouge*.

There is also the
Arthur Seelan Studio
Theatre in the base-
ment. It's a modified
black box that seats
sixty people and is used
for special events, book
signings, workshops,
and the resident theater
company Back House
Productions (a group
that does works that
are socially relevant, as
well as workshops with
children and ex-cons).
The theater's namesake
was the owner of the
Drama Book Shop for
fifty years. He passed
away three years ago
and his wife, Rozanne
Seelan, is co-owner.

Kimshelley sat down
for a chat with Allen
and Domenic Silipo,
general managers.

K: Tell me about your
staff.
AH: We have the best
staff at the moment.
They are mostly per-
formers and writers.
They know a lot
about theater.
DS: We try to be very
supportive. We know
they have careers
they work hard for.
K: What are the best re-
sources for actors in
New York?
Both: *(Laughing.)*
What, other than us?
The Performing Arts
Library [at Lincoln
Center].
DS: For playwrights:
the Dramatists Guild.
For Filmmakers:
AIVF, the Association

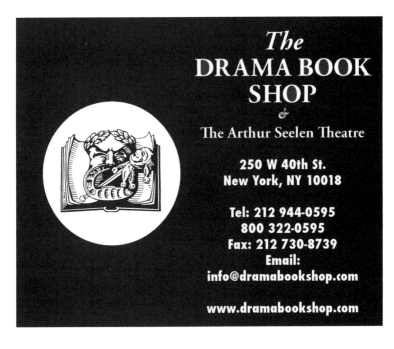

The
DRAMA BOOK SHOP
&

The Arthur Seelen Theatre

**250 W 40th St.
New York, NY 10018**

**Tel: 212 944-0595
800 322-0595
Fax: 212 730-8739
Email:
info@dramabookshop.com**

www.dramabookshop.com

of Independent Video and Filmmakers.

K: Do you have any advice for actors in New York City?

AH and DS: To get a job you have to be there. Meaning go out and audition as much as you can. Learn the business: read plays, go to the theater, see films. Really know your stuff.

The Drama Book Shop
259 W. 40th Street
(bet. 7th and 8th Aves.)
New York, NY 10018
(212) 944-0595

Hours: Mon.–Fri. 10–8 PM;
10:30 AM–8:30 PM;
Sat. 12 PM–6 PM, Sun.

Dramatists Guild Web site:
www.dramaguild.com
AVIF Web site: www.avif.org

Other Bookstores

**Applause
Theatre Books**
211 W. 71st Street
(off Amsterdam Ave.)
New York, NY 10023
(212) 496-7511

**Barnes and Nobles
Booksellers**
Not only do they cover every subject you need, can special order, and have a café in each store, they also have clean bathrooms! Here are a few of the locations in New York City.

1280 Lexington Avenue
(bet. 86th and 87th Sts.)
New York, NY 10028
(212) 423-9900

4 Astor Place
(bet. Broadway and
Lafayette St.)
New York, NY 10003
(212) 420-1322

33 E. 17th Street
(bet. Broadway and Park
Ave.; at Union Square)
New York, NY 10003
(212) 253-0810

600 Fifth Avenue
(at 48th St.; Rockefeller Center)
New York, NY 10020
(212) 765-0590

675 Sixth Avenue (at 21st
St.)
New York, NY 10010
(212) 727-1227

385 Fifth Avenue
(bet. 35th and 36th Sts.)
New York, NY 10016
(212) 779-7677

750 Third Avenue
(bet. 46th and 47th Sts.)
New York, NY 10017
(212) 697-2251

2289 Broadway
(at 82nd St.)
New York, NY 10024
(212) 362-8835

240 E. 86th Street
(bet. 3rd and 2nd Aves.)
New York, NY 10028
(212) 794-1962

396 Sixth Avenue (bet.
Waverly Place and 8th St.)
New York, NY 10011
(212) 674-8780

160 E. 54th Street
(bet. Lexington and 3rd
Aves; Citigroup Building)
New York, NY 10022
(212) 750-8033

1972 Broadway
(at 66th St.)
New York, NY 10023
(212) 595-6859

Blue Danube Gifts
217 E. 83rd Street
New York, NY 10028
(212) 794-7099
www.blue-danube.com

**Borders Books, Music
and Café (2 locations)**
550 Second Avenue
(bet. 29th and 30th Sts.)
New York, NY 10016
(212) 685-3947

461 Park Avenue
(at 57th St.)
New York, NY 10022
(212) 980-6785

Gotham Book Mart
41 W. 47th Street
New York, NY 10036
(212) 719-4448

Gryphon Bookshop
2246 Broadway
New York, NY 10024
(212) 362-0706

**Last Word Used
Books & Records**
1181 Amsterdam Avenue
New York, NY 10027
(212) 864-001

Lenox Hill Bookstore
1018 Lexington Avenue
New York, NY 10021
(212) 472-7170

Mercer Street Books
206 Mercer Street (bet.
Bleecker and Houston Sts.)
New York, NY 10012
(212) 505-8615
www.mercerstreetbooks
andrecords.com

**Oscar Wilde
Memorial Bookshop**
15 Christopher Street
(bet. 6th and 7th Aves.)
New York, NY 10014
(212) 255-8097

Revolution Books
9 W. 19th Street
New York, NY 10011
(212) 691-3345

**Richard Stoddard
Performing Arts Books**
43 E. 10th St. #6D
New York, NY 100033
(212) 598-9421
E-mail: rs@richardstoddard.
com
www.richardstoddard.com
Rare books in the field of
drama

Samuel French
45 W. 25th Street
New York, NY 10010
(212) 206-8990
Bookstore and reading
room.

**Shakespeare and Co.,
Greenwich Village**
716 Broadway
(at Washington Place)
New York, NY 10003
(212) 529-1330

St. Marks Bookshop
31 Third Avenue
New York, NY 10003
(212) 260-7853
Fax: (212) 598-4950
E-mail: stmarksbooks@
mindspring.com
www.stmarksbook shop.com

**Strand Bookstores
(3 locations)**
The Strand is a New York

treasure! "8 miles of books,"
both new and used. If you
specifically know what you
want, see if they have it by
checking their Web site:
www.strandbooks.com. The
Broadway store is not air-
conditioned and can get
very hot and crowded, but
it's worth it!

828 Broadway (at 12th St.)
New York, NY 10003
(212) 473-1452
www.strandbooks.com

95 Fulton Street (bet.
William and Gold Sts.)
New York, NY 10038
(212) 732-6070

45 W 57th Street, 5th Floor
New York, NY 10019
(212) 688-7600

**Unoppressive
Non-Imperialist
Bargain Books**
34 Carmine Street (at
Bleecker St.)
New York, NY 10014
(212) 229-0079
This wonderful little place in
the village has a great selection of titles and very impressive prices.

Urban Center Books
457 Madison Avenue
New York, NY 10022
(212) 935-3595

36.
VIDEOs, DVDs,
AND CDs

Kimshelley's
Spotlight On:
Kim's Video

Let the nonartists have
the big corporate video
chains, we have Kim's

video. Since Yongman Kim opened his first store in 1986 (Kim's Avenue A), he has sought to be different from other video stores. He gears his selection and store setup toward those who care about and respect the art of filmmaking. The videos are in order by director, and the number of separate titles is incredible. There are five Kim's, ranging in size from the smallest on Avenue A, to Mondo Kim's on St. Marks Place. And rentals aren't all they offer. Mondo Kim's has three floors: one for music sales, one for film sales, and one for film rentals. Kim's Mediapolis does all this, plus they have an impressive range of film-themed books.

To rent, membership is free, but you will need either a $150 cash deposit (returned at cancellation of membership), or, preferably, a credit card to which the deposit can he held, meaning it's never charged unless necessary. Again, the deposit is released with cancellation of membership. Rental fees are currently $2 per day for new releases and $1.25 per day for others (but be careful, late fees are $3.50 and $1.50 re-

spectively). Their Web site (www.kimsvideo.com) allows you to see all the titles they carry, but make sure to call ahead to see if the one you want is in.

Mondo Kim's
6 Saint Marks Place
(at 3rd Ave.)
New York, NY 10003
Hours: 9 AM–12 midnight
Music: (212) 598-9985
Rental: (212) 505-0311
Sales: (212) 614-8941

Kim's Avenue A
85 Avenue A
New York, NY 10009
Rental: (212) 529-3410

Kim's Mediapolis
2906 Broadway
(at 113th St.)
New York, NY 10025

Kim's Underground
144 Bleecker Street
(at LaGuardia)
New York, NY 10012
Rental, Sales: (212) 260-1010

Kim's West
350 Bleecker Street
(at 10th St.)
New York, NY 10014
Music, Rental, Sales: (212) 675-8996
Music, Rental, Sales: (212) 864-5321

Other Video Stores

Blockbuster Video (several locations)
250 E. Houston Street (bet. Aves. A and B)
New York, NY 10002
(212) 420-8186

151 Third Avenue
(at 15th Ave.)
New York, NY 10003
(212) 505-7766

780 Broadway (at 9th St.)
New York, NY 10003
(212) 677-8859

312 First Avenue (at 19th St.)
New York, NY 10009
(212) 353-0413

155 E. 34th Street (bet. 3rd and Lexington Aves.)
New York, NY 10016
(212) 686-0022

829 Eighth Avenue (at 51st St.)
New York, NY 10019
(212) 765-2021

199 Amsterdam Avenue
(at 69th St.)
New York, NY 10023
(212) 787-0300

726 Columbus Avenue
(at 93rd St.)
New York, NY 10025
(212) 665-2777

2689 Broadway
(at 103rd St.)
New York, NY 10025
(212) 663-3332

121 W. 125th Street
(bet. 7th and Lennox Aves.)
New York, NY 10027
(212) 665-9101

1302 Amsterdam Avenue
(at 123rd St.)
New York, NY 10027
(212) 316-9143

1646 First Avenue
(at 86th St.)
New York, NY 10028
(212) 794-9001

1251 Lexington Avenue
(at 81st St.)
New York, NY 10028
(212) 439-0960

344 Third Avenue
(bet. 25th and 26th Sts.)
New York, NY 10010
(212) 481-4035

Channel Video
472 Columbus Avenue
New York, NY 10024
(212) 496-2759
www.channelvideo.com

Cinema Classics
332 E. 11th Street
(bet. 1st and 2nd Aves.)
New York, NY,10003
(212) 677-6309

**Couch Potato Video
(2 locations)**
1456 Second Avenue
New York, NY 10021
(212) 517-8666

9 E. Eighth Avenue
New York, NY 10003
(212) 260-4260

DVD Chelsea
234 7th Avenue, 2nd flr.
New York, NY 10011
(646) 638-3996

DVD Palace
733 Eighth Avenue
(at 46th St.)
New York, NY 10036
(212) 265-5213

Express Video
1577 Third Avenue
New York, NY 10128
(212) 410-3456

**Fliks Video and DVD to
Go (2 locations)**
175 W. 72nd Street
New York, NY 10023
(212) 721-0500

1093 2nd Ave. E.
New York, NY 10022
(212) 752-3456

Thunder Video
100 Greenwich Street
New York, NY 10006
(212) 385-1313

Kimshelley's Spotlight On: Joe's CDs

A boss whose philosophy is to hire only nice people who aren't planning to be there for the rest of their lives? A little unheard of here, but that's Joe Randisi for you. He is the owner of Joe's CDs in the East and West Villages.

Joe has been in the music business for twenty-five years. He loves what he does and it shows. His stores have a great range in new and used CDs and the prices are very competitive (usually around $9.99)

He opened Joe's East (on St. Marks) in 1995. It started small but grew so much in only a year, he decided to open Joe's West (on Bleecker St.) in 1996. Then in 1997 he added a downstairs area to the still expanding Joe's East.

When it comes to styles, both locations run the gamut, with West specializing in House, Dance and R&B (it also has a great soundtrack and show-tunes selection) and East specializing in rap, hip-hop and electronic.

Joe, a native of Brooklyn, tends to hire young people who have a good knowledge of and love of music. He also feels it's very important that they have a long-range career goal. Joe's East has been featured in films, television shows, and is a favorite of many celebrities.

Joe's East
11 St. Marks Place,
New York, NY 10003
(212) 673-4606
Hours: 11 AM–11 PM
Sun.–Thurs.; 11 AM–12 PM
Fri. and Sat.

Joe's West
96 Christopher Street,
New York, NY 10014
(212) 463-0884
Hours: 11 AM–9 PM
Sun.–Thurs.; 11 AM–11 PM
Fri. and Sat.

Other Music Stores

Best Buy
60 W. 23rd Street
New York, NY 10010
(212) 366-1373
www.bestbuy.com

Bleecker Street Records
239 Bleecker Street
New York, NY 10014
(212) 255-7899

Colony Records
1619 Broadway (at 49th St.)
New York, NY 10019
(212) 265-2050
www.colonymusic.com
A haven for musical theatre actors — tons of sheet music and karaoke tapes.

Disc-O-Rama Music World (3 locations)
Discorama sells new and used CDs, tapes, vinyl, videos, and DVDs.
www.discorama.com

186 W. 4th Street (bet. Barrow and Jones Sts.)
New York, NY 10012
(212) 206-8417

(annex)
40 Union Square
New York, NY 10003
(212) 260-8616

(classical and clearance)
146 West 4th St.
New York, NY 10012
(212) 477-9410

FYE (2 locations)
716 Lexington Avenue
New York, NY 10022
(212) 826-3500

405 Sixth Ave.
New York, NY 10014
(212) 243-1446

Heartbeat Records
107 W. 10th Street
New York, NY 10011
(212) 255-5260

I B Records, Inc.
658 10th Avenue
New York, NY 10036
(212) 10036

J & R Music World
31 Park Row (bet. Ann and Beekman Sts.)
New York, NY 10038
(212) 238-9100

Nervous Records
363 Seventh Avenue
New York, NY 100001
(212) 273-1135

Norman's Sound & Vision
67 Cooper Square
New York, NY 10003
(212) 473-6599

Rebel Rebel
319 Bleecker Street (bet. Grove and Christopher Sts.)
New York, NY,10014
(212) 989-0770

Sam Goody (2 locations)
390 Sixth Avenue (at W. 8th St.)
New York, NY 10011
(212) 674-7131

19 Fulton Street
New York, NY 10038
(212) 571-9706

Sinamen's Sounds Music Store
2431 Seventh Avenue
New York, NY 10030
(212) 368-7005

Sound & Fury
192 Orchard Street
New York, NY 10002
(212) 598-4300

The Sound Library
214 Avenue A
New York, NY 10009
(212) 598-9302

Subterranean Records
5 Cornelia Street (corner of W. 4th and 6th Ave.)
New York, NY 10014
(212) 463-8900

Take it Uptown Music
2024 Third Avenue
New York, NY 10029
(212) 876-4723

Tower Records (3 locations)
1961 Broadway
New York, NY 10023
(212) 799-2500

692 Broadway
New York, NY 10012
(212) 505-1500

725 5th Ave.
New York, NY 10022
(212) 838-8110

Virgin Megastores (2 locations)
Times Square
1540 Broadway
New York, NY 10036
(212) 921-1020

Union Square
52 E. 14th Street
New York, NY 10003
(212) 598-4666

37. INTERNET CAFÉS

A & G Internet Café
8618 Whitney Avenue
Flushing, NY 11373
(718) 205-0503

Alt.Coffee
139 Avenue A
New York, NY 10009
(212) 259-2233
www.altdotcoffee.com
Café serves coffee, tea, cookies, bagels, etc., and offers classes and full range of Internet service.

Bay's Internet Café
1241 Nostrand Avenue
Brooklyn, NY 11225
(718) 462-8400

Cranberry Café
9506 Fourth Avenue
Brooklyn, NY 11209
(718) 833-7979
Baked entrées and desserts, Tuesday lecture series, open for breakfast, lunch, and dinner

Cybercafe (2 locations)
Cafés serve organic foods in addition to the usual offerings (coffee, tea, pastries) and offers classes and full range of Internet services.

273 Lafayette Street
New York, NY 10012
(212) 334-5140
www.cyber-café.com

250 W. 49th Street (Times Square)
New York, NY 10019
(212) 333-4109
www.cyber-café.com

Cyber Station
Internet Café
2255 31st St. #207
Astoria, NY 11105
(718) 777-5900

Internet Cyber Café
32 Third Avenue
New York, NY 10003
(212) 777-5544

Internet Café
82 E. 3rd Street
New York, NY 10003
(212) 614-0747
www.bigmagic.com
Live music during the week,
and shows work of painters
and photographers and of-
fers classes and full range of
Internet services. Available
for private parties and business functions. Specialize in
Web-page launches.

Internet Café
5820 Roosevelt Avenue
Flushing, NY 11377
(718) 424-2227
Fax: (718) 424-4202

Jackson Heights
Café Internet
8917 3Seventh Avenue
Flushing, NY 11372
(718) 505-0594

Keelum Broadband
Internet Café
273 W. 38th Street
New York, NY 10018
(212) 921-9791

Log On Café
41 E. 30th Street
New York, NY 10016
(212) 889-1555
Café offers premade sand-
wiches, coffee, etc. No classes; Internet only

The easyEverything
Internet Café
234 W. 42nd Street
(Times Square)
New York, NY 10036
(212) 398-0775
Open 24 hours a day,
7 days a week. No café, no
classes, unassisted Internet
use only

William Christy
Internet Café
159 Avenue C
New York, NY 10009
(212) 477-6000

NINE

getting healthy

38. HEALTH CLUBS

Although health clubs can be expensive, it may be beneficial for you to join one where you can go to several locations if you're temping or rehearsing all over the city.

Asphalt Green
1750 York Avenue
New York, NY 10128
(212) 369-8890
www.asphaltgreen.org

Bally Total Fitness (several locations)
Bally's is well priced comparatively and has many locations around the city.
www.ballyfitness.com

45 E. 55th Street
New York, NY 10022
(212) 688-6630

641 Sixth Avenue
New York, NY 10011
(212) 645-4565

2100 Bartow Avenue
Bronx, NY 10475
(212) 320-4000

162 W. 83rd Street
New York, NY 10024
(212) 875-1902

144–146 E. 86th Street
New York, NY 10028
(212) 722-7371

335 Madison Avenue
(Bank of America Plaza)
New York, NY 10017
(212) 983-5320

Chelsea Piers Sports and Entertainment Complex
(The Sports Center at Chelsea Piers)
Pier 60
New York, NY 10001
(212) 336-6000
www.chelseapiers.com

Core Fitness Inc.
12 E. 86th Street
New York, NY 10028
(212) 327-4197

Crunch (several locations)
www.crunch.com

162 W. 83rd Street
New York, NY 10024
(212) 875-1902

144 W. 38th Street
New York, NY 10018
(212) 869-7788

555 W. 42nd Street
New York, NY 10036
(212) 594-8050

404 Lafayette Street
New York, NY 10003
(212) 614-0120

152 Christopher Street
New York, NY 10014
(212) 366-3725

1109 Second Avenue
New York, NY 10022
(212) 758-3434

623 Broadway
New York, NY 10012
(212) 420-0507

554 Second Avenue
New York, NY 10016
(212) 545-9757

54 E. 13th Street
New York, NY 10003
(212) 475-2018

25 Broadway
New York, NY 10004
(212) 269-1067

**Curves of
Manhattan**
345 W. 14th Street
New York, NY 10014
(212) 647-7100

**Equinox (several
locations)**
www.equinoxfitness.com

897 Broadway
New York, NY 10003
(212) 780-9300

1633 Broadway
New York, NY 10019
(212) 541-7000

10 Columbus Circle (at 60th
St.)
New York, NY 10019
(212) 871-0425

54 Murray Street
New York, NY 10007
(212) 566-6555

140 E. 63rd Street
New York, NY 10021
(212) 750-4900

250 E. 54th Street
New York, NY 10022
(212) 277-5400

344 Amsterdam Avenue
New York, NY 10024
(212) 721-4200

2465 Broadway
New York, NY 10025
(212) 799-1818

205 E. 85th Street
New York, NY 10028
(212) 439-8500

Gladiator's Gym
503 W. Sixth Street
New York, NY 10009
(212) 674-9803

**Lucille Roberts (for
women only; several
locations)**
www.lucilleroberts.com

2700 Broadway
New York, NY 10025
(212) 961-0500

143 Fulton Street
New York, NY 10038
(212) 267-3730

1387 St. Nicholas
Avenue
New York, NY 10033
(212) 927-8376

505 W. 125th Street
New York, NY 10027
(212) 222-2522

300 W. 40th Street
New York, NY 10018
(212) 268-4199

**New York Sports Club
(several
locations)**
www.nysc.com

1605 Broadway
New York, NY 10019
(212) 977-8880

1372 Broadway
New York, NY 10018
(212) 575-4500

19 W. 44th Street
New York, NY 10036
(212) 768-3535

1657 Broadway
New York, NY 10019
(212) 307-9400

50 W. 34th Street
New York, NY 10001
(212) 868-0820

2162 Broadway
New York, NY 10024
(212) 496-2444

2527 Broadway
New York, NY 10025
(212) 665-0009

30 Wall Street
New York, NY 10005
(212) 482-4800

230 W. 41st Street
New York, NY 10036
646-366-9400

160 Water Street
New York, NY 10038
(212) 363-4600

1637 3rd Street
New York, NY 10128
(212) 987-7200

3 Park Avenue
New York, NY 10016
(212) 686-1085

2311 Frederick
Douglass Blvd.
New York, NY 10027
(212) 316-2500

151 E. 86th Street
New York, NY 10028
(212) 860-8630

102 North End Avenue
New York, NY 10281
(212) 945-3535

1221 Sixth Avenue
New York, NY 10020
(212) 840-8240

125 Seventh Avenue South
New York, NY 10014
(212) 206-1500

200 Madison Avenue
New York, NY 10016
(212) 686-1144

502 Park Avenue
New York, NY 10022
(212) 308-1010

575 Lexington Avenue
New York, NY 10022
(212) 317-9400

179 Remsen Street
Brooklyn, NY 11201
(718) 246-0600

633 Third Avenue
New York, NY 10017
(212) 661-8500

131 E. 31st Street
New York, NY 10016
(212) 213-1408

614 Second Avenue
New York, NY 10016
(212) 213-5999

61 W. 62nd Street
New York, NY 10023
(212) 265-0995

270 Eighth Avenue
New York, NY 10011
(212) 243-3400

128th Eighth Avenue
New York, NY 10011
(212) 627-0065

34 W. 14th Street
New York, NY 10011
(212) 337-9900

23 W. 73rd Street
New York, NY 10023
(212) 496-6300

10 Irving Place
New York, NY 10003
(212) 477-1800

349 E. 76th Street
New York, NY 10021
(212) 288-5700

248 W. 80th Street
New York, NY 10024
(212) 873-1500

503–511 Broadway
New York, NY 10012
(212) 925-6600

151 Reade Street
New York, NY 10013
(212) 571-1000

217 Broadway
New York, NY 10007
(212) 791-9555

**Printing House Fitness
and Racquet Club**
421 Hudson Street
New York, NY 10014
(212) 243-7600

39. YOGA AND MARTIAL ARTS

Kimshelley's Spotlight On: Jivamukti Yoga Center

Wonder why yoga has become so popular lately? You can thank Sharon Gannon and David Life. Sharon and David have developed a form of Hatha yoga that integrates chanting, asanas, music, and meditation and is strongly grounded in Eastern philosophies. It's called Jivamukti Yoga, and Jivamukti Yoga Center is *the* place in New York for yoga.

Both Sharon and David are artists. David majored in fine art and Sharon in dance, and both were both very involved in the New York theatrical and creative scenes. They started practicing yoga in the early 1980s and are now the leading yoga teachers in the United States. From just meeting this sweet couple, you can tell how passionate they are. They have several books out, including a photography book that shows off their incredible, awe-inspiring partner work.

Jivamukti Yoga

Center has hundreds of students per day. Celebrities and stressed-out New Yorkers alike flock to Sharon and David's center. But this isn't just for the aesthetic effects of yoga; this place is for those who want the spiritual aspects also. There are five tenets incorporated into every class:

Scripture: Studying the ancient yogic teachings, including Sanskrit chanting.

Bhakti: Acknowledging that God realization is the goal of all yoga practices.

Ahimsa: Practicing a nonviolent, compassionate lifestyle that emphasizes ethical vegetarianism and animal rights.

Nada Yoga: Developing a sound body and mind through deep listening.

Meditation: Connecting to that eternal unchanging reality within.

They offer a free introductory class the last Sunday of every month for anyone who wants an introduction to Jivamukti Yoga, given on a first come, first serve basis. Check out their Web site for fees and information: www. jivamuktiyoga.com.

**Jivamukti Yoga Center
(2 locations)**
Downtown
404 Lafayette Street
New York, NY 10003
Fax: (212) 995-1313
E-mail: andrea@jivamukti
yoga.com
www.jivamuktiyoga.com

Uptown
853 Lexington Avenue,
2nd Floor (bet. 64th and
65th Sts.)
New York, NY 10021
(212) 396-4200
Fax: (212) 396-2366

Other Yoga
Centers

Astango Yoga Shala
611 Broadway
New York, NY
(212) 982-0753

**Atmananda Yoga and
Holistic Center Inc.**
552 Broadway (bet. Prince
and Spring Sts.)
New York, NY 10012
(212) 625-1511
Fax: (212) 625-8559
E-mail: atmananda@mac.com
www.atmananda.com

Aum Supreme Truth
8 E. 48th Street
New York, NY 10017
(212) 421-3687

**Be Yoga LLC (several
locations)**
Eastside
1319 Third Avenue, 2nd
Floor (bet. 75th and
76th Sts.
New York, NY 10021
(212) 650-9642
www.beyoga.com

Westside
2121 Broadway, 3rd Floor
New York, NY 10022
(877) 723-9642

Downtown
138 Fifth Avenue, 4th Floor
New York, NY 10011
(212) 647-9642

Midtown
160 E. 56th Street,
12th Floor
New York, NY 10022
(212) 935-9642

Bhava Yoga
638 E. 6th Street (bet. Aves.
B and C)
New York, NY 10009
(212) 254-1384

**Bikram Yoga
College of India
(several locations)**
208 W. 72nd Street (at
Broadway)
New York, NY 10023
(212) 824-7303
E-mail: BikramNYC@aol.com
www.bikramyoganyc.com

235 E. 49th Street
New York, NY 10017
(212) 832-1833
E-mail: NYBikramEast@aol.
com
www.bikramyogaeast.com

250 W. 26th Street,
3rd Floor
New York, NY 10014
(212) 929-9052
E-mail: info@bikram
yogaChelsea.com
www.bikramyogachelsea.
com

182 Fifth Avenue (bet. 22nd
and 23rd Sts.)
New York, NY 10010
(212) 206-9400
E-mail: info@bikram
yoganyc.com
www.bikramyoganyc.com

797 Eighth Avenue (bet.
48th and 49th Sts.)
New York, NY 10019
(212) 245-2525

150 Spring Street (bet. West
Broadway and Wooster St.)

New York, NY 10012
(212) 245-2458
E-mail: BikramNYC@aol.com
www.bikramyoganyc.com

**Bikram Yoga Union
Square**
37 Union Square West
(bet. 16th and 17th Sts.)
New York, NY 10003
(212) 929-8926
E-mail: otto@bikramyoga
unionsquare.com
www.bikramyogaunion
square.com

**Himalayan Institute of
Yoga Science and
Philosophy**
78 Fifth Avenue, 2nd Floor
(bet. 13th and 14th Sts.)
New York, NY 10011
(212) 243-5995
1-877-742-6844 (toll free)

Integral Yoga Center
200 W. 72nd Street (at
Broadway)
New York, NY 10023
(212) 721-4000
E-mail: wogsol@bestweb.net
www.integralyogany.org

Integral Yoga Institute
227 W. 13th Street
New York, NY 10011
(212) 929-0586
Fax: (212) 675-3674
E-mail: info@iyiny.org
www.integralyogany.org

Iyengar Yoga Institue
27 W. 24th Street (bet.
Broadway and 6th Ave.)
New York, NY 10010
(212) 691-9642

Kula Yoga
28 Warren Street, 4th Floor
New York, NY 10007
(212) 945-4460
E-mail: info@kulayoga.com
www.kulayoga.com

Kundalini Yoga East
873 Broadway, Suite 614
(bet. 18th and 19th Sts.)

New York, NY 10003
(212) 982-5959

L'chaim Yoga
415 E. 52nd Street
New York, NY 10022
(212) 751-9642

Laughing Lotus Yoga
55 Christopher Street
(bet. 6th and 7th Aves.)
New York, NY 10014
(212) 414-2903
E-mail: info@laughinglotus.
com
www.laughinglotus.com

**New York Yoga
(2 locations)**
E-mail: info@newyorkyoga.
com
www.newyorkyoga.com

1629 York Avenue
(at 86th St.)
New York, NY 10028
(212) 717-9642

132 E. 85th Street (at
Lexington Ave.)
New York, NY 10028
(212) 717-9642

**Pilates Shop
Yoga Garage**
42 W. 96th Street
(Central Park West and
Columbus Ave.)
New York, NY 10025
(212) 316-9164

Prana Studio
300 W. 108th Street
(bet. 5th and 6th Aves.)
New York, NY 10025
(212) 666-5816
E-mail: instructor@theprana
studio.com
www.thepranastudio.com

Rasa Yoga Center
246 W. 80th Street, 4th
Floor
New York, NY 10024
(212) 875-0475
E-mail: info@rasayoga.com
www.rasayoga.com

**Sivananda Yoga
Vedanta Center, Inc.**
243 W. 24th Street
(bet. 7th and 8th Aves.)
New York, NY 10011
(212) 255-4560

Urban Yoga Workout
900 Broadway
New York, NY 10003
(212) 505-0902

Virayoga
580 Broadway, Suite 1109
New York, NY 10012
(212) 334-9960
www.virayoga.com

World Yoga Center
265 W. 72nd Street
(off West End Ave.)
New York, NY 10023
(212) 787-4908
www.worldyogacenter.com

**Yoga Connection
Tribeca**
145 Chambers Street
New York, NY 10007
(212) 945-9642
E-mail: contactus@yoga
connectionnycc.com
www.yogaconnectionnyc.
com

**Yoga Studios of
New York**
351 E. 84th Street
(bet. 1st and 2nd Aves.)
New York, NY 10028
(212) 988-9474
Private lessons only.

Yoga Zone
138 Fifth Avenue
New York, NY 10011
(212) 647-9642

Yoga Zone Ltd.
160 E. 56th Street,
12th Floor
New York, NY 10022
(212) 935-9642

Martial Arts Studios

Ahn Tai Chi Studio
15 E. 30th Street, Suite 301
(bet. 5th and Madison Aves.)
New York, NY 10016
(212) 481-2553
E-mail: don@ahntaichi.com
www.ahntaichi.com

Aikido Arts
425 W.14th Street
New York, NY 10014
(212) 691-1378

**Aikido Dojo of
New York**
142 W. 18th Street
(bet. 6th and 7th Aves.)
New York, NY 10011
(212) 242-6246

Aikido of Manhattan
60 W. 39th Street, 3rd Floor
New York, NY 10018
(212) 575-0151
E-mail: aikidoofmanhattan@
yahoo.com
www.aikidoofmanhattan.com

Capoeira Angola Center
104 W. 14th Street,
3rd Floor
New York, NY 10011
(212) 989-6975
E-mail: tishotto@panix.com
www.panix.com/~tishotto/
capoeira

**Eagle Claw Kung-Fu
Tai Chi Academy**
40 W. 27th Street
(bet. Broadway and 6th Ave.)
New York, NY 10001
(212) 213-8805

Harlem Karate
2234 Third Avenue
New York, NY 10035
(212) 410-1658
www.geocities.com/harlem
karate/Harlem_Goju_Karate.
html

Impact Self Defense
147 W. 25th Street
(bet. 6th and 7th Aves.)
New York, NY 10001
(212) 255-0505
Ken Zen Institute
54 Thomas Street
New York, NY 10013
(212) 406-9104
E-mail: KenZenInst@aol.com
www.kenzendojo. com

Ken Zen Institute
54 Thomas Street
New York, NY 10013
(212) 406-9104
E-mail: KenZenInst@aol.com
www.kenzendojo.com

Krav Maga
John Jay College of
Criminal Justice
899 10th Avenue
(at 58th St.)
New York, NY 10019
(212) 580-5335
E-mail: contact@krav
magainc.com
www.kravmagainc.com

**Natural Chinese
Martial Arts**
320 W. 37th Street, Suite
2B (8th and 9th Aves.)
New York, NY 10018
(212) 967-3978
www.infinite.org/nma

**New York School of
T'ai Chi Chuan**
Ripley/Grier Studios
520 Eighth Avenue (bet.
36th and 37th Sts.)
(212) 502-4112
www.taichichuan.org
Free introductory classes.

Oishi Judo Club
79 Leonard Street (bet.
Broadway and Church St.)
New York, NY 10013
(212) 966-6850
Fax: (212) 274-8656
www.oishi-judo.com

**Positive Impact
Martial Arts**
122 W. 27th Street,
2nd Floor
New York, NY 10001
(917) 749-5169
www.pi-ma.com

Tiba Capoeira
The Ailey Studio
211 W. 61st Street,
3rd Floor
New York, NY 10023
(646) 228-7268
www.tibacapoeira.com

40. MASSAGE

Kimshelley's Spotlight On: Massage America

I must admit I'd always thought of professional massage as an extravagance. No longer! Having had my first professional massage with Gregory Serdahl, owner of Massage America, I am now an avid fan.

The moment you walk into Massage America, you feel a sense of calm. There is a strict rule of no "sports talk" (loud, intrusive language), and you must remove your shoes (even if you're just visiting). The rooms are small and cozy, the temperature just right, and the smells and sounds relaxing. A full body massage takes about an hour, and the therapist will focus extra attention where needed (for me, my shoulders and upper back from carrying a bag around all day).

Massage not only has an internal effect, but external too. For the rest of the day, after my massage, I was glowing and people commented on how vibrant I looked. At Massage America they offer yogic neuromuscular therapy, sports massage, deep tissue massage, and shiatsu.

Gregory started as an actor and has a theater degree from University of California. He became a masseur to supplement his income and found the field of healing arts to be very creative in itself. He has attended the Swedish Institute, the Esalen Institute, and the Institute of Yogic Neuromuscular Therapy. Gregory chose to open his practice in New York because it is both the creative and stress capital of the world. He feels people should get a massage once a week. Though I agree, most of us can't afford that. I'd say put a little money away each month and try to go at least twice a year. In these times, it's no longer an extravagance, but a necessity.

Massage America
32 Union Square East,
Suite 115
New York, NY 10003
(212) 539-1690
E-mail: massageamerica@
earthlink.net
www.massageamerica.com
Business hours:
9 AM–9 PM, Mon.–Fri.
10 AM–5 PM, Sat. and Sun.

Fees: $75–$150 per hour,
$40–$60 per half hour
(depending on type of
massage. See Web site
for more details.)

Other Massage Facilities

Back to Basics Massage
315 W. 57th Street
(at 8th Ave.)
New York, NY 10019
(212) 974-0988
E-mail: backtobasicsm@
aol.com
www.backtobasicsmassage.
com

**Great American
Backrub (3 locations)**
53 W. 36th Street
New York, NY 10018
(212) 750-7046

529 Third Avenue (at 39th
St.)
New York, NY 10016
(212) 447-9062

958 Third Avenue
New York, NY 10022
(212) 832-1766

**Jane's Aromatherapy &
Massage Therapy**
135 E. 56th Street (at Lexington Ave.)
New York, NY 10022
(212) 486-9550

**Lexington
Beauty Center**
714 Lexington Avenue
(bet. 57th and 58th Sts.)

New York, NY 10022
(212) 752-1060

Manhattan Massage
116 E. 36th Street
New York, NY 10016
(917) 687-4109
www.manhattan-massage.
com

Massage on Park
Contact: Joy Schwartz
49 Park Avenue (at 37th St.)
New York, NY 10016
(212) 696-0043
www.massageonpark.com

**Much Kneaded
Massage & Wellnes**
280 Madison Avenue
New York, NY 10016
(917) 612-8492

**New York Wellness
Bodywork Center**
80 E. 11th Street (bet.
University Plaza and
Broadway)
New York, NY 10003
(212) 505-5034

Oasis Day Spa
108 E. 16th Street
(bet. Union Square East
and Irving Plaza)
New York, NY 10003
(212) 254-0840
www.nydayspa.com

**One-Stop
Wellness Center**
222 E. 75th Street
(bet. 2nd and 3rd Aves.)
New York, NY 10021
(212) 249-2044

Salon de Tokyo
200 W. 57th Street
(at 7th Ave.)
Room 1308
New York, NY 10019
(212) 757-2187

Swedish Institute
226 W. 26th Street
New York, NY 10001
(212) 924-5900
www.swedishinstitute.org

Toa Healing Arts
1 Union Square West
(at 14th St.)
New York, NY 10003
(212) 242-1410

41. HEALTH FOOD STORES

Kimshelley's Spotlight On: Westerly Health Foods

For those actors who are vegan, vegetarian, allergic to wheat or dairy, or who are just into living a healthy lifestyle, there is a great health food store on the corner of Eighth Avenue and 54th Street.

Westerly Health Foods has something for everyone. The small aisles are packed with organic produce, natural grains, nitrate- and hormone-free meat, grain alternatives to wheat, and sugar-free products. Westerly has been family owned since it started thirty years ago. It began as a pharmacy, focus then moved to vitamins and sports supplements. When owner Michael Toback took over, he expanded it into an impressive health food store, which is continually evolving.

One of the things you'll notice pretty quickly is how competitively priced things are.

"Price is king in New York," said Michael, "and we work to be less expensive than others." Michael is very involved with his store. He will gladly listen to suggestions and special requests. He has both a doctor and a nutritionist working for him, and he is very knowledgeable about the food he sells.

Coming soon to the store will be a deli counter, which will have all sorts of goodies, including organic coffee and juice. Stop by and try some OatsCream, a nondairy frozen dessert, or pick up some of Westerly's own brand of vitamins.

Westerly Health Foods
913 Eighth Avenue (at 54th St.)
New York, NY 10019
(212) 586-5262
E-mail: westerlyfoods@
aol.com
www.westerlyhealthfood.com
Hours: 8 AM–10 PM,
Mon.–Fri.; 9 AM–10 PM,
Sat. and Sun.

Other Health Food Stores

Balanced Health Product
215 E. 68th Street
New York, NY 10021
(212) 794-9878

Better Health Foods, Inc.
389 Third Avenue
New York, NY 10016
(212) 684-5260

C & C Natural Health Foods
1554 St. Nicholas Avenue
New York, NY 10040
(212) 923-6366

Columbus Natural Food
725 Columbus Avenue
New York, NY 10025
(212) 663-0345

Creative Natural Food Store
805 Broadway
New York, NY 10003
(212) 866-5637

Earthmatters
177 Ludlow Street
New York, NY 10002
(212) 475-4180

Food for Health, Inc.
1653 Third Avenue
New York, NY 10128
(212) 369-9202

Health & Harmony
470 Hudson Street
New York, NY 10014
(212) 691-3036

Health 4-U Natures Market
432 Park Avenue South
New York, NY 10016
(212) 532-2644

Health Is Wealth
184 Seventh Avenue
New York, NY 10011
(212) 620-3074

Lotus Health Food, Inc.
1309 Lexington Avenue
New York, NY 10128
(212) 423-0345

Matter of Health
1478 First Avenue
New York, NY 10021
(212) 288-8280

May Wah Healthy Vegetarian Food, Inc.
213 Hester Street
New York, NY 10013
(212) 344-4428

Natural Frontier Market (2 locations)
266 Third Avenue
New York, NY 10010
(212) 288-9133

1424 Third Avenue
New York, NY 10028
(212) 794-0922

Nature Food Centers (several locations)
364 Seventh Avenue
New York, NY 10001
(212) 971-7375

682 Broadway
New York, NY 10012
(212) 777-2330

2871 Broadway
New York, NY 10025
(212) 666-8285

1050 Sixth Avenue
New York, NY 10018
(212) 869-6373

Natural Green Market
162 Third Avenue
New York, NY 10003
(212) 780-0263

New Age Nutrician Health Food Store
4532 Broadway
New York, NY 10040
(212) 304-2755

Organic Market V
275 Seventh Avenue
New York, NY,10010
(212) 420-9247

Organic Traditions
388 Second Avenue
New York, NY 10010
(212) 420-9247

Seven Grains Health Foods
2259 Seventh Avenue
New York, NY 10027
(212) 862-3760

Step Down to Nature
835 Second Avenue
New York, NY 10017
(212) 490-2979

275 Organic Market
275 Seventh Avenue
New York, NY 10001
(212) 243-9927

**Whole Earth
Bakery & Kitchen**
130 St. Marks Pl.
New York, NY 10009
(212) 677-7597

42.
RESTAURANTS
AND CAFÉS

Kimshelley's Spotlight On: The Cupping Room

From the outside, the Cupping Room is deceptively small. But once you go in, you will find that the small café up front expands to a larger restaurant with a full bar in the back. This friendly place is like a second home to many regulars. After September 11, owner Natalie Azari opened her doors to serve free coffee and cake to those who were in need of some quiet comfort. The Cupping Room is a much-loved neighborhood hangout, open twenty-four hours on Friday and Saturday.
Opened in 1977, Natalie Azari's Cupping

Room was a coffee warehouse where she sold coffee accessories and would have coffee tasting in little cups (hence the name). In time she expanded to a café and then the current restaurant/bar.
From her trips abroad, Natalie got to know Benny Kish, who was working at a hotel she regularly stayed in. She asked him to come to the United States and be the general manager of her restaurant — a position Benny has held for fifteen years.
The Cupping Room staff are friendly and loyal (some people have been working there since it opened). According to Benny, the quietest time to stop in for some coffee, or something off the very eclectic restaurant menu, is Monday, Tuesday, or Sunday nights.
In 2000, Natalie opened The Cupping Room — Village, on Hudson Street. This is more of a bakery and coffee bar. There are tables outside and a few bar stools inside. She plans to open another bakery/coffee house on the East Side soon.

The Cupping Room
359 West Broadway
(bet. Broome and Watts Sts.)
(212) 925-2898

The Cupping Room — Village
496 Hudson Street
(212) 638-2800

Affordable Restaurants

In the windows of most restaurants you will see a Zagat write-up. This very handy little guide will tell you all sorts of things about a restaurant. Pick up the latest Zagat Survey New York City Restaurants Guide; it's updated annually and available at Barnes and Nobles, Borders, and The Strand. It lists restaurants and gives you price range, food ratings, reviews, and other pertinent information. Oh, and you'll hear it pronounced all sorts of ways, but the folks at Zagat tell us that it's pronounced za-gat (rhymes with "the cat").

Midtown
Basilico
676 Ninth Avenue
(bet. 46th and 47th)
(212) 489-0051
This Italian restaurant is rather small, but the food is delicious and the atmosphere cozy.

Café Des Sports
329 W. 51st Street (bet. 8th and 9th Aves.)
(212) 581-1283
This French restaurant has a great prix fixé and

appetizer. (Not great for vegetarians.)

La Bonne Soup
48 W. 55th Street (bet. 5th and 6th Aves.)
(212) 586-7650
This French restaurant does indeed have great soup and also fondue. It's a wonderful post-theater stop.

McHales
750 Eighth Avenue (bet. 46th and 47th Sts.)
(212) 997-8885
Great burgers to be had at this popular Irish bar/restaurant.

Pax
736 Seventh Avenue (bet. 48th and 49th Sts.)
(212) 399-9100
There are several Pax locations across Manhattan. Pax offers a whole menu of organic, healthy foods. The healthiest fast-food joints around.

Poseidon Bakery
629 Ninth Avenue
(bet. 44th and 45th Sts.)
(212) 757-6173
A wonderful Greek pastry shop. Try the spanakopita (spinach pie).

Rachel's
American Bistro
608 Ninth Avenue
(bet. 43rd and 44th Sts.)
(212) 957-9050
An American restaurant with some French mixed in. Gil suggests the chicken pot pie.

Serendipity 3
225 E. 60th Street
(bet. 2nd and 3rd Aves.)
(212) 838-3531
If you like desserts, you have to try this place! My personal fav is the frozen hot chocolate.

Times Square Bagels
200 W. 44th Street (at 7th Ave.)
(212) 997-7300
Obviously this place does bagels—and very well!

West Village

Café Mona Lisa
282 Bleecker Street
(at 7th Ave. S.)
(212) 929-1262
One of our favorite places to chill out, late at night, in the big, comfy chairs with a dessert and coffee/hot chocolate. It's jam-packed during summer, but during winter it's less busy and truly delightful.

Café Torino
139 W. 10th Street (bet. 7th and Greenwich Aves.)
(212) 675-5554
The food here is very yummy and well priced, but the best thing is the tiramisu—they give you a piece the size of a small brick!

Caffe Rafaella
134 Seventh Avenue
(bet. Charles and 10th Sts.)
(212) 929-7247
No credit cards. The wait staff is generally crazed, so less than courteous, but the food is divine—fabulous Italian desserts.

Caffe Vivaldi
32 Jones Street
(bet. Bleecker and 4th Sts.)
(212) 691-7538
A charming, comfortable little place. Wonderful variety of delicious Italian desserts, and they serve alcohol.

Chumley's
86 Bedford Street (bet. Grove and Bleecker Sts.)
(212) 675-4449
This historical pub was a popular speakeasy during Prohibition. It has been the hangout of numerous literary luminaries. It's one of the stops on the Greenwich Village Pubcrawl, and it continues to be incredibly popular to this day. They have their own beers (other beers also) and the burgers are good, but my favorite is the house salad with house dressing. It's a little pricey for a salad but it is to die for!

Cones
272 Bleecker Street (bet. Morton St. and 7th Ave.)
(212) 414-1795
Ice cream lovers, this place will make you very happy! Cones makes gelato (softer and creamier than ice cream) fresh daily. They also have delicious sorbet.

Cookies and Couscous
230 Thompson Street
(at W. 3rd St.)
(212) 477-6562
A Moroccan eatery that boasts delicious homemade sorbet.

Grano Trattoria
21 Greenwich Avenue
New York, NY 10014
(212) 645-2121
www.granonyc.com
Great Italian food in a cozy atmosphere.

Grove
314 Bleecker Street
(at Grove St.)
(212) 675-9463
This lovely little restaurant has a great outdoor area in the garden in back.

Magnolia Bakery
401 Bleecker Street
(at 11th St.)
(212) 462-2572
For those with a strong sweet tooth, Magnolia is heaven! The cupcakes are famous and the Banana Pudding

with Nilla wafers is addictive. Be prepared to stand in line (sometimes out the door); this place is very popular.

Moustache
90 Bedford Street
(bet. Barrow and Grove Sts.)
(212) 229-2220
No credit cards
An incredibly popular Mediterranean eatery, the dining area of Moustache is almost always full. You can wait or you can always order to go. Try the spinach pie.

Out of the Kitchen
456 Hudson Street
(at Barrow St.)
(212) 242-0399
Not a restaurant per se, but more delilike. Wonderful sandwiches, and their own yummy version of the black and white cookie.

Peanut Butter and Co.
240 Sullivan (bet. Bleecker and W. 3rd Sts.)
(212) 677-3995
Just as the name suggests, this restaurant is a wonder for those who have an affinity for PBJ's, fluffernutters, and so on.

East Village

Bendix Diner
167 First Avenue
(bet. 10th and 11th Sts.)
(212) 260-4220
Mainly diner food but also has some Thai cuisine.

Frank
88 Second Avenue
(bet. 5th and 6th Sts.)
(212) 420-0202
No credit cards. This is a homey, comfy Italian eatery.

St. Dymphna's
118 St. Marks Place
(bet. Ave. A and 1st Ave.)

(212) 254-6636
This Irish bar/restaurant offers live Irish folk music on the weekends

Yaffa Café
37 St. Marks Place
(212) 674-9302
(bet. Ave. A and 1st Ave.)
This cool vegetarian eatery is open 24/7.

SoHo/ Lower East Side

Mrs. K's Italian Deli & Gourmet
118 Madison Avenue
New York, NY 10016
(212) 689-2250
Fax: (212) 576-1425

Chelsea

Restivo's
209 Seventh Avenue
(212) 366-4133
Great Italian restaurant. Not for those who are sensitive to cigarette smoke as the smoke tends to travel into the nonsmoking area from the smoking area and the bar.

7A
109 Avenue A
New York, NY 10009
(212) 475-9001
Open 24 hours. Great ginger dressing and big burritos.

Zoe
90 Prince Street
New York, NY 10012
(212) 966-6722
New American food.
250-label wine list.

Union Square

Chat n' Chew
10 E. 16th Street
(bet. 5th Ave. and Union Square West)
(212) 243-1616
Good ol' American comfort food (pot pies, mac and

cheese, etc.). Often the wait staff are overworked and as a result are not the cheeriest.

The Farmer's Market at Union Square
A great gathering of merchants selling all sorts of goodies, a lot organic foods, as well as handmade crafts and flowers. Usually on Wednesdays, Fridays, and Saturdays in summer and Wednesdays and Saturdays the rest of the year.

Republic
37 Union Square
(bet. 16th and 17th Sts.)
(212) 627-7172
This funky, Asian restaurant can be very busy, so it can get rather loud.

Kimshelley's Spotlight On: A Salt and Battery and Tea and Sympathy

I'm a Brit and proud of it! I love living in the United States and plan to stay here, but I miss English food. Yes, contrary to popular American belief, English food is delicious! Luckily for me, and all the other expats and anglophiles living in the city, Nicky Perry feels the same way.

When Nicky came to visit New York in 1981, she fell in love with the city instantly and moved here two months later. But the lack of good tea upset this dyed-in-the-wool Brit, and she vowed to do something about it. This was the beginning of Tea and Sympathy. Opened in 1990, Tea and Sympathy offers not only the best tea at the best price, but all sorts of English favs like Bangers and Mash, Beans on Toast, Treacle Pudding, Sticky Toffee Pudding, and an assortment of veggie stuff too!

In October 2000, Nicky opened A Salt and Battery, a fish-and-chip shop. With only seven bar stools inside, it's in true English take-away fashion. (For those who want to experience fish and chips in a restaurant setting, try their other location on Second Avenue, between 4th and 5th Streets.) A Salt and Battery offers more English delicacies: Chip Butty, Steak and Kidney Pie, Deep Fried Cream Egg or Mars Bar, and my favorite, Ribena.

In the middle of the two restaurants is Carry On Tea and Sympathy. Here they sell English food, beverages, videos, T-shirts, and other merchandise, as well as handle the delivery aspect of the two restaurants.

Thanks to Nicky, and husband Sean Kavanagh-Dowsett (actor/model/ Brit), there is a place to go and have good English food,

served by good English people. Brilliant!

Tea and Sympathy
108-110 Greenwich Avenue
(bet. 12th and 13th Sts.)
(212) 989-9735
E-mail: info@teaandsympathy
newyork.com
www.teaandsympathy
newyork.com

A Salt and Battery
(2 locations)
112 Greenwich Avenue
(bet. 12th and 13th Sts.)
(212) 691-2713
E-mail: info@asaltand
battery.com
www.asaltandbattery.com
80 Second Avenue
(bet. 4th and 5th Sts.)
(212) 254-6610

Budget Restaurants

Budget a little tight? Check out these low-cost budget restaurant delights!

AQ Café
58 Park Avenue (at 38th St.)
(212) 847-9745
Scandinavian.

B & H Dairy Restaurant
127 Second Avenue
(bet. 7th and 8th Sts.)
(212) 505-8065
Kosher.

Bella Napoli
130 Madison Avenue
(bet. 30th and 31st Sts.)
(212) 683-4510
Italian (pizza and other).

B. Frites
1657 Broadway
(bet. 51st and 52nd Sts.)
(212) 767-0858
Specializing in fries.

Benny's Burrito's
(2 locations)
113 Greenwich Avenue
(bet. Jane and W. 12th Sts.)
(212) 727-3560
Cash only. Mexican.

93 Avenue A
New York, NY 10009
(212) 254-2054

Bread from Beirut
24 W. 45th Street
(bet. 5th and 6th Aves.)
(212) 764-1588
Lebanese.

Bulgin' Waffles
49½ First Avenue
(at 3rd St.)
(212) 477-6555
Waffles and sundaes.

Café Gigi
417 E. 9th Street
(bet. 1st Ave. and Ave. A)
(212) 505-3341
Pizza and other. This is a very cute little place. Non-smokers be aware that there are no smoking/nonsmoking areas.

Congee Village
100 Allen Street
(at Delancy St.)
(212) 941-1818
Chinese.

Crif Dogs
113 St. Marks Place
(bet. 1st Ave. and Ave. A)
(212) 614-2728
One-half dozen types of hot dogs (including tofu dogs) and old-school arcade games.

Da Andrea
557 Hudson Street
(bet. Perry and W. 11th Sts.)
(212) 367-1979
Italian.

Dinerbar
1569 Lexington Avenue
(bet. 100th and 101st Sts.)

(212) 348-0200
American. Try the mac and cheese.

Dumpling
99 Allen Street (bet. Delancey and Broome Sts.)
New York, NY 10002
(212) 941-9975
Chinatown
Chinese. You gotta love a place where you can get five dumplings for $1!

El Malecon
4141 Broadway
(at W. 175th St.)
(212) 927-3812
Dominican. Known for their great chicken. You can get an entire meal under $10.

Ess-A-Bagel
(2 locations)
359 First Avenue (at 21st St.)
(212) 260-2252
Bagels, also has a wide range of salads.

831 Third Avenue
New York, NY 10022
(212) 980-1010

F & B
269 W. 23rd Street
(bet. 7th and 8th Aves.)
(212) 486-4441
Hot dogs and other. Try a Great Dane with pomme frites. Vegetarians, try a tofu dog.

Flea Market Café
131 Avenue A (bet. 9th Street and St. Marks Pl.)
(212) 358-9282
French. The place to go when craving well-priced escargot .

Franklin Station Café
222 West Broadway
(at Franklin St.)
(212) 274-8525
French and Malaysian. Comfort food. Try the Chick-

en Istawema and fruit tart of the day.

Gray's Papaya
(3 locations)
2090 Broadway
(at 72nd St.)
(212) 260-3532
Cash only; open 24 hours a day. Hot dogs and other. There's nowhere to sit down, but heck they've got the Recession Special: two hot dogs and a drink for $2.

402 Sixth Avenue (at 8th St.)
New York, NY 10011
(212) 799-0243

539 Eighth Avenue
New York, NY 10018
(212) 904-1588

Grilled Cheese
168 Ludlow Street
(bet. Stanton and Houston)
(212) 982-6600
American and international. Don't worry, they serve more than just grilled cheese.

Hale and Hearty Soups
(several locations; see a few below)
849 Lexington Avenue
(bet. 64th and 65th Sts.)
(212) 517-7600
Cash only. Soups and other. Good for vegetarians.

55 W. 56th Street
(bet. 5th and 6th Aves.)
(212) 245-9200

75 Ninth Avenue
(bet. 14th and 15th Sts.)
(212) 255-2400

Hampton Chutney Co.
68 Prince Street
(at Crosby St.)
(212) 226-9996
Indian (well-Americanized Indian food).

Hop Shing
9 Chatham Square (bet. Bowery and East Broadway)

(212) 267-0220
Chinese, dim sum.

'ino
21 Bedford Street (bet. 6th Ave. and Downing St.)
(212) 989-5769
Cash only. Italian.

Island Burgers and Shakes
766 Ninth Avenue
(bet. 51st and 52nd Sts.)
(212) 307-7934
Cash only. Hamburgers and other. Sixty-three varieties of burgers, but no fries to be had. On the upside: the burgers were voted Best in New York City by Citysearch in 2001.

Jackson Hole (several locations; see a few below)
232 E. 64th Street
(bet. 2nd and 3rd Aves.)
(212) 371-7187
American diner and coffee shop. More than twenty-four varieties of seven-ounce beef or turkey burgers

1270 Madison Avenue (at 91st St.)
New York, NY 10128
(212) 427-2820

517 Columbus Avenue
New York, NY 10024
(212) 362-5177

Johnny Rockets
42 E. 8th Street (bet. Broadway and University Place)
(212) 253-8175
Hamburgers and hot dogs.

John's Pizzeria
278 Bleecker Street
(bet. 6th and 7th Aves.)
(212) 243-1680
Cash only. Pizza. This place is a major cause for debate—some love it, some hate it. Go judge for yourself.

Katz's Deli
205 Houston Street
(at Ludlow St.)
(212) 254-2246
Deli/international. Go if you
love pastrami, knishes, or
When Harry Met Sally
(yes, it's the famous "I'll
have what she's having"
restaurant).

Kossar's Bialys
367 Grand Street
(at Essex St.)
(212) 473-4810
Bialys. Full name is Kossar's
Bialystoker Kuchen Bakery.
Basically, its just Bialy's.
Open 24 hours a day. Ex-
cept closed sundown Friday
to sundown Saturday (for
Shabbat).

La Taza de Oro
96 Eighth Avenue
(bet. 14th and 15th Sts.)
(212) 243-9946
Cash only. Puerto Rican,
Caribbean, and American
diner.

Lombardi's Pizza
32 Spring Street (bet. Mott
and Mulberry Sts.)
(212) 941-7994
Cash only. Italian/pizza.
They may have long lines,
but fans swear it's worth it.

Papaya King
(3 locations)
179 E. 86th Street
(at 3rd Ave.)
(212) 369-0648
Cash only. Hot dogs.

121 W. 125th Street
(bet. Lennox and 7th Ave.)
(212) 665-5732

255 W. 43rd Street
New York, NY 10036
(212) 944-4590

Pastrami Queen
1269 Lexington Avenue
(bet. 85th and 86th Sts.)
(212) 828-0007

Upper east side. Deli. Has a
small bar that serves wine
and beer.

Sapporo
152 W. 49th Street
(bet. 6th and 7th Aves.)
(212) 869-8972
Cash only. Authentic Japanese food.

71 Irving Place
71 Irving Place
(bet. 18th and 19th Sts.)
(212) 995-5252
Coffeeshop.

Soba-ya
229 E. 9th Street
(bet. 2nd and 3rd Aves.)
(212) 533-6966
Japanese. Try the soba,
freshly made and cut by
hand.

Sorrento
4 W. 18th Street
(bet. 5th and 6th Aves.)
(212) 627-0572
Diner

Tal Bagel
333 E. 86th Street
(bet. 1st and 2nd Aves.)
(212) 427-6811
Cash only. Deli. The downside: they won't toast your
bagel; the upside: nominat-
ed for Best Bagel by Citysearch.

Taqueria de Mexico
93 Greenwich Avenue
(bet. Bank and W. 12th Sts.)
(212) 255-5212
Cash only. Mexican.

Times Square Eatery
42nd Street (bet. 7th and
8th Aves.)
New York, NY 10036
At this food court you can
find Chili's, Applebee's,
Manchu Wok, Ruby's Diner,
California Pizza Kitchen,
Cinnabon, and Carvel.

Tortilla Flats
767 Washington Street (at
12th St.)
New York, NY 10014
(212) 243-1053
West Village. Mexican.
Place is tiny, but they have
bingo nights!

Vatan
409 Third Avenue
(at 28th St.)
(212) 689-5666
Indian/healthy/vegetarian.
The menu is $19.95 prix
fixé, but it's all you can eat.
Make a reservation and be
prepared to remove your
shoes.

Veselka
144 Second Avenue (at 9th
St.)
(212) 228-9682
East Village. Open 24
hours. Diner/Eastern Euro-
pean. Try the raspberry
blintzes and the pierogies.

Wo Hop
17 Mott Street
(bet. Bowery and Mosco)
(212) 267-2536
Americanized Chinese food.

Wrapp Factory
2857 Broadway
(bet. 110th and 111th Sts.)
(212) 665-5870
Harlem. American and
international.

Book Review: Vegetarian NYC: The Essential Guide to Dining, Shopping and Lodging by Suzanne Gerber

For vegetarians, vegans,
and all health-conscious
actors, *Vegetarian
NYC: The Essential*

Guide to Dining, Shopping and Lodging (Globe Pequot Press, 2004) is a most handy, well-organized guide. Suzanne Gerber, the former editor-in-chief of *Vegetarian Times*, has put together a fabulous book that is clearly the first and last word in eating healthfully in New York. *Vegetarian New York, NY* contains reviews of some 200 restaurants, scores of healthy markets, as well as tips for navigating the vegetarian world of New York as only insiders can tell you.

Suzanne will not just send you to well-known vegetarian haunts; she lets you in on secrets even longtime New Yorkers don't know, namely where someone who doesn't eat meat can get the absolutely best and most-exciting meals in New York. Each write-up includes a review based on a personal recent visit, all pertinent information (hours and payment accepted), and is indexed according to type of cuisine, cost, and "vegebility." Organized by location, each chapter includes a description of the neighborhood, a map, and an alphabetical list of local restaurants, markets, and places to stay. Addition-

ally, there are fun and informative sidebars that include:

- Best of the best: from best bargains to best karma to most romantic places.
- Green markets: every location and days and hours of operation.
- Culinary destinations: Chinatown, Little Italy, Little Korea, and three Little Indias!
- Top ten vegan desserts.
- The best vegetarian sushi places.
- Brooklyn's hip Smith Street.
- Mock meat bastions.
- Food co-ops and home delivery outfits.
- Earthsave, vegan shoes, and raw events.

Wow, this is some book! We suggest you run out and get a copy.

In the meantime, here are Suzanne's top ten restaurant suggestions for health-minded folks on a budget.

Angelica Kitchen
300 E. 12th St (bet. 1st and 2nd Aves.)
(212) 228-2909
Hours: Daily,
11:30 AM–10:30 PM
Organic whole-food vegan. This is the place that's launched a thousand imitators. There are a few daily

specials (with groaner names like Charlie's Triangles), but most regulars love to order from the extensive all-veg menu, featuring inventive salads, soups, appetizers, sandwiches, entrées, and dragon bowl combinations. Some people come just for the vegan desserts (chocolate when the moon is full).

Ayurveda Café
716 Amsterdam (bet. 94 and 95th Sts.)
(212) 932-2400
Hours: Daily, 11:30
AM–11:30 PM
Indian. Major credit cards accepted. No alcohol; no BYOB. Since 1999, the cozy café has been serving multi-regional vegetarian Indian cuisine prepared fresh — and with compassion and love. Every day there's a different menu at lunch and dinnertime from lunch; in theory you could come every day and sample a completely different original creation — and many regulars do. One friend who's lived in India says this is the only truly authentic Indian place in New York.

B & H Dairy
127 Second Avenue (bet. 7th St. and St. Marks Pl.)
(212) 505-8065
Hours: Daily, 7 AM–10 PM
Kosher, dairy, vegetarian. Cash only. B & H will take you back in time to the days when Jewish delis dotted the East Village. This tiny deli is known for its all-veg soups (try the borscht or mushroom/barley), served with thick fresh challah bread. But its blintzes and pierogis are equally renowned. At less than $5 apiece for any of the above, you won't go home hungry — or broke.

Burritoville (several locations)
Tex-Mex. Days and hours vary. Major credit cards accepted. Burritoville is the quick-fix escape for the vegetarian on the run. With twelve locations around the city, you'd be hard-pressed not to stumble upon one. Choose from an extensive (and tasty) menu of tacos, quesadillas, wraps, enchiladas, salads, soups, nachos, soups, chilis, burritos, or weekly specials. The mandates posted on the wall assure the customers that: They press all their own tortillas daily; No lard; no preservatives; no cans in the kitchen; bo prepared products. Every recipe is made fresh every day.

451 Amsterdam Avenue
(212) 787-8181

166 West 72nd Street
(212) 580-7700

625 Ninth Avenue
(212) 333-5352

352 West 39th Street
(212) 563-9088

264 West 23rd Street
(212) 367-9844

298 Bleecker Street
(212) 633-9249

144 Chambers Street
(212) 964-5048

36 Water Street
(212) 747-1100

20 John Street
(212) 766-2020

141 Second Avenue
(212) 260-3300

866 Third Avenue
(212) 980-4111

1487 Second Avenue
(212) 472-8800

Café Mogador
101 St. Marks Place (bet. 1st Ave. and Ave. A)
(212) 677-2226
Moroccan. Hours: Sun.–Thurs., 9 AM-1 AM; Fri.–Sat., 9 AM–2 AM. Major credit cards accepted. This East Village staple claims to churn out the best couscous in town, but you'd be remiss to skip the appetizers (mezes), which you can make a full meal of. Mix and match the cucumber yogurt, smoky roasted eggplant, falafel, humus, roasted red peppers, all served with pita bread. In warm weather, try to get a sidewalk table and enjoy prime people-watching.

Candle Café
1307 Third Avenue (at 75th St.)
(212) 472-0970
Seasonal organic vegan. Hours: Mon–Sat., noon–10:30 PM; Sun. noon–9:30 PM. Major credit cards. Open for over a decade now, Candle is one of the leading organic veggie places in the country. Start with a fresh-squeezed juice or glass of organic wine. Menu staples span the globe, and there are nightly specials featuring such stars as grilled tofu, rosemary-crusted tempeh, and exotic grains. And the desserts are killer. Who knew veggie could be so gourmet?

Caravan of Dreams
405 E. 6th Street (bet. 1st Ave. and Ave. A)
(212) 254-1613
Organic vegan. Hours: Mon., 5–11 PM; Tue.–Thurs. and Sun 11 AM–11 PM; Fri.–Sat., 11–midnight. Major credit cards accepted. This downtown fave boasts

the 3 H's: hearty, healthy, and hip. Dine on tofu, grains, an all-raw platter, huge salads, or pretty much anything your veg heart desires. Caravan serves organic beers and wine and exciting desserts, and many nights there's even live entertainment. Lean on a throw pillow and relax: you'll be here a while.

Café Madras
79 Second Avenue (bet. 4th and 5th Sts.)
(212) 254-8002
Indian. Hours: Daily, 1 PM–11 PM. This way-above-average Indian joint is named for the owner's hometown of Madras, which is famous for its skilled chefs and vivid spices. You'll find plenty of your favorite northern dishes (curries, sag paneer), but if you've never had a dosa, try one. The humongous lentil-flour crepe is stuffed with potatoes or other veggies and served with two delectable dips,. If that's not enough food, order the Thali, a full traditional meal that includes lentil soup, rice, roti bread, riatha, two entrées, and dessert for $10.95. Kosher South Indian vegetarian. Major credit cards.

18 Arhans
227 Centre Street (Grand and Broome)
(212) 941-8986
Pan-Asian vegetarian. Hours: Mon.–Sat., 12 PM–7 PM. Cash only. Lower Manhattan's only vegetarian café/Buddhist shrine serves up made-to-order Pan-Asian food for no more than $7 a plate. Try the Curry Spring Roll and House Special B—Chinatown's closest cousin to Southern American com-

fort food. Arhans is famous for its tofu, which is made fresh in the neighborhood and bought by the restaurant daily.

Sacred Chow
522 Hudson Street (bwt. Charles and W. 10th Sts.)
(212) 337-0863
Vegan Asian. Hours: Mon.–Fri., 7:30 AM–9:30 PM; Sat.–Sun., 8:30 AM–9:30 PM. Major credit cards. The eclectic, organic fare at this little West Village lunchtime counter is priced at $7 to $8 a pound. Favorites include marinated, then grilled chunks of South Western tofu, black olive roasted seitan, rosemary roasted tempeh, and spicy peanut udon. For dessert, there are cookies, muffins, bars, carrot cakes, a gorgeous fruit cobbler, halva, chocolate pie, and a to-die-for vanilla tofu and pear pie with a wheat-free crust.

Liz's Favorite Cafés

Latte, espresso, café au lait, or just a straight up cup o'Joe — there is no shortage of coffee shops in New York City. Have a hankering for a homemade marshmallow? Take your sweet-tooth self to The City Bakery. Bop or over to Edwin's Café and treat yourself to a night of traditional Puerto Rican music on Yerba Buena whilst you sip. Coffee shops make a perfect place to relax after an exhausting au-

dition or to give you that perk you need after spending a day in rehearsal. Of course, true caffeine addicts know there's no need to make an excuse for a jolt of java, so here's a few you might enjoy:

Alt.coffee
139 Avenue A
New York, NY 10009
(212) 529-2233

Ansonia Espresso Bar
2113 Broadway (at 72nd St.)
New York, NY 10023
(212) 873-3245

Arthur Avenue Café
2329 Arthur Avenue
Bronx, NY 10458
(718) 562-0129

Big Cup
228 Eighth Avenue
New York, NY 10011
(212) 206-0059

Breadsoul Café
30 Lincoln Plaza
New York, NY 10023
(212) 765-7309

Café Grand Marnier
1752 Broadway (at 56th St.)
New York, NY 10019
(212) 581-5130

Café Pick Me Up
145 Avenue A
New York, NY 10009
(212) 673-7231

Caffe Tosca
260 E. 72nd Street
New York, NY 10021
(212) 744-4155

The City Bakery
3 W. 18th Street
New York, NY 10011
(212) 366-1414

Coffee Mug
233 Broadway (Park Pl. and Barclay St.)
New York, NY 10007
(212) 349-6040

Drip
489 Amsterdam Avenue
New York, NY 10024
(212) 875-1032

Edwin's Café
181 E. 111th Street
New York, NY 10029
(646) 672-1808

Fluffy's Café & Bakery
855 Seventh Avenue
New York, NY 10019
(212) 247-0234

The Grey Dog's Coffee
33 Carmine Street
New York, NY 10014
(212) 462-0041

In the Black
180 Varick Street
New York, NY 10014
(212) 807-8322

World Cup Café & Bakery
956 Lexington Avenue
New York, NY 10021
(212) 717-6888

43. CLEAN RESTROOMS

All Barnes and Nobles!
For a list of locations, see pages 165–166

Starbucks (several locations)
494 Eighth Avenue (at 35th St.)
(212) 947-3860
You must get a key from the counter.

370 Seventh Avenue (bet. 30th and 31st)
(212) 967-8463

1 Battery Park Plaza (bet. Broadway and Greenwich)
(212) 482-1180

45 Wall Street
(at William St.)
(212) 269-8717

304 Park Avenue South
(at 23rd St.)
(212) 475-9025

93 Greenwich Avenue
(bet. 12th and Bank Sts.)
(212) 462-4697

261 Fifth Avenue
(bet. 28th and 29th Sts.)
(212) 779-1557

424 Park Avenue South
(bet. 55th and 56th Sts.)
(212) 725-0637

575 Fifth Avenue (at 47th St.)
(212) 490-3189

757 Third Avenue
(at 47th St.)
(212) 715-9884

639 Third Avenue (at 41st St.)
(212) 973-1376

109 E. 42nd Street (bet. Lexington and Park Aves.)
(212) 599-4368

280 Park Avenue (48th St.)
(212) 573-9869

462 Fashion Avenue
(at 35th St.)
(212) 279-6432

750 Seventh Avenue
(bet. 49th and 50th Sts.)
(212) 974-0032

325 W. 49th Street
(bet. 8th and 9th Aves.)
(212) 765-2205

116 E. 57th Street (bet. Lexington and Park Aves.)
(212) 486-1632

48 W. 73rd Street
(bet. Central Park West and Columbus Ave.)
(212) 579-7834

2 Columbus Avenue
(at 59th St.)
(212) 489-6757

1841 Broadway
(bet. 60th and 61st Sts.)
(212) 307-0162

540 Columbus Avenue
(at 86th St.)
(212) 496-4139

444 Columbus Avenue
(at 81st St.)
(212) 769-2296

2851 Broadway
(bet. Cathedral Parkway and W. 11th St.)
(212) 280-7268

83 W. 125th Street
(bet. 7th and Lennox Aves.)
(917) -492-2453

25 W. 45th Street
(bet. 5th and 6th Aves.)
(212) 505-0738

682 Ninth Avenue (at 47th St.)
(212) 397-2288

1460 Broadway
(bet. 41st and 42nd Sts.)
(212) 869-0191

38 Park Row (bet. Beekman and Ann Sts.)
(212) 587-8400

450 Fashion Avenue
(bet. 31st and 32nd Sts.)
(212) 279-1122

1642 Third Avenue
(at E. 92nd St.)
(212) 360-0425

665 Broadway
(bet. Bond and W. 3rd Sts.)
(917) 534-0799

2498 Broadway
(at 93rd St.)
(917) 441-1643

95 East Broadway
(at Forsyth St.)
(212) 791-6368

450 Lexington Avenue
(at 45th St.)
New York, NY 10017
(212) 682-5139

400 Madison Avenue
(bet. 47th and 48th Sts.)
(212) 319-1676

1 Penn Plaza
(bet. 7th and 8th Aves.)
(212) 760-3001

250 Vesey Street
(at North End Ave.)
(212) 945-0282

100 Wall Street (at Front St.)
(212) 809-1556

100 William Street
(at Platt St.)
(212) 509-9709

334 Fifth Avenue
(at 33rd St.)
(212) 279-2799

545 Fifth Avenue
(at E. 45th St.)
(212) 687-1026

600 Eighth Avenue (at 39th St.)
(212) 997-7337

871 Eighth Avenue
(at 52nd St.)
(212) 246-7699

150 E.42nd Street (bet. Lexington and 3rd Aves.)
(212) 949-4122

1 E. 57th Street (at 5th Ave.)
(212) 755-1339

135 E. 57th Street
(at Lexington Ave.)
(212) 935-1866

2929 Broadway (bet. 114th and 115th Sts.)
(212) 932-1748

830 Third Avenue (bet. 50th and 51st Sts.)
(212) 980-1748

1166 Sixth Avenue (bet. 45th and 46th Sts.)
(212) 354-3730

1185 Sixth Avenue (bet. 46th and 47th Sts.)
(212) 382-0352

1345 Sixth Avenue (at 54th St.)
(212) 265-8610

335 Madison Avenue (at 43rd St.)
(212) 370-3510

100 Church Street (at Park Pl.)
(212) 513-1006

909 Third Avenue (at 55th St.)
(212) 735-9910

55 Park Avenue Plaza (bet. 52nd and 53rd Sts.)
(212) 750-7140

Downtown

ABC Carpet and Home
888 Broadway (at 19th St.)
2nd and 4th floors

Battery Park
In Castle Clinton Park, on the north end of Battery Park, within the castle's walls.
Open from 8:30 AM–5 PM.

Forbes Magazine Galleries
62 Fifth Avenue
(bet. 12th and 13th Sts.)

KMart
770 Broadway (bet. Lafayette and 8th Sts.)
2nd floor

Midtown

Brooks Brothers
346 Madison (at 44th St.)
Women on 3rd floor
Men on 5th floor

Citigroup Center
850 Third Avenue (bet. 52nd and 53rd Sts.)

Doral Park Avenue
70 Park Avenue (at 38th St.)

Doral Tuscany Hotel
120 E. 39th Street (bet. Park and Lexington Aves.)

Drake Hotel
440 Park Avenue (bet. 56th and 57th Sts.)

Gramercy Park Hotel
2 Lexington Avenue (at 22nd St.)

Grand Central Station
42nd Street (bet. Lexington and Vanderbilt Aves.)

Grand Hyatt Hotel
42nd Street (Park Ave. at Grand Central Station)

Henri Bendel
712 Fifth Avenue
(bet. 55th and 56th Sts.)
Women on lower level, 3rd and 4th floors
Men on lower level

Hotel Edison
228 W. 47th Street (bet. Broadway and 8th Ave.)

Jacob Javits Convention Center
655 W. 34th Street (at 11th Ave.)
Open 24 hours a day.

KMart
1 Penn Plaza (bet. 33rd and 34th Sts.)

Le Parker Meridian Hotel
118 W. 57th Street (bet. 6th and 7th Aves.)

Lord and Taylor
424 Fifth Avenue
(bet. 38th and 39th Sts.)
Women on 4th and 5th floors
Men on 10th floor

Macy's
6th and Seventh Avenues
(bet. 38th and 39th Sts.)
Women on 2nd, 6th, and 7th floors
Men on 4th and 7th floors

Marriott Marquis Hotel
1535 Broadway (bet. 45th and 46th Sts.)
Levels 3 through 9

New York Hilton at Rockefeller Center
1335 Sixth Avenue (at 53rd St.)

New York Public Library (Donnell Branch)
20 W. 53rd Street (bet. 5th and 6th Aves.)

New York Public Library (Mid-Manhattan)
455 Fifth Avenue (at 42nd St.)
Ground floor and 3rd floor

Novotel Hotel
226 W. 52nd Street (bet. Broadway and 8th Ave.)

Omni Berkshire
21 E. 52nd Street (bet. Madison and 5th Aves.)

Paramount Hotel
235 W. 46th Street (bet. Broadway and 8th Ave.)

Park Avenue Plaza
52nd Street (bet. Madison and Park Aves.)
Open 8 AM–10 PM

Port Authority
40th and 42nd Streets
(bet. 8th and 9th Aves.)
Lower level, 1st and 2nd floors

Roosevelt Hotel
45 E. 45th Street
(bet. Madison and Vanderbilt Aves.)

Roger Smith Hotel
501 Lexington Avenue (at 47th St.)

Roger Williams Hotel
131 Madison Avenue
(at 31st St.)

Royalton Hotel
44 W. 44th Street
(5th and 6th Aves.)

Saks and Co.
611 Fifth Avenue
(bet. 49th and 50th Sts.)
Women on 4th floor
Men on 6th floor

Shelburne Hotel
303 Lexington Avenue
(bet. 37th and 38th Sts.)

Sheraton New York
811 Seventh Avenue
(at 53rd St.)

Southgate Tower Hotel
371 Seventh Avenue (bet.
30th and 31st Sts.)

St. Regis Hotel
2 E. 55th Street (at 5th Ave.)

Urban Center
457 Madison Avenue
(bet. 50th and 51st Sts.)
Hours: 8 AM–6 PM

Waldorf Astoria Hotel
Park Avenue (at 50th St.)

Uptown

Barbizon Hotel
140 E. 63rd Street
(at Lexington Ave.)

Bergdorf Goodman
754 Fifth Avenue
(bet. 57th and 58th Sts.)
Women on 7th floor
Men on 3rd floor

Bloomingdales
1000 Third Avenue
(bet. 59th And 60th Sts.)
Women on 4th and
7th floors
Men on lower level, 5th
and 7th floors

Cooper-Hewitt Museum
2 E. 91st Street (at 5th Ave.)

**Delacorth Theatre
(Central Park)**
81st Street, midpark

Hotel Pierre
6 E. 61st Street (bet. 5th
and Madison Aves.)

Lincoln Center Library
111 Amsterdam Avenue
(at 65th St.)
2nd and 3rd floors

Plaza Hotel
768 Fifth Avenue
(at 59th St.)

Regency Hotel
540 Park Avenue
(bet. 60th and 61st Sts.)

Ritz Carlton Hotel
50 Central Park South
(bet. 5th and 6th Aves.)

**Sherry
Netherland Hotel**
781 Fifth Avenue
(at 59th St.)

Tiffany's
757 Fifth Avenue (at 57th St.)

44.
HEALTH CARE
PROVIDERS

Dentists

For those who are
very strapped for cash,
there are the low-cost
dental care offices of
Toothsavers.

**Toothsavers
(2 locations)**
57 W. 57th Street
New York, NY 10019
(212) 753-0123
1-800-287-8338

231 W. 96th Street
New York, NY 10025
(212) 865-8280
www.toothsaversdental.com

Howard Brodsky, DDS
115 E. 57th Street
(in The Galleria)
New York, NY 10022
(212) 832-8664

**Robert Castracane,
DMD**
225 E. 64th Street (bet. 2nd
and 3rd Aves.)
New York, NY 10021
(212) 838-7676

Jeffrey Dorfman
18 E. 50th Street
Penthouse C
New York, NY 10022
(212) 754-6555
Dr. Dorfmann is on the higher end of the price scale, but
during the school year, he
has Columbia University
graduate students working at
his office, and he offers a
discount if you wish to work
with them.

**Manhattan Dental
Associates**
2 W. 45th Street
Suite 1008
(bet. 5th and 6th Aves.)
New York, NY 10036
(212) 944-2836

Ramona Olivera
30 E. 40th Street,
Suite 207(bet. Park and
Madison Aves.)
New York, NY 10016
(212) 696-4979

Nancy Schnur, DDS
275 Madison Avenue,
Suite 1318 (at 40th St.)
New York, NY 10016
(212) 972-6340

Optometrists

**American Eye
Care Center**
38-03 Broadway
Astoria, NY 11103
(718) 956-3000

Eyes of Broadway
651 Broadway (bet.
Bleecker and Bond Sts.)
New York, NY 10012
(212) 614-0069

Eyetech
142 E. 49th Street (bet.
Lexington and 3rd Aves.)
New York, NY 10017
(212) 753-1466

**Grammercy Park
Optical**
344 Third Avenue
(bet. 25th and 26th Sts.)
New York, NY 10010
(212) 679-9690

Myoptics
42 St. Marks Place
(bet. 1st and 2nd Aves.)
New York, NY 10003
(212) 533-1577

**Pearl Vision (several
locations)**
2177 Broadway
(at 77th St.)
New York, NY 10024
(212) 787-9100

1548 First Avenue
(at 81st St.)
New York, NY 10028
(212) 717-5412

6 E. 23rd Street (bet.
Broadway and Madison Ave.)
New York, NY 10010
(212) 982-7850

Featured Doctor: Dr. Richard Kowal

Dr. Kowal has been a practicing nutritionist and chiropractor serving New York City performers since 1983. He received a B.S. in human development from Cornell University, an M.S. in human nutri-

tion from the University of Bridgeport, and a D.C. from New York Chiropractic College.

Dr. Kowal's first experience with the special problems of performers came while working with the dancers from the Joffrey Ballet, who combine traditional ballet with modern dance. Because they were artists, Dr. Kowal offered the dancers a reduced rate and many came for care. Dr. Kowal told us how much he loved working with the dancers and how, out of that experience, he continues to use many of the dance repair techniques that he developed fifteen years ago.

Dr. Kowal has also worked extensively with Broadway performers. He has treated musicians' injuries to the shoulders, arms, forearms, and hands. He also wrote a popular series of articles for the New York musician's magazine, *Allegro*. Dr. Kowal said that actors and singers on raked stages working eight shows a week have also needed special care of the frequent spine-related complaints associated with the grueling obligations of a Broadway show. Actors, said Dr. Kowal,

have an almost transparent quality that translates into great sensitivity to his work.

We discovered that much of Dr. Kowal's work as a nutritionist and chiropractor revolves around opening, sensitizing, and freeing. Dr. Kowal had an obvious love for nutrition. He said that when we eat in a way that makes us chronically tired and low, it's very difficult to relate it to our food choices. It simply seems like our chronic state, dissociated with the daily choices we make. But when we begin to refine our diet and lifestyle choices, we can actually feel the specific vibration created in us by what we eat, how we exercise, the quality of our rest, etc. This refinement is an endless study, and anyone who thinks that they can grow inwardly and outwardly, without taking the body along on the journey, is mistaken.

Dr. Kowal became very passionate as he talked about improving his clients' health. He said that as we become older, the effort to maintain ourselves becomes both more challenging and more rewarding. As we age, it becomes progressively more difficult to maintain perfect weight and body composition, especially for women. Fortunately, there is a solution. And perhaps more important, the same strategies that help to improve body composition also improve the quality of our skin, reduce our inflammatory problems, and reduce our risk of heart disease and other serious illnesses. Dr. Kowal has actually coached countless actors and actresses in these strategies and has seen, time after time, tremendous success.

Dr. Richard Kowal
23 W. 73rd Street
New York, NY 10023
(212) 799-2520

Doctors

Claudia Holland, MD (2 offices)
16 E. 60th Street, 4th Floor
(bet. 5th and Madison Aves.)
New York, NY 10022
(212) 305-5572

161 Fort Washington Avenue (at 165th St.)
New York, NY 10032
(212) 305-5572

Mark E. Horowitz, MD
Midtown Family Medicine
315 W. 57th Street
(at 7th Ave.)
Suite 304
New York, NY 10019
(212) 262-9285

Alan Kadet, MD
65 Central Park West
New York, NY 10023
(212) 721-5600
Kimshelley's doctor: a very charming man with a friendly and helpful staff.

Andrew Stiber, MD
220 E. 30th Street
(bet. 2nd and 3rd Aves.)
New York, NY 10016
(212) 686-0499

Psychotherapists

Robert Curtis, CSW
(917) 415-5232
Free consultation.

Portia Franklin, CSW
(212) 427-6921
Mind/body process developed by former Martha Graham dancers. Moderate fee. Free telephone consultation.

Myra Friedman, MSW
Psychotherapy/hypnosis.
(212) 330-9331

Dolores Walker, CSW
(212) 691-6073
Former AEA/SAG member.

Robert Wool
(212) 245-7698
Free consultation; sliding scale.

45. HOSPITALS

Beth Israel Medical Center
First Avenue and 16th Street
New York, NY 10001
(212) 420-2000 (general information)

Columbia Presbyterian Medical Center
622 W. 168th Street
New York, NY 10032
(212) 305-3101
www.nyp.org

Coney Island Hospital
2601 Ocean Parkway
(at Avenue Z)
Brooklyn, NY 11235
(718) 616-3000

Gracie Square Hospital
420 E. 76th Street
(bet. 1st and York Aves.)
New York, NY 10021
(212) 988-4400
E-mail: info@nygsh.org
www.nygsh.org

Harlem Hospital Center
506 Lenox Avenue
(bet. 136th and 137th Sts.)
New York, NY 10037
(212) 939-1401
E-mail: harlemmed2@
earthlink.org
www.harleminternal
medicine.org

Hospital for Joint Diseases Orthopaedic Institute
301 E. 17th Street
New York, NY 10003
(212) 598-6000
www.jointdiseases.com

Lenox Hill Hospital
100 E. 77th Street
(at Park Ave.)
New York, NY 10021
(212) 434-2000
www.lenoxhillhospital.org

Lincoln Medical and Mental Health Center
234 E. 149th Street
(bet. Morris and Park Aves.)
Bronx, NY 10451
(718) 579-5000

Manhattan Eye, Ear, and Throat Hospital
210 E. 64th Street
(at 3rd Ave.)
New York, NY 10021
(212) 838-9200

Mt. Sinai Hospital
19 E. 98th Street, #4E (bet.
Madison and 5th Aves.)
New York, NY 10029
(212) 241-6500

**New York Hospital,
Cornell Medical Center**
525 E. 68th Street
(at York Ave.)
New York, NY 10021
(212) 746-5454

North General Hospital
1879 Madison Avenue
New York City, NY 10035
(212) 423-4000

**NYU Downtown
Hospital**
170 William Street
New York, NY 10038
(212) 312-5000
www.nyudh.org

NYU Medical Center
550 First Avenue
New York, NY 10016
(212) 263-7300
www.nyumc.org

St. Claire's Hospital
426 W. 52nd Street
New York, NY 10019
(212) 586-1500

**St. Vincent Catholic
Medical Center**
153 W. 11th Street
(at 7th Ave.)
New York, NY 10011
(212) 604-7000
www.svcmc.org

**Westchester Medical
Center**
Vahalla Campus
Vahalla, NY 10595
(914) 493-7000
www.worldclassmedicine.
com

TEN

getting around and staying there

46. TRANSPORTATION

Subways and Buses

New York City has an incredible public transportation system. OK, when it's summer and you're stuffed inside a subway car with so many people you can't even move enough to check the time on your watch and some of the people in this over-stuffed aluminum can aren't wearing deodorant, it doesn't seem so incredible.

To ride, you can buy a MetroCard at the subway booths, or you can purchase Metro-Cards through the MetroCard vending machines, usually locat-ed close to the booths. Sometimes MetroCards are available at stores in the city such as Hall-marks or drugstores (they usually post a sign to that effect if they do carry them).

The cost is $2 per ride. There are also oth-er options — a one-day Fun Pass or a weekly or monthly unlimited ride card. You will have to plan out how many rides you will take every day, but if you know you're going to take sev-eral rides, one of the un-limited ride cards may be worth it. Be aware, once you swipe your un-limited card at a turn-stile, you cannot use it again for another eight-een minutes. You can also use your Metro-cards on MTA buses.

Subway maps are usually posted when you first walk down into a station, close to the booths. There's also usually a map posted somewhere in every subway car. You can get subway maps all over the place, but get-ting a map for the bus-es is harder. Despair not, until you can get your hands on a map, all that information can be found online at the MTA Web site: www.mta.nyc.ny.

There never seems to be a time when they're not doing work on at least one of the lines, so always be prepared for delays, schedule changes, and line changes. There is an MTA Hotline that is updated hourly from

6 AM to 9 PM: (718) 243-7777.

One constant on the subways is the panhandlers (beggars). It is technically illegal for them to beg on the subways, but that is never a deterrent. Most people will completely avoid eye contact, and the panhandler will continue through the cars. For a new person in New York, the amount of people panhandling can seem overwhelming. And you will see the same people over and over again. The MTA would prefer that you not give to them, but of course, it's up to you. Be aware you will also see a lot of bogus charities on the streets trying to drum up money. If you want to give to a charity, there are plenty of legitimate ones to be found on www.city search.com. You will see a lot of musicians playing in Times Square and other stations also. Some are there legitimately. There is a program that musicians audition for and get chosen to showcase their talents in the subway. But a lot of times, the musicians, singers, dancers, and novelty acts are trying to raise some cash. Don't blow them off completely

though. There's some wonderful talent to be found there!

Rush hour for the subways is approximately 8 to 10 AM and 5 to 7:30 PM. This is when riding is just no fun. The trains are supposed to be on a schedule, but it never really works out that way. People holding the doors and delaying the train, train malfunctions, or accidents can set back the whole schedule. Trains run about every five to ten minutes during the day, but slow down considerably at night. Also, if you're on a shared line, be aware of what train you're getting on. For example, on the N/R line, if an N passes, it's not always safe to assume the next train will be an R. If you're just riding within Manhattan, that doesn't tend to matter, but if you are planning on taking it out of Manhattan, you'll want to make sure you have it right.

Most stations have a newspaper kiosk, and they usually carry *Backstage* and *Show Business Weekly*.

Taxi Cabs

Yellow taxi cabs are synonymous with New York City. They are *everywhere*. And yet, it can be really hard to catch one. It's simple to hail one — simply raise your arm and flag one down. It's finding one that's empty that's the hard part. Just remember, if the numbers on the top of the cab are lit, it's available.

The base fee is $2.50 and on top of that you will pay $0.40 each one-fifth mile (approximately four blocks). Additional riders are free. Pay only what's on the meter, plus a 15 to 20 percent gratuity. Tolls for outside the metropolitan New York area or New Jersey are also your responsibility. Make sure to take your receipt.

Should you run into any problems, all yellow cabs have an ID number and the driver's name is usually displayed as well. This information should also be on your receipt. The Taxi and Limousine Commission number is (212) 692-8294. For more information, go to www.ny.com/transportation/taxis.

Car Service

If you want to make sure you have a car instead of taking a chance of catching a cab, you can always call a car service. Remember, find out what kind of charge you'll be looking at before you accept. The following car services will pick up from any of the boroughs:

Allen Car Service
154 Allen Street
New York, NY 10002
(212) 228-1111

Allstate Car and Limousine, Inc.
163 Eighth Avenue
New York, NY 10011
(212) 333-3333

Crown Limousine and Car Service
554 W. 48th Street
New York, NY 10036
(212) 246-2626

Hoyt Car Service
23-03 Astoria Blvd
Astoria, NY 11102
(718) 204-5861

Lincoln Car Service
347 E. 109th Street
New York, NY 10029
(212) 722-0939

Original Uptown Car Service
961 Washington Avenue
Bronx, NY 10456
(718) 993-8070

Taxi Service by Carmel
2642 Broadway
New York, NY 10025
(212) 666-6666
1-800-9-CARMEL

PATH

The PATH train is run by the Port Authority of New York and New Jersey. It runs from Hoboken and Newark (with a few stops on the way) to Christopher (at Hudson), 9th Street at Sixth Avenue, 14th Street at Sixth Avenue, 23rd Street at Sixth Avenue, and 33rd Street at Sixth Avenue in Manhattan. The PATH runs Monday through Friday: 6 AM to 11 PM. Saturday, Sunday, and holidays: 9 AM to 7:30 PM. Go to www.panynj.gov/path for more information.

47. AIRPORTS AND AIRLINES

LaGuardia Airport

Located in Queens, LaGuardia only handles domestic flights. It's a very busy little airport so be prepared for delays. To reach LaGuardia you can call Hoyt Car Service at (718) 204-5861 or you can take the M60 bus.

John F. Kennedy Airport

Also located in Queens, though further out away from the city. If you take a cab, it is a set fee of $35 from Manhattan, plus tolls. Most car services are the same, but ask in advance and make sure. Also allow ample time for traffic. To get there by public transport, take the E or F subway to Union Turnpike (in Kew Gardens), and then take the Q10 to the airport. Again this is a lengthy trip, so plan accordingly.

From Manhattan to and from JFK, LaGuardia, or Newark Airport in New Jersey, you can also take the Super Shuttle. Its costs around $13 to $22. The downside is you have to deal with other passengers not being ready at their pickup time. Also, there is a long wait if you try to get a Super Shuttle in the very early hours of the morning. Rates are subject to change with no notice so make sure to ask when you make your reservation. Try to make it at least twenty-four hours in advance. Call Super Shuttle: (212) 258-3826 or www.supershuttle.com

Be aware that gypsy cabs are at both LaGuardia and JFK, as well as at most elevated subways. These cab drivers generally work for legitimate car services but on their own time try to pick up customers at the subway and airports. Doing this at the airports is illegal. For your own safety, avoid gypsy cabs; get a registered yellow taxi from the taxi stand. If, for whatever reason, you must use one, make sure you establish a price and agree to it before you get in the car. Otherwise, you will likely pay two times the amount you would pay a registered taxi. And once you've accepted a gypsy cab's services, you're obligated to pay the driver whatever he or she decides to charge you. It's also wise to establish an approximate figure when using a legitimate car service, just so you have an idea what your fare should be.

Airline Telephone Numbers and Web Sites

Air Canada
1-888-247-2262
www.aircanada.com

Alaska Airlines
1-877-502-5357
www.alaskaair.com

American Airlines
1-800-433-7300
www.aa.com

America West
1-800-235-9292
www.americawest.com

Air Canada
1-800- 422-7533
www.aircanada.com

Austrian Airlines
1-800-843-0002
www.austrianair.com

China Airlines
(917) 368-2000
www.china-airlines.com

Continental Airlines
1-800-525-0280
www.continental.com

Delta Airlines
1-800-221-1212
www.delta-air.com

Frontier Airlines
1-800-265-5505
www.frontierairlines.com

Lufthansa
1-800-581-6400
http://cms.lufthansa.com

Mexicana
1-800-531-7921
www.mexicana.com

National Airlines
1-888-757-5387
www.nationalairlines.com

Northwest Airlines
1-800-225-2525
www.nwa.com

Southwest Airlines
1-800-435-9792
www.southwest.com

Spirit Airlines
1-800-772-7117
www.spiritair.com

United Airlines
1-800-241-6522
www.ual.com

US Air
1-800-428-4322
www.usair.com

Virgin Atlantic
1-800-862-8621
www.virgin-atlantic.com

If you want to find a good price, try these Web sites:

www.travelocity.com
This site gives you rates from several airlines; also does lodging, cars, railways, vacations, cruises, and more.

www.expedia.com
This site gives you airline rates, lodging, cars, and so on; also does maps and guides to cities.

48.
LIMOUSINES

Limousine services will charge you from garage to garage, meaning they will charge you more if they have to travel far from their base to pick you up and drop you off. If you live outside the city, you may want to find a limo company that is close to you.

Allstate Car and Limousine
163 Eighth Avenue
New York, NY 10011
(212) 333-3333

American Classic Limousines
237 First Avenue
New York, NY 10003
(212) 979-0500

Bermuda Limousine International, Inc.
537 W. 20 th Street
New York, NY 10011
(212) 647-8400

Carey A Limousine NY, Inc.
27-10 4Ninth Avenue
Long Island City 11101
(212) 599-1122

**Carnegie Limousine
Network Inc.**
Contact: Sam
64 North Pier
New York, NY 10011
(212) 929-1111

**Crown Limousine
and Car Service Inc.**
554 W. 48th Street
New York, NY 10036
(212) 246-2626

**Farrell's Limousine
Service**
428 E. 92nd Street
New York, NY 10128
(212) 570-9800

**First Class Car and
Limousine Service**
4980 Broadway
New York, NY 10036
(212) 304-1111
(Picks up from Manhattan
only.)

The Garage
348 E. 15th Street (at 2nd
Ave.)
New York, NY 10003
(212) 674-0060
www.thegarage-ny.com
info@thegarage-ny.com

Grand Transportation
621 W. 55th Street
New York, NY 10019
(212) 956-6600

**Kennedy Radio
Dispatch Limousine**
3760 Broadway (at 157th
St.)
New York, NY 10032
(212) 283-5858

**Lower East Side
Car Service**
169 Avenue C (at 11th St.)
New York, NY 10009
(212) 477-7777

**Madison Avenue
Limousine**
348 E. 15th Street
New York, NY 10003
(212) 674-0060

Nice Guys Limousine
622 W. 57th Street
New York, NY 10019
(212) 757-7788

**Prestige Executive
Service**
973 Columbus Avenue
(at 107th St.)
New York, NY 10025
(212) 663-8140

**Rainbow Limousine
Service**
35-28 Union Street
Flushing 11354
(212) 769-2929

RSVP
51 Little W. 12th Street
(at 6th Ave.)
New York, NY 10014
(212) 242-7787

**Spectacular Limousine
Service, Inc.**
250 W. 61 Street
New York, NY 10023
(212) 501-7400

Star Limo
373 W.52nd Street
(at 9th Ave.)
New York, NY 10019
(212) 586-6666

**Tri-State Car and
Limousine Service**
326 Second Avenue
New York, NY 10003
(212) 777-7171

**Universal International
Limousine Inc.**
141 W. 28th Street
(at 6th Ave.)
New York, NY 10001
(212) 279-1700

49. BUDGET HOTELS

OK, so family or
friends are coming into
town, and they can't all
fit in your tiny apart-
ment. Hotels in New
York City can be astro-
nomically expensive, so
if you want a nice, af-
fordable place, call
these places and see
what their current
prices are.

Chelsea Lodge
318 W. 20th Street
(bet. 8th and 9th Aves.)
New York, NY 10011
(212) 243-4499

Comfort Inn Midtown
129 W. 46th Street
(bet. 6th and 7th Aves.)
New York, NY 10036
(212) 221-2600

Da Vinci Hotel
244 W. 56th Street
New York, NY 10019
(212) 489-4100

Gershwin Hotel
7 E. 27th Street
New York, NY 10016
(212) 545-8000

Herald Square Hotel
19 W. 31st Street (bet. 5th
Ave. and Broadway)
New York, NY 10001
(212) 279-4017

Hotel Carlyle
983 Madison Avenue
New York, NY 10021
(212) 744-1600

Hotel Edison
228 W. 47th Street
(bet. Broadway and
8th Ave.)
New York, NY 10036
(212) 840-5000

Hotel Riverview
113 Jane Street
New York, NY 10014
(212) 929-0060

**Howard Johnson
Express Inn**
135 East Houston Street
(bet. 1st and 2nd Aves.)
New York, NY 10002
(212) 358-8844

Kimberly Hotel
145 E. 50th Street
New York, NY 10022
(212) 755-0400

Lucerne
201 W. 79th Street
New York, NY 10024
(212) 875-1000

Marriot Marquis
1535 Broadway
New York, NY 10036
(212) 398-1900

Mayfair New York
242 W. 49th Street (bet.
Broadway and 8th Aves.)
New York, NY 10019
(212) 586-0300

New Yorker Hotel
481 Eighth Avenue
New York, NY 10001
(212) 971-0101

On the Avenue Hotel
2178 Broadway
New York, NY 10024
(212) 362-1100

Portland Square Hotel
132 W. 47th Street
New York, NY 10036
(212) 382-0600

Quality Hotel
215 W. 94th Street
(bet. Broadway and
Amsterdam Ave.)
New York, NY 10025
(212) 866-6400

Radisson Hotel
511 Lexington Avenue
New York, NY 10017
(212) 755-4400

**Red Roof Inn
Manhattan**
6 W. 32nd Street (bet.
Broadway and 5th Ave.)
New York, NY 10001
(212) 643-7100

Roger Williams Hotel
131 Madison Avenue
(at 31st St.)
New York, NY 10016
(212) 448-7000

Cheap Rooms

If all you want is a cheap room where you can leave your bags while you explore New York City and have a clean bed to sleep in, check these places out. Remember to check if the bathrooms are communal or private.

Hotel Wolcott
4 W. 31st Street (bet.
5th Ave. and Broadway)
New York, NY 10001
(212) 268-2900

Pickwick Arms Hotel
230 E. 51st Street (bet. 2nd and 3rd Aves.)
New York, NY 10022
(212) 355-0300
The less expensive rooms in this place share bathrooms. If that bothers you, make sure you pay a little more and get your own bathroom.

Pioneer Hotel
341 Broome Street
(Elizabeth and Bowery)
New York, NY 10013
(212) 226-1482

Seton Hotel
144 E. 40th Street (bet. 3rd and Lexington Aves.)
New York, NY 10016
(212) 889-5301

50. HOUSING

There are ways of getting an apartment without using a realtor, though it requires more work on your part. Check the *Village Voice, New York Sunday Times*, www.craigslist.org, and, in the boroughs, any local papers with classified sections.

There are also rental listing companies that can be found online (check www.panix.com or use your search engine to find lists). You will pay a fee and they will give you lists of available apartments, but you will have to set up appointments to see the places. Although using a realtor can be a lot easier, using a listing company can be a lot less expensive.

You can check the boards at SAG and the papers to see if anyone is looking for a roommate or is looking for someone to sublease.

Harlem is an area of Manhattan that is becoming increasingly popular because the rents are lower. Apartments in Manhattan can be incredibly expensive, so a lot of people live in the other boroughs and commute. You might want to check out Astoria/Long Island City in

Queens, Pelham Bay, Throggs Neck, and Country Club in the Bronx and Park Slope, Williamsburg, and Brooklyn Heights in Brooklyn.

As a tenant you have rights that the landlord/lady must uphold. Make sure you educate yourself on what those rights are by checking out www.tenant.net/Rights.

Hiring a Realtor

Realtors will charge you a fee of around 15 percent, due only when they have found you an apartment. You should not have to pay a fee up front. Make sure you ask the realtors which areas are safe. Don't be pressured; if you don't feel safe in an area; go with your instincts. Here are some realtors to try:

Aamen Realty
2255 31st Street
Astoria, NY, 11105
(718) 545-2474

Buff Real Estate
40 Clinton Street, Suite 1J
Brooklyn, NY 11201
(718) 625-5201

City Sites Real Estate Group
425 E. 61st Street
New York, NY 10021
(212) 588-9490

E. Green Realty Co
352 Seventh Avenue
New York, NY 10001
(212) 997-7709

John P. Burke Realty
412 Seventh Avenue
Brooklyn, NY 11215
(718) 768-1001

Metropolis International Realty
2917 23rd Avenue
Astoria, NY 11105

Pepe Real Estate
85 Kingsland Ave.
Brooklyn, NY 11222
(718) 388-8600
www.peperealestate.com

Trust Real Estate
211 East Broadway
New York, NY 10002
(212) 505-9281

Venus Realty
3805 31st Avenue
Astoria, NY 11103
(718) 204-1616

Veronica Christensen Realty
3009 Westchester Avenue
Bronx, NY 10461

51. BANKS

There are many different types of banks in New York. There are the popular ones such as Chase, Citibank, and Fleet that are all over the city. But be aware that they tend to charge a large monthly fee if you don't have a lot of money in your account. Smaller banks may not charge you, but they also may only have one or two locations. It's well worth your time to go to several banks and find which will suit you the best.

Actors Federal Credit Union
165 W. 46th Street
New York, NY 10036
(212) 869-8926

Chase Manhattan
Individual branch phone numbers are not available but dialing the service line/current account information number should get you the help you need regardless of the branch you use.

Toll free number:
1-800-242-7324

Service line/current account information:
(212) 935-9935

Chinese service line:
(212) 809-6464

Korean service line:
(212) 809-3737

Spanish service line:
(212) 935-9935

Service line for hearing impaired with TDD equipment:
1-800-242-7383

Foreign money exchange:
1-888-242-7384

Outside NY, NJ, and CT:
1-800-935-9935

Mastercard and Visa information:
1-800-356-5555

Mortgage information:
1-800-524-3642

302 W. 12th Street
New York, NY 10016

525 Broadway
New York, NY 10012

281 Broadway
New York, NY 10007

270 Park Avenue
New York, NY 10017

2065 Second Avenue
New York, NY 10029

3940 Broadway
New York, NY 10032

160 E. 125th Street
New York, NY 10035

71 W. 23rd Street
New York, NY 10010

969 Eighth Avenue
New York, NY 10019

Citibank
Citiphone 24-hour automated service: (212) 627-3999

Citigroup directory assistance: 1-800-285-3000

Citiphone TDD (hearing impaired): 1-800-945-0258

Report a lost or stolen ATM card: (212) 627-3999

Citibank Visa/Mastercard: 1-800-950-5114

Citicorp Investment Services (existing clients): 1-800-846-5200

Citicorp Investment Services (new clients): 1-800-721-1899

Citigold: 1-800-756-1200

US Private Banking Group: 1-800-870-1073

Investor Services: 1-800-422-2066

Student loans: 1-800-967-2400

Foreign Currency Exchange: (212) 308-7863

Retirement Plan Services: 1-800-695-5911

Real Estate Commercial Loans: (212) 922-5902

Official Checks and Money Orders: 1-800-223-7520

111 Wall Street
New York, NY 10005
(212) 248-6600

800 Third Avenue
New York, NY 10022
(212) 688-0992

1107 Broadway
New York, NY 10010
(212) 645-3200

1440 Broadway
New York, NY 10018
(212) 944-6227

717 Sixth Avenue
New York, NY 10010
(212) 229-3520

90 Park Avenue
New York, NY 10016
(212) 682-2726

785 Fifth Avenue
New York, NY 10022
(212) 421-7776

800 Third Avenue
New York, NY 10022
(212) 688-0992

1Rockefeller Ctr.
New York, NY 10020
(212) 765-3315

5 Penn Plaza
New York, NY 10001
(212) 947-3374

866 United Nations Plaza
New York, NY 10017
(212) 688-3922

50 Avenue A
New York, NY 10009
(212) 533-3087

201 W. 125th Street
New York, NY 10027
(212) 663-3282

401 W. 42nd Street
New York, NY 10036
(212) 594-5134

734 Third Avenue
New York, NY 10017
(212) 682-0290

55 South Street
New York, NY 10005
(212) 245-0247

4249 Broadway
New York, NY 10033
(212) 781-7882

555 LaGuardia Pl.
New York, NY 10012
(212) 387-7270

322 W. 23rd Street
New York, NY 10011
(212) 627-6300

1 Broadway
New York, NY 10004
(212) 248-6805

108 Hudson Street
New York, NY 10013
(212) 274-8044

1310 Amsterdam Avenue
New York, NY 10027
(212) 663-2390

Emigrant
Executive Offices
5 E. 42nd Street
New York, NY 10017
(212) 850-4000

Telephone Service Center:
(212) 850-4444

Mortgage Servicing:
(212) 850-4555

Human Resources:
(212) 850-4888

Pensions: (212) 414-2600

Phone Access:
(212) 850-3333

Phone Access (TDD):
(212) 850-3334

Telephone Service Center (TDD): (212) 850-4900

110 Church Street
New York, NY 10007
(212) 285-3220

261 Broadway
New York, NY 10007
(212) 748-7550

5 E. 42nd Street
New York, NY 10017
(212) 850-4521

465 Grand Street
New York, NY 10002
(212) 979-5550

1270 Lexington Avenue
New York, NY 10028
(212) 987-3690

395 Sixth Avenue
New York, NY 10014
(212) 647-7270

250 W. 23rd Street
New York, NY 10011
(212) 367-7830

Fleet Bank
TDD Access: 1-800-637-4031
1-800-225-5353

Customer Service (individual branch numbers are not listed but this number should get you assistance regardless of the branch you use):
1-800-841-4000

515 Fashion Avenue
New York, NY 10018

1775 Broadway
New York, NY 10019

260 Canal Street
New York, NY 10017

100 Church Street
New York, NY 10007

1140 Sixth Avenue
New York, NY 10036

1143 Lexington Avenue
New York, NY 10021

116 Fifth Avenue
New York, NY 10011

126 Delancey Street
New York, NY 10002

150 Broadway
New York, NY 10038

1675 Broadway
New York, NY 10019

2250 Third Avenue
New York, NY 10035

318 Grand Street
New York, NY 10002

345 Park Avenue
New York, NY 10154

50 Bayard Street
New York, NY 10013
56 E. 42nd St.
New York, NY 10017

589 Broadway
New York, NY 10012

72 Second Avenue
New York, NY 10003

215 W. 125th Street
New York, NY 10027

HSBC
All branches: 1-800-975-4722

250 Park Avenue South
New York, NY 10003

268 Canal Street
New York, NY 10013
27 E. Broadway
New York, NY 10002

140 Broadway
New York, NY 10005

North Fork Bank
2 Park Avenue
New York, NY 10016
(212) 679-1140

300 E. 79th Street
New York, NY 10021
(212) 535-3810

2025 Broadway
New York, NY 10023
(212) 580-4000

1180 Third Avenue
New York, NY 10021
(212) 744-6670

845 Third Avenue
New York, NY 10022
(212) 935-7563

404 Fifth Avenue
New York, NY 10018
(212) 967-9400

2 Park Avenue
New York, NY 10016
(212) 679-1140

1258 Second Avenue
New York, NY 10021
(212) 737-3974

1407 Broadway
New York, NY 10018
(212) 869-0021

1001 Broadway
New York, NY 10023
(212) 764-1001

750 Third Avenue
New York, NY 10017
(212) 450-9700

Sterling National
Operations Center
148 W. 37th Street
New York, NY 10018
(212) 760-9610

Personal Loan Department
622 Third Avenue
New York, NY 10017
(212) 490-9814

Equipment Leasing
(212) 490-9822

500 Fashion Avenue
New York, NY 10018
(212) 575-8886
(212) 575-5016

650 Fifth Avenue
New York, NY 10019
(212) 757-3300

If you're an actor in SAG/AFTRA you might want to check out:

ELEVEN

getting it on

52. FUN AND (SOMETIMES) FREE THINGS TO DO

Kimshelley's Spotlight On: Central Park

Designed by Frederick Law Olmstead and Calvert Vaux, Central Park is twice the size of the principality of Monaco. It runs from 59th Street to 110th Street between Fifth Avenue and Central Park West. The park is open between 6 AM and 1 AM.

On your first visit to Central Park, you may want to start by stopping by The Dairy visitor center, located midpark at 65th Street. There you can see a small-scale model of the entire park, learn about its history, and, best of all, pick up a free pamphlet that contains a detailed map and all sorts of park-related phone numbers. (Closed on Mondays.) There is also a map posted by the museum at 80th Street and Fifth Avenue.

There are, of course, the famous areas that you'll want to visit. The running track around the reservoir: 1.58 miles of soft surface that gives you incredible views of the buildings along Central Park East and Central Park West, located between 86th and 96th Streets and Fifth Avenue and just east of Central Park West. Strawberry Fields: a small area of the park that is financially maintained by Yoko Ono in memory of John Lennon, located at 72nd Street and Central Park West; it features flowers sent from all over the world. Tavern on the Green: the famous restaurant located at 66th Street and Central Park West. The Chess and Checkers House: featured in many movies, located midpark at 64th Street; open Saturday and Sunday 11:30 AM to 3:45 PM; chess pieces available for rent at The Dairy.

But there are also other areas that you may want to visit. The Shakespeare Garden: a beautiful path of flowers with a bench in the center where you can

201

sit quietly and rumi-
nate, located at 79th
and Central Park West.
The Carousel: a fa-
vorite of children and
adults, located midpark
at 64th Street; open
weekends. $1 per ride.
Bethesda Terrace: de-
signed by Frederick
Law Olmstead and
Calvert Vaux to be an
"open air hall of recep-
tion," a stunning area
with Emma Stebbins's
"Angel of the Waters"
overlooking all, located
midpark at 72nd Street.
Belvedere Castle: a
small highland castle
built in 1872, where
you can climb up to the
top and look out over
the park (the stairs are
very narrow — not for
those with claustropho-
bia), located midpark at
79th Street. The Zoo:
featuring some 450 ani-
mals, from piranhas to
polar bears, located at
64th Street and Fifth
Avenue ($3.50 for
adults). And, of course,
you'll want to visit the
Delacorte Theatre, with
its enchanting statues
from *Romeo and Juliet*
and *The Tempest,* locat-
ed midpark at 81st
Street.

Make the most of
this treasure. See it in
winter when it's a
snow-covered wonder-
land, in spring when
the flower are in
bloom, in summer

when it's full of life,
and of course in fall
when the colors are tru-
ly rapturous. Whether
you go to relax or exer-
cise, lie in the sun or sit
in the shade, get away
from it all or meet up
with friends, the most
important thing is that
you go.

Central Park
59th Street to 110th Street
(bet. 5th Ave. and Central
Park West)

Other Free Things

Central Park Summerstage
72nd Street and Fifth Av-
enue
Info. Hotline: (212) 360-2777
Held at Rumsey Playfield, for
eight weeks of summer (call
the hotline or see www.city
search for play list and
dates) you can see shows of
music, poetry readings,
opera and dance. Free un-
less otherwise noted.

HBO Bryant Park Summer Film Festival
Bryant Park, located at 42nd
and Sixth Avenue
The show is at sunset on
Mondays (rain dates are
Tuesday). But you'll want to
get there a lot earlier because this is a very popular
event, and take a blanket
and food because you'll be
sitting on the lawn. The
movies are a mix of old and
new; check www.citysearch
for the list of what's playing.

Macy's Thanksgiving Day Parade
The famous parade that runs
from 79th Street and Central

Park West to Macy's Herald
Square. You have to get
there early (like 7 AM at
least) to get a good spot,
and during the hours leading
up to the parade, people
will push in front of you, but
it's worth it to go. Every year
they add new floats, but the
old favorites return. Make
sure you dress warmly and
wear very comfortable
shoes. Also be prepared for
the mass exodus after the
parade; everyone will push
and fight to get to the subways and get home.

New York Stock Exchange
20 Broad Street (bet. Wall
St. and Exchange Place)
You've seen it on TV and in
the movies, now see it for
yourself. Watch from the
gallery for free. Be aware it
can sometimes be very hard
to get in. Tickets available at
20 Broad Street.

Shakespeare in the Park at the Delacorte Theater
Held during summer
(July–September). Tickets are
free. Go as early as possible
to make sure you get tickets.

South Street Seaport
89 South Street, Pier 17
New York, NY, 10038 (bet.
Fulton and South Sts.)
What now is a bustling center of 120 shops, restau-
rants, and a museum was
originally a trading port in
the 1600s. Though it's a little
disappointing to see a GAP
store and the like in the
beautiful buildings set on
cobblestone streets, it is nice
to get away from the sky-
scrapers and enjoy the wa-
terfront for a little while. (Museum is not free.)

Staten Island Ferry at the South Ferry Terminal
South Ferry Plaza, New York, NY 10004 (Battery Park bet. South and Whitehall Sts.)
Cruise for twenty-five minutes around the southern tip of Manhattan — Statue of Liberty, Ellis Island, plus the shorelines of Brooklyn and New Jersey — and dock on Staten Island. All for free! For a fun date, try a ferry ride at sunset.

Washington Square Park
W. 4th Street (bet. MacDougal and University Place)
Known for it's beautiful arch celebrating George Washington, if you love to people-watch, this is your place. All sorts of people go to Washington Square Park for all sorts of reasons. There are dancers, musicians, poets, and multiple variations of personalities. On Memorial and Labor Days, there's an outdoor art fair.

Fun (But, Alas, Not Free)

Liz's Spotlight On: Maila Mills Swimwear

Take note as a curvy, twenty-something blonde exits the Maila Mills headquarters and outlet, positively beaming and gushing thank-yous as she leaves. This is a woman whose attitude has made a complete 180.

"She's a typical gal who can't find a suit."

Gals like that say, 'I haven't bought a bikini in years,'" Carol Mills said. "I get them in a bikini, and they can visualize being on vacation and being really happy. They're going away and they're feeling beautiful."

For more than a decade, Carol and Malia Mills, sisters and owners of Malia Mills Swimwear, have made it their mission to make wearing a bathing suit a joyous experience.

If you're a woman and you have a body, chances are you're already sizing up your skinny legs or your less-than-taut tummy and thinking, "Joyous? Yeah, right." But the Mills sisters know exactly what's on your mind and they refer you to their motto: "We don't want to change the way you look; we want to change the way you look at yourself. Love thy differences!"

The key to one of these suits, Carol explains, comes in changing your mind about individual proportions; not buying into the myth that if you don't fit into a particular category, if you are small-breasted or wide-hipped, something is wrong with your body. Carol says the idea

came to her sister one day as they were shopping. "Malia said, 'I don't know why you can't buy a bathing suit the way you buy lingerie,'" that is, separate tops and separate bottoms.

The sisters took it upon themselves to do just that. Eleven years later, they're happy to report their idea was a well-received one.

Here's how it works: First, a salesperson will ask your bra and bottom size. Using that information, she'll recommend a few different combinations, like the Country Girl above the Skinny Dipper or the Bettie Bandeau top with an It's-a-Cinch bottom.

And a one-of-a-kind fit doesn't mean having to settle when it comes to style. Mixing and matching is encouraged among the many available colors, fabrics, and prints to create a unique look. "I always ask people, 'Do you wear the same tops with the same pants all the time?' We want to change the mindset that tops have to go with bottoms," Carol says. It all adds up to what makes Malia Mills different from the average swimsuit experience.

Being bombarded by fantasy notions of

beauty every day, it's easy to miscalculate how you measure up.

"Women are our own worst enemies," Carol Mills said. "The fashion magazines always say crazy stuff like, 'Wanna look thinner? Wear vertical stripes!'

"Chicks are busty, chicks are round, chicks are narrow. Most companies design suits with a medium-size build top to bottom, and that's not reality. With so many negative images out there, we want to change the way women think, particularly young girls. Buying a bathing suit should be an empowering, fun experience not a mortifying one. You just come in and we totally take care of you."

New York and Connecticut locations and store hours
Headquarters and Outlet
263 W. 38th Street,
16th Floor
Monday–Friday
12 PM–6 PM

New York Uptown
960 Madison Avenue,
2nd Floor
Monday–Saturday
12 PM–7 PM

New York Downtown
199 Mulberry Street
Monday–Saturday
12 PM –7 PM
Sunday, 12 PM–5 PM

Connecticut location
By appointment
Westport, CT.
(203) 341-8737

www.maliamills.com

Other Fun Things

Now, there's so much to do in New York, what with the many museums, clubs, theaters, cinemas, parades, festivals, and wonderful shops. Here's just a few things to try.

Annex Antique Fair and Flea Market
Sixth Avenue
(bet. 24th and 26th Sts.)
New York, NY 10116
(212) 243-5343
On the weekends, this market of mixed wares attracts a fitting mixed crowd. This is not a thrift market, the prices aren't unbelievable low, but they are not bad either. Check it out if you're looking to furnish your new apartment (remember it's a flea market, bring cash). Clothing accessories also available. $1 entry fee.

Broadway City Arcade
241 W. 42nd Street
(bet. 7th and 8th Aves.)
New York, NY
(212) 997-9797
A great place to take kids of all ages. You gotta love a place where you can play Whack-a-Mayor.

Bronx Zoo
2300 Southern Blvd.
Bronx, NY 10460
Info. Hotline:
(718) 367-1010
Web site: www.wcs.org
The zoo is huge and really beautiful. The animals are kept in areas designed to replicate their natural habitat. You can spend the whole day there (well, from 10 AM-4:30 PM anyway), but be aware, if you're not a big fan of children (and mass amounts of them), you might want to skip this one. It's even more child-filled on Wednesdays because it's "by donation" day. You may prefer to spend the $11 to get in on the other days.

The Cloisters
Fort Tryon Park
(upper Manhattan)
Info. Hotline:
(212) 923-3700
A lot of people describe the Cloisters as a way to get away from New York without leaving New York. The Cloisters takes you back to the Middle Ages with tapestries, illuminated manuscripts, fountains, gardens, and more. It's a branch of the Metropolitan Museum of Arts division of Medieval Arts and Architecture (your entrance fee also allows you same-day admittance to the Metropolitan Museum of Art). Currently the suggested donation is $12 for adults, $7 for seniors and students. Closed every Monday, and also on Thanksgiving Day, Christmas Day, and New Years Day. Take the Madison Avenue M4 bus to the last stop, which is "Cloisters."

Mets Clubhouse Shop
143 E. 54th Street (bet. 3rd and Lexington Aves.)
New York, NY 10022
1-888-7508

11 W. 42nd Street
(bet. 5th and 6th Aves.)
New York, NY 10036
(212) 768-9532

Our Name Is Mud
(several locations)

For $5 per half hour plus the cost of the readymade forms, you can paint a piece of pottery that will then be glazed and fired by the pros. It may not sound like a blast, but it really is. A great idea for a date or a relaxing afternoon with friends. They also offer pottery classes.

59 Greenwich Avenue
(bet. Seventh Avenue and 11th St.)
(212) 647-7899

506 Amsterdam Avenue
(bet. 84th and 85th Sts.)
(212) 579-5575

1566 Second Avenue
(bet. 81st and 82nd Sts.)
(212) 570-6868

Grand Central Terminal
New York, NY 10017
212-388-9559

Shea Stadium
(The Mets)

123-01 Roosevelt Avenue
Flushing, NY 11368
(718) 507-8499
Take the 7 to Willets Point-Shea Stadium. Just as important! Tickets can be purchased through ticketmaster or the Mets Store (in person only at this time).

Mets Clubhouse Shop
143 E. 54th Street (3rd and Lexington Aves.)
New York, NY 10022
(212) 1-888-7508

11 W. 42nd Street (5th and 6th Aves.)
New York, NY 10036
(212) 768-9532

Yankees Clubhouse
Shop (two locations)

110 E. 59th Street (bet. Park and Lexington Aves.)
New York, NY 10022
(212) 758-7844

245 W. 42nd Street
(bet. 7th and 8th Aves.)
New York, NY 10036
(212) 768-9555

Yankees Stadium

161st Street (at River Ave.)
Bronx, NY 10451
(718) 293-4300
Take the D or 4 to 161st Street. Even if you're not a baseball fan, you should go at least once. Tickets can be purchased through ticket master or the Yankees Store (in person only at this time).

53. WHAT TO DO WHEN GUESTS ARE IN TOWN

Kimshelley's Spotlight On: The Greenwich Village Literary Pubcrawl

Surprisingly, my mum isn't really into seeing theater (unless I'm in it, of course). So when my parents came to visit me recently, I needed to find something for us to do that I knew she would enjoy. Solution: The Greenwich Village Literary Pubcrawl, a fantastic walking tour that stops at four pubs and also covers a good deal of the Village.

The guides are members of the New Ensemble Theatre Company. They are there on a volunteer basis, so all profits go to the theater company. The great part is, because they are actors, they not only tell you about the famous playwrights and authors who frequented the pubs, the guides also act out scenes from works by the writers.

Paul Angelo and Mike Nickols founded the New Ensemble Theatre Company in 1997. Soon after they began the pubcrawl, they were able to fund their first production (*Romeo and Juliet*). In 2000, after directing several productions for New Ensemble, Steven McElroy became coartistic director. An actor who received his MFA from the Alabama Shakespeare Festival, Steven is in charge of both the ensemble and the pubcrawl. The New Ensemble has up to fifteen members and holds auditions every year. A season typically has two new works and a Shakespearian piece.

The pubcrawl is currently $15 per person (not including drinks) and is held every Saturday, year-round; at 2 PM. Reservations are recommended.

The New Ensemble Theatre Company will accept new plays and headshots and résumés. Send to:

**The New Ensemble
Theatre Company**
444 W. 49th Street, Apt. 3B
New York, NY 10019

To make reservations,
call (212) 613-5796.
For more information,
go to www.geocities.
com/newensemble.

Other Things to
Do with Guests

Here is a quick guide to
places your guests will
likely want to visit. Surprisingly, a lot of places
will only take cash, so
be prepared.

Apollo Theater
253 W. 125th Street
Harlem, NY 10027
(212) 531-5300
E-mail: box-office@apollo
theater.com
www.apollotheater.com

Bergdorf Goodman
754 Fifth Avenue
(at 57th St.)
New York, NY 10019
1-800-558-1855
E-mail: clientservices@
bergdorfgoodman.com
www.bergdorfgoodman.com

Bloomingdales
1000 Third Avenue
(bet. 59th and 60th Sts.)
New York, NY 10022
1-800-558-1855
www.bloomingdales.com

Blue Note New York
131 W. 3rd Street
New York, NY 10012
(212) 475-8592
E-mail: club@bluenote.net
www.bluenote.net

Carnegie Deli
854 Seventh Avenue
(bet. 54th and 55th Sts.)
New York, NY 10019
www.carnegiedeli.com

Carnegie Hall
W. 57th Street and 7th
Avenue
New York, NY 10019
(212) 247-7800
E-mail: boxoffice@carnegie
hall.org
www.carnegiehall.org
(If you go to see a show, this
is one of the only theaters
that has a dress code of no
jeans).

**Chelsea Piers
Sports Center**
Pier 60
23rd Street and the
Hudson River
New York, NY 10011
(212) 336-6000
www.sportscenter
@chelseapiers.com

Chrysler Building
405 Lexington Avenue
(at 42nd St.)
New York, NY 10017
E-mail: cb@luciddreams.com
www.luciddreams.com

City Hall
Broadway at Murray Street
New York, NY 10007

Dylan's Candy Bar
1011 Third Avenue
New York, NY 10021
(212) 620-2704
www.dylanscandybar.com

Empire State Building
350 Fifth Avenue (at 34th
St.)
New York, NY 10118
www.esbnyc.com
The color of the Empire State
Building lights varies all the
time. Check out www.
esbnyc.com to find out what
they stand for; for example,
purple and white: Alzheimer's

Awareness; green: St.
Patrick's Day, March of
Dimes, Rainforest Aware-
ness, or Earth Day; no lights:
Day without Art/Night with-
out Lights, AIDS awareness.

Gracie Mansion
59 E. 89 Street
Carl Schurtz Park Entrance
(bet. 89th Street and
East End Ave.)
New York, NY 10128
www.ci.nyc.ny.us/html/om/
html/gracie.html

**Harry Winston
(Jewelers)**
718 Fifth Avenue (at 56th
St.)
New York, NY 10019
www.harry-winston.com

Indoor Market
714 Broadway
New York, NY 10003
(212) 868-2000

**Intrepid Sea Air
Space Museum**
86 N. River Pier (46th Street
at 12th Ave.)
New York, NY 10036
(212) 245-0072

The Juilliard School
60 Lincoln Center Plaza (bet.
64th and Broadway)
New York, NY 10023
www.juilliard.edu

Macy's
151 W. 34th Street
(bet. 6th Ave./Broadway
and 7th Ave.)
New York, NY 10001
www.macys.com

**Madison Square
Garden**
2 Pennylvania Plaza
(at 7th Ave. bet. 32nd
and 33rd Sts.)
New York, NY 10001
E-mail: msgnetpr@msgnet
work.com
www.thegarden.com

**MET (Metropolitan
Opera House)**
30 Lincoln Center Plaza
(bet. 64th and Broadway)
New York, NY 10023

**New York
Botanical Garden**
Bronx River Parkway at
Fordham Road
Bronx, NY 10458
(718) 817-8700
www.nybg.org

Prada
724 Fifth Avenue (bet. 56th
and 57th Sts.)
New York, NY 10019

Radio City Music Hall
1260 Sixth Avenue
(at 50th St.)
New York, NY 10020
(212) 247-4777
www.radiocity.com

Rockefeller Center
30 Rockefeller Plaza
(bet. 48th and 51st Sts.)
New York, NY 10012
(212) 332-6868
www.rockefellercenter.com

Saks Fifth Avenue
611 Fifth Avenue (at 51st
St.)
New York, NY 10022
(212) 753-4000
www.saksfifthavenue.com

St. Patrick's Cathedral
14 E. 51st Street
New York, NY 10019
(212) 753-2261
www.ny-archdiocese.org/
pastoral/cathedral_about.
html

Statue of Liberty
17 Battery Place
New York, NY 10004
(212) 269-5755
www.statueoflibertyferry.com
E-mail: nytix@circlelineferry.
com
Liberty Island reachable by
ferry leaving from Battery

Park. (The statue and museum are currently closed, but
there are plans to reopen the
statue for visitors again
soon. Regardless, you can
go to the island. Be pre-
pared for security checks).

**Tiffany and Co.
(aka Tiffany's)**
727 Fifth Avenue (bet. 56th
and 57th Sts.)
New York, NY 10022
(212) 755-8000
www.tiffanys.com

**Times Square
Visitor Center**
1560 Broadway, Suite 800
New York, NY 10036
(212) 768-1560
E-mail: info@timessquare
bid.org
www.timessquarebid.org

Trinity Church
74 Trinity Plaza (bet.
Broadway and Wall St.)
New York, NY 10006
(212) 602-0800
www.trinitywallstreet.org
(Closed until further notice
due to 9/11)

Yankee Stadium
161st Street and River
Avenue
Bronx, NY 10451
(718) 293-4300
http://newyork.yankees.mlb.
com

54. TECH ZONE

Welcome to the *Act
New York* "Tech
Zone," our new sec-
tion, which features the
most fun and useful
digital innovations. In
each edition of *Act
New York*, after exten-
sive testing at the *Act*

New York digital head-
quarters, we will give
out our awards for best
products of the year.
Here now, the two win-
ners for 2005.

The *Act New
York* Tech
Awards

Best Photo Product
for 2005: The Hi
Touch Imaging
730PS Photo Printer
Almost every actor we
have talked with is
shooting photos with a
digital camera, and one
thing that became clear
in our survey was that
everyone wants an easy
and high-quality way to
print the digital images.
Well, we have the most
exciting new printer for
you. It is fast and fun,
and it produces the
most gorgeous prints
you will ever see. Inter-
ested? Read on.

About the Company
Hi Touch Imaging was
established in January
2001, and it is growing
fast. Most people know
the company as HiTi
(pronounced "high
tee"). The folks at HiTi
are dedicated to a tech-
nology known as dye
diffusion thermal trans-
fer, which they have put
to good use in their
fabulous lineup of
photo-quality printers.
   They are the clear

winners in a field that is seeing rapid advancements both in quality of printing and the numbers of printers available. Don't just take our word, though, HiTi has received numerous awards for its printers, including the "Top 35 Products of the Year" award from *PC Photo Magazine,* "Top 100 Products of 2003" award from *Computer Shopper,* and the prestigious PMA "Innovative Digital Product Award," and it won the 2004 "Digital Printer Shootout" at the 2004 PMA convention and trade show.

The 730PS Printer

Of HiTi's many printers, the 730 is the newest and most versatile. Though incredibly compact in size, the 730 will print 4 by 6, 5 by 7 and 6 by 8 prints in a very fast forty-five to seventy seconds. And what prints these are! The best way to describe them is stunning. As good as lab prints you ask? No, better!

How Does HiTi Do It?

First of all, dye diffusion printers do not lay down dots of ink like the inkjet printers do. This is continuous tone printing with 256 gradation levels per color. Also, you never have to watch the levels on your ink cartridges again. The HiTi uses a specially designed ribbon that lasts as long as the number of sheets of photo paper it came with. So, when you run out of paper, you know it is time to change the ribbon. It couldn't be any easier!

Here's how it works: After you tell the 730 to print, it pulls the special photo paper through the machine four times, each time laying down a new coat of yellow, magenta, and cyan. Wait, that's only three coats, you say. Yep, you're right. When the print makes its fourth pass, the 730 applies its "magic coating technology" to make the print waterproof, protecting it from fingerprints and UV radiation. This process also gives the print a brilliant gloss finish. When you watch your first photo being printed, this process will make you go "Wow!"

Also, your photos, printed on the special HiTi photo paper, never need to be cut down to size (which you often have to do when you print on an ink jet printer, resulting in much wasted paper).

When your photo pops out of the machine, simply fold the paper on the perforated seams, and you have a perfect, borderless photo.

The 730 will work with your computer, or it will print standing all on its own. If you want to go the computer route, you can hook up your 730 via USB to either a PC or a Mac. If you are a PC user, the 730 comes with professional photo-editing software called "Photo-Desiree." This nicely designed software has creative color-toning buttons with options for color adjustment, contrast, sharpness, brightness, and hues. It also helps you create personalized calendars; poster greeting cards, ID photos, and CD labels. Of course, on a Mac, you can use any photo-editing programs, such as Photoshop and iPhoto.

Now if you want to make prints without use of a computer, all you have to do is take your media card right from your camera and plug it in to the 730, which accepts any type of media card you throw its way. Once you punch in the media card, you can then view the images on the very nicely designed external, handheld controller, which features a 1.6-inch color LCD screen. Here, you can adjust the photo before printing it, as well as choosing the size and type of print you want to make.

The Costs

Yes, you can go get a pretty decent photo-printing ink jet these days for under $200. But if you are looking for ease of operation with outstanding results every time, then it is our advice to "buy once and buy right"! At a retail price of $399, the 730 is more expensive, but if you plan to keep on shooting those digital pics, all the benefits of this beautiful machine turn it into the best photo-making investment you can make.

The prints themselves will cost you a mere 40 cents each for 4 by 6s, 80 cents each for 5 by 7s and one dollar a piece for the 6 by 8s. And remember, you will never have to buy all those expensive ink cartridges and ink jet photo paper ever again.

(By the way, if you only need to print 4 by 6 prints, the HiTi 640PS costs about a hundred dollars less, and it has all the same great technology built in.)

So let's sum it up: When you own the HiTi 730PS, what you actually have is a true digital photo lab right in your own home. The people at HiTi have made a marvel of a machine that is so simple to use you will be producing the most vivid and luscious photographic prints from your very first try.

The supersmooth gradations and true continuous tone colors result in pictures that have a heightened realism. And the Magic Coating gives you prints that will last forever. Also, the ability to print directly from your media card or to operate via a PC or Mac makes this beautiful little printer the most versatile and advanced printer on the market today!

For more information, please visit the Hi Touch Imaging Web site: www.hitouch imaging.com

Best Digital Video Camera of 2005: The Panasonic AG-DVC30

We were invited to the office of Steve Golub, at Panasonic's New Jersey headquarters to test their newest digital marvel, the AG-

DVC30. Knowing how interested the actors-craft staff is in digital moviemaking, Steve gave us a thorough demonstration of this powerful and compact camera under every possible shooting situation.

We tested many cameras this past year, and we have determined that for the high quality of its three chip image, the available options of shooting modes, the beautiful Leica lens, and its very low cost, the DVC30 is the clear winner.

Take a look at the technical details: Total mobility, easy carrying, and advanced audio specs. With the multi-style handle, you get it all. Designed with the professional in mind, the DVC30 introduces a new detachable handle that adds versatility by letting you use this compact DV camera three different ways. Style 1: With handle detached, this supercompact 3CCD camera fits easily into a bag or pack for top mobility. Style 2: With handle in place, the DVC30 is easy to carry and easy to use, even when shooting at difficult angles. Style 3: With the optional XLR adapter mounted to the handle, the DVC30 has outstanding audio specs, plus an external phantom mic and line input.

With features like time/date superimposition and the "No-Light IR mode" — the world's first infrared nighttime shooting mode in a 3CCD camcorder — the DVC30 is also ideal for professional monitoring and surveillance use. Add a slow shutter mode for high-sensitivity color recording, Cine-Like gamma curves, and 30-fps frame recording that gives images a film-like appearance, and you've got multiperformance to meet a host of professional needs.

The DVC30 also features the newly developed Leica Dicomar 16X optical zoom lens, which answers a broad range of shooting needs, delivering superb results from 39.5-mm wide angle all the way to 632-mm telephoto (both 35-mm lens equivalents). In wide-angle performance, this lens is tops in its class. Behind this outstanding performance are the advanced optical technologies and know-how that have made Leica one of the most respected names in the camera world. This new 16X optical zoom lens system uses low-dispersion glass and aspherical lenses to reduce color aberration and boost resolution. Use of a special multicoating process dramatically reduces flare and ghosts. The result: sharp, crisp, beautifully rendered pictures with vivid colors, delicate nuances, and exceptional shading.

And here is the great news for your filmmaking efforts. The DVC30 can capture and reproduce images that are strikingly similar in tone to film images, thanks to Panasonic's unique Cine-Like gamma curves and a 30-fps frame recording function that electronically interpolates interlaced images to create frames with no time differences between fields. Settings for this mode are preset in the "Movie-Like" scene function. Also, the slow shutter function uses image accumulation to allow shutter speeds with frame rates reduced by half or more. The accumulation method provides bright color images with less noise than those captured using conventional gain-up, so you get the higher sensitivity needed for nighttime shooting without illumination. This slow shutter function can also be used to obtain movie-like effects.

The DVC30 comes equipped with two built-in microphones for stereo. Adding the optional AG-MYA30G XLR adapter gives you the +48 V phantom mic and line input. Featuring two XLR audio input terminals and level controls, the adapter lets you independently switch channel 1 or channel 2 to mic or line input, with each having its own level adjustment. Audio-level meters can be displayed in the viewfinder and LCD monitor, making it easy to check the signal as you record.

So, if you are already self-producing digital movies or thinking about gearing up for production, you will be thrilled with the DVC30. There isn't one shooting demand it can't handle. Our advice? Head over to our favorite store, B&H Photo on 34th and Ninth, where the camera currently sells for $2,299.95. Then what? Stock up on some Panasonic mini-DV tape and start having fun!

For more information, go to:
www.panasonic.com

For purchasing information, go to:
www.bhphotovideo.com.

55. A LITTLE TRIVIA

Broadway, originating from lower Manhattan at Bowling Green and ending in Albany, is one of the world's longest streets at 150 miles (241 km). The official name of this street is Highway 9.

New York City has 722 miles of subway track.

St. Patrick's Cathedral seats about 2,200 people.

The *New York Post*, established 1803 by Alexander Hamilton, is the oldest running newspaper in the United States.

New York City was the first capital of the United States (from 1789–1790).

In 1789, George Washington took his oath as president on the balcony at Federal Hall.

Joseph C. Gayetty, of New York City, invented toilet paper in 1857.

New York was the first state to require license plates on cars.

Peter Minuit established the first public brewery in America at the Marckvelt (market) field in lower Manhattan.

Brooklyn was called "Broken Land" by the Dutch.

The Empire State Building has 10 million bricks in it.

Central Park is almost twice the size of the principality of Monaco.

More Italians live in New York City than in Rome.

New York produces more than 26,400,000 pounds of garbage a day.

The first theater in the city was opened in 1732.

The first subway line opened in 1904.

Manhattan, the Bronx, Queens, Staten Island, and Brooklyn joined to form Greater New York on January 1, 1898.

One mile is the equivalent of twenty city blocks in New York.

The best seats in a Broadway theater are fifth row center.

New York City has the largest Jewish population of any city in the world.

Cab drivers in the city communicate in around sixty different languages.

About 19,000 buildings in the city have some degree of landmark status.

Stuyvesant is pronounced Sty-va-san

Zagat is pronounced Za-gaht (like the cat)

Houston (Street) is pronounced How-ston

Flatiron is pronounced Flat Iron

Murray (Hill) is pronounced Murry

TriBeCa stands for the TRiangle BElow CAnal Street

SoHo stands for South of Houston

NoLita stands for North of Little Italy

Greenwich Village is generally referred to as just "The Village."